Animal Production in the Tropics

Animal Production in the Tropics

the late
Jean Pagot

Honorary Veterinary Inspector General
Honorary Director of the Institute
of Animal Production and
Veterinary Medicine in the Tropics
(IEMVT)
Maisons-Alfort, France
Formerly Director of the
International Livestock Centre for Africa
Addis Ababa

translated by
John Wilding
Tropical Agriculture Consultant

MACMILLAN CTA

First edition 1992
Reprinted 1993

Published by THE MACMILLAN PRESS LTD
London and Basingstoke
Associated companies and representatives in Accra,
Auckland, Delhi, Dublin, Gaborone, Hamburg, Harare,
Hong Kong, Kuala Lumpur, Lagos, Manzini, Melbourne,
Mexico City, Nairobi, New York, Singapore, Tokyo.

Original French edition published in 1985 under the title
L'Elevage en Pays Tropicaux
in the series Techniques Agricoles et
Productions Tropicales (Series Editor, Professor R Coste)
by the ACCT and Maisonneuve et Larose,
15, rue Victor-Cousin, 75005 Paris, France.
No responsibility is taken·by the holders of the copyright
for any changes to the original French text.

Published in co-operation with the Technical Centre for
Agricultural and Rural Co-operation, P.O.B. 380,
6700 AJ Wageningen, Netherlands,

ISBN 0 – 333 – 53818 – 8

Printed in Hong Kong

A catalogue record for this book is available from
the British Library.

Contents

PART II THE ANIMALS

PART III ANIMAL PRODUCTION SYSTEMS

Acknowledgements

Professor René Coste was the series Editor of the Techniques Agricoles et Productions Tropicales Series in which the original French edition was published.

The opinions expressed, as well as the spelling of proper names and the territorial limits shown in the present document are only attributable to the authors and in no way are they attributable to the official position nor are they the responsibility of the Agency for Cultural and Technical Cooperation or the CTA.

Dr Noel and Dr Christy of IEMVT (Institute d'Elevage et de Medicine Veterinaire des Pays Tropicaux), Maisone-Alfort, France, provided advice on the translation.

The publishers would like to thank Dr M J Bryant, Dr G Farmer, Dr A J Smith, Anne Pearson and Archie Hunter for help and advice on the editing and translation of portions of the manuscript.

1

Introduction: the role of tropical animal production in the world

by P. Auriol

In this chapter the word 'tropical' is taken in its widest sense. Several countries that are called tropical, such as India, largely spread beyond the strict geographical limits of the intertropical zone, namely the Tropic of Cancer to the north and the Tropic of Capricorn to the south. Conversely, other countries, essentially temperate ones, encroach on the tropics. This is the case, for example, with Argentina, Australia, the United States and China. A demarcation which corresponds better to the zoological reality would be that which includes all the territories contained within the latitudes 30° north and 30° south.

In light of the difficulty of obtaining statistics relating purely to the tropical regions, it has been decided, sometimes arbitrarily, to omit the following regions and countries from this book: Europe and North America in total; the Near East; Asia – Afghanistan and Pakistan, Bhutan, Nepal, China, Japan, Mongolia and the USSR; Africa – Morocco, Algeria, Tunisia, Libya, Egypt, South Africa, Lesotho and Swaziland; South America – Argentina, Chile and Uruguay; and Oceania – Australia and New Zealand.

After some discussion of the specificity and diversity of the tropical environment, forage resources and animal resources will be examined in order to enable a better analysis of the statistics concerning production, supply and demand, international trade, as well as their evolution in time.

Diversity and characteristics of the tropical environment

Diversity of the tropical environment

Numerous factors other than latitude modify climate in a very sensitive way: altitude and proximity to the sea are examples. Combined with the presence of mountains, the dominant wind regime and the great marine currents, these factors contribute to the creation of the hyperhumid equatorial forest and the semi-arid steppes passing through the intermediate stages of the deciduous forests and the tree savannas. In fact the climates encountered in the intertropical zone have, perhaps as their only things in common, the absence of low temperatures (with the exception of some regions of high altitude), a limited variation in day length during the year and the violent, or even very violent, characteristic of the rainfall, which itself is very poorly spread over the year. The one or two dry seasons can reach 9 months at the latitude of the Tropics of Capricorn and Cancer. To this varied physical environment comes into play the diversity of the human element, historically established or more or less recently arrived.

The association of these numerous factors has engendered multiple systems of animal production from the most extensive to the most intensive, but in general strongly dependent upon climatic conditions. The latter largely explain the distribution of the cattle population on the intertropical zone. A map would bring out forcibly the scarcity, if not the absence, of cattle in the domain of the dense equatorial forest and their concentration in the savanna and steppe regions, which lie to the north and south of it. The disease environment, itself linked partly to climate, has sometimes played a determining role. The most striking example of this given by the influence of the tsetse fly and trypanosomiasis, and of ticks and babesiosis, on the distribution of the cattle population in tropical Africa. Finally man, by the socio-economic conditions he has created, has largely contributed to the dissemination of cattle in the tropics. It is man who introduced them, after having domesticated them in Mesopotamia and the Indus Valley, into Europe, the Far East and Africa, before adapting them to America and Oceania. Cattle very often accompanied man in his great migrations. In this respect, it should be noted that the expansion of cattle into the tropical environment happened in different ways according to the regions concerned:

1. In Africa humpless cattle (*Bos taurus*) were introduced first followed by the Zebu (*Bos indicus*).
2. In North and South America *Bos taurus*, essentially originating from the Iberian peninsula, was introduced in colonial times, followed at the end of the nineteenth century by an importation of *Bos indicus*, originating particularly from India, into the Antilles and Brazil from where it spread into the whole of tropical America and the southern United States.

The introduction of cattle into South-east Asia seems to have been made essentially in the form of Zebus in the monsoon region and with humpless cattle in the plains and high plateaux of Central Asia. Zebus × humpless cattle, which predominate very far into the tropics, are thus originally from two regions which are not correctly called tropical, namely Mesopotamia and the Indus basin, whose climate is characterised by very high maximum temperatures (distinctly more than in the tropics) for 3–4 months of the year, a low humidity and infrequent, poor rains. This, without doubt, explains the best adaptation of Zebus to the semi-arid tropical climates. Genes with resistance to humid tropical climates would be worth searching for in the subgroup of bovines represented by the semidomesticated or wild species of

South-east Asia (Gaur, Banteng, Gayal and Kouprey), which are perfectly adapted to the Monsoon. In fact it is the domesticated buffalo (*Bubalus bubalis*) which predominates in this region.

The penetration into the tropics of the European type of specialised milking breeds has come about more recently in the course of the last half century. This penetration is continuing. It will probably lead, in the tropical milking areas, to the creation of populations of Zebus and humpless cattle more or less crossed with European blood according to the degree of control of the environment by man.

Homogeneity of the tropical environment

Tropical climates, by their direct and indirect effects on cattle, create stress which is more or less permanent according to the situation: stress due to the combination of high temperatures and high humidities for certain periods of the year; stress due to chronic underfeeding and to water shortage; also the risk of diseases, notably parasites, is much higher than in temperate climates.

However the large majority of tropical regions have other characteristics which influence the development of cattle rearing.

1. Systems of agricultural production which ignore cattle rearing or treat it in a way which is independent of crop production, to such a point that livestock rearing and agriculture are often the business of different ethnic groups. Two notable exceptions are the use of cattle for draught purposes and the use of cows for family milk production in some regions of Asia.
2. There is often some underdevelopment of infrastructure and basic services, such as communication networks, research institutes and teaching institutions specialised in the subject of livestock production, veterinary and agricultural extension services.
3. Production zones (particularly for meat) are often very distant from the principal urban markets.
4. Traditional commercial circles are often solidly established and allow few chances for producers to be involved in fixing of prices for slaughtering cattle; also there are very seasonal and very large variations in prices.
5. Consumer prices (milk and meat) are generally limited by the government and hardly reflect differences in quality. On the majority of markets in the tropics, only two categories of meat exist – with or without bone, whereas in sophisticated markets the range of prices currently runs from one to five according to the category of the cuts and their quality. With only two categories, however, the tropical situation might be unfavourable from a nutritional point of view.
6. There are generally high prices for equipment and certain inputs which must be imported.

Points 4, 5 and 6 mean that beef production is, in general, fairly unprofitable (net benefit less than the rate of interest in force) and does not attract new capital. The very extensive systems are only viable where these rely on family labour who are otherwise underemployed. On the subject of milk, the situation is completely different: in the regions close to the large urban centres, the relationship between the cost of production and price of milk can be very favourable. On the other hand, in the less suitable areas, prices can be very low, particularly during the period of peak production, and only very extensive systems (mixed meat/milk production, one milking per day, little or no supplementary feed, on site conversion of the milk into milk products) can keep going.

7. Processing establishments (abattoirs, dairies) are often badly sited, badly managed and costly to maintain.
8. There are low individual levels of milk consumption (pastoralists excepted) and of beef consumption, despite the relatively low price of these products compared with those of cereals for human consumption.
9. There is often a considerable unsatisfied demand for these products and potentially significant domestic markets if one considers the low level of actual consumption.
10. Home consumption is very significant in the case of cow's milk and very limited for beef, which is most often consumed in the setting of religious rites or feasts on the occasion of marriages or funerals. It is all of these elements, as much as the climate, which contribute to giving tropical cattle rearing its specificity.

Principal resources

Forage resources

In the intertropical zone, the basic forage resources come from the natural vegetation (meadows, savanna grasslands and steppes). The contribution of improved or artificial meadows and forage crops, although always on the increase, still remains negligible on an overall regional level. The same applies to concentrates for cattle feed. Furthermore, the salvaging of crop by-products as well as those from the agro-industries for feeding local cattle is far from complete, even in the regions where small mixed farming is carried on and where the pastures are scarce or non-existent (as is the case in parts of India). As an example, for the whole of Latin America (Argentina and Uruguay included), the following estimates have been made:

1. More than 90 per cent of the energy consumed by cattle comes from pasture, (Thurston, 1969).
2. Less than 10 per cent of pastures are used in a rational way (rotation, pasture resting, bringing forward of the harvest etc.) (McDowell, 1966).

Table 1.1 Permanent pastures and human population (1988)

	Permanent pastures		Human population		Total area	
	1 000 ha	Percentage	Thousands	Percentage	1 000 ha	Percentage
World	3 214 352	100.0	5 114 788	100.0	13 389 055	100.0
Tropical Africa*	634 985	19.7	462 393	9.0	2 328 511	17.1
Tropical America†	400 874	12.5	382 806	7.5	1 683 357	12.6
Tropical Asia and Oceania‡	29 577	0.9	1 383 211	27.0	854 445	6.4
Tropical countries (total)	1 065 436	33.1	2 228 410	43.5	4 866 313	36.4
Developed countries§	1 261 433	39.2	1 235 303	24.1	5 620 266	41.9

* Africa minus Morocco, Algeria, Tunisia, Libya, Egypt, Lesotho, Swaziland, South Africa.
† Latin America minus Argentina, Chile and Uruguay.
‡ Asia = the Near East and Middle East excluded as well as Pakistan, Bhutan, Nepal, China, Mongolia, USSR, North and South Korea, Japan. Oceania minus Australia and New Zealand.
§ All beyond the tropical zone, except the north of Australia and the extreme south of the United States.
(Source FAO, *Production Yearbook*, **42**, 1988)

The tropical countries have almost one-third of the permanent pasture in the world (Table 1.1). If one takes account of the fact that, in the tropics, much of the zones classed as 'forest' are in fact exploited as pasture and one can consider, as a rough approximation, that half of the permanent pastures are in the tropics. Table 1.1 shows however that the different tropical regions are about this level, considering that tropical Africa alone would possess almost 20 per cent of the world pastures, Latin America 12 per cent, whereas Asia and Oceania (Australia excluded) would only account for 1 per cent.

It should also be remembered that the productivity of tropical pastures is extremely variable over time and according to place, taking account of the differences in rainfall and the fertility of the soils. On the other hand, their exploitation can be limited by shortage of drinking water or by health factors (tsetse fly for example). The area of permanent pasture is thus only a small element in the estimation of the forage potential of a region. Whereas the area of permanent pastures is generally reducing (Asia: − 2 per cent in the course of the last 15 years), it is expanding in South America (+ 8.7 per cent in the same period).

The statistics concerning the consumption of cereal grains by livestock are still far too imprecise and fragmentary in most of the tropical countries for the purposes of determining their role in animal feeding with any sort of precision. Nevertheless, a study by the Food and Agricultural Organisation (FAO) (1979a) showed an increase in this consumption of 4.2 per cent per year for all the developing countries in the course of the 1963–1973 decade, the average rate of growth for the period 1973–1985 being estimated at 3.9 per cent per year. If one compares these rates with those concerning the increase in poultry meat and egg production over the first period (+ 6.8 per cent and 3.9 per cent respectively), one can deduce that the essential increase in consumption of grains occurred in the poultry sector, the cattle sector only accounting for a modest part (notably in the intensive milk production sector).

Only a drastic change in the relationship of the price of beef to the price of cereals, coinciding with the appearance of large surpluses of cereals on the national markets, could lead to a significant consumption of grains by ruminants in the tropics. Such a change is hardly forseeable, at least in the course of the next decade. From the estimates made in the study cited before, one can calculate that in 1973, tropical cattle consumed a maximum of 2 per cent of the concentrate food used in the world by livestock (on the basis of their energy value), or 1.6 per cent of forage cereals.

Animal resources

More than half of the world bovine herd (buffalo included) is found in the tropics, which also has 20 per cent of the sheep, 60 per cent of the goats, 40 per cent of the horses and mules, about 50 per cent of the donkeys and 70 per cent of the camels, including only the domesticated herbivores (Table 1.2). But the distribution of this animal population is very unequal and is a function of the physical environment and socio-economic factors prevailing in each region. This is also the case in tropical Asia, which accounts for 45 per cent of tropical bovines (the impact of the Indian herd) and only 8 per cent of the horses and mules. In tropical America, the figures are 33 per cent of tropical bovines but 77 per cent of horses and mules, while Africa has 51 per cent of the sheep, 53 per cent of the goats and 90 per cent of the dromedaries and camels kept in

Table 1.2 Livestock populations 1988

	Cattle and buffalo		Sheep		Goats		Horse and mules	
	Thousands	Percentage	Thousands	Percentage	Thousands	Percentage	Thousands	Percentage
World	1 400 910	100.0	1 150 952	100.0	520 376	100.0	80 754	100.0
Tropical Africa	161 787	11.5	125 934	10.9	146 733	28.2	4 682	5.8
Tropical America	246 335	17.6	56 533	4.9	31 125	6.0	25 268	31.3
Tropical Asia and Oceania	341 292	24.4	58 845	5.1	133 176	25.5	2 602	3.2
Tropical countries (total)	749 414	53.5	241 312	20.9	311 034	59.7	32 552	40.3
Developed countries	425 704	31.9	528 538	46.7	24 983	5.3	22 683	28.9

	Donkeys		Camels		Pigs	
	Thousands	Percentage	Thousands	Percentage	Thousands	Percentage
World	41 599	100.0	18 964	100.0	823 403	100.0
Tropical Africa	10 670	25.6	13 543	71.4	11 473	1.4
Tropical America	7 454	17.9	–	–	72 833	8.8
Tropical Asia and Oceania	1 355	3.3	1 390	7.3	52 123	6.3
Tropical countries (total)	19 479	46.8	14 933	78.7	136 429	16.5
Developed countries	1 576	3.8	275	1.4	337 969	41.0

(Source FAO, *Production Yearbook*, **42**, 1988)

Table 1.3 Density of animal populations (1988)

	Cattle and buffalo		Sheep		Goats		Horses and mules		Donkeys		Camels		Pigs	
	S	P	S	P	S	P	S	P	S	P	S	P	S	P
World	10.4	43.6	8.6	35.8	3.9	16.2	0.6	2.5	0.3	1.3	0.1	0.6	6.1	25.6
Tropical Africa	6.9	25.5	5.4	19.8	6.3	23.1	0.2	0.7	0.4	1.1	0.6	2.1	0.05	1.8
Tropical America	14.6	61.4	3.3	14.1	1.8	7.7	1.5	6.3	0.4	1.9	–	–	4.3	18.2
Tropical Asia and Oceania	39.9	115.3	6.8	198.8	15.6	449.9	0.30	8.8	0.1	4.5	0.2	4.7	6.1	17.6
Tropical countries (total)	15.4	70.3	4.9	22.6	6.4	29.2	0.66	3.0	0.4	1.8	0.3	1.4	2.8	12.8
Developed countries	7.2	32.1	9.8	43.8	0.5	2.2	0.40	1.7	0.03	0.1	0.004	0.002	6.0	26.8

S = density per square kilometre of ground; P = density per square kilometre of permanent pasture.
(Source FAO, Production Yearbook, **42**, 1988)

the tropics. More than 82 million buffalo, or 62 per cent of the world population, live in the tropics. In fact, if one included the tropical areas of China and Pakistan among the latter, the proportion would be even greater.

Related to the area of land and available permanent pastures in each large region, the distribution of the tropical herd makes the disparities appear even greater (Table 1.3). Thus the cattle density per square kilometre of pasture is respectively between 6.9 and 25.5 in tropical Africa to 40 and 1153 in tropical Asia/Oceania (Australia excluded). The same table also shows, at the regional level, the insignificant role that pastures play in Asia: each hectare of permanent pasture contributes to the maintenance of 11 cattle, 2 sheep, 5 goats, 0.08 horses, 0.05 camels and 10.04 donkeys, without mentioning pigs which are still largely herbivores in this part of the world.

All the animals have to find their nutritional essentials outside of the resource of the permanent pasture (natural vegetation on roadsides and embankments, straw and other by-products, fallow and forage crops etc.).

Table 1.4 Number of cattle, sheep, goats and pigs per 100 inhabitants (1988)

	Cattle and buffalo	Sheep	Goats	Pigs
World	27.4	22.5	10.1	16.1
Tropical Africa	34.9	27.2	31.7	2.5
Tropical America	64.3	14.7	8.1	19.0
Tropical Asia and Oceania	24.6	4.2	9.6	3.7
Tropical countries	33.6	10.8	13.9	6.1
Developed countries	32.8	44.8	2.3	27.3

(Source FAO, *Production Yearbook*, **42**, 1988)

Table 1.4 indicates that the tropical countries are, as a group, well provided for in ruminant numbers compared with developed countries: per 100 inhabitants, the former have 34.0 cattle and buffalo, and 14 goats as against 33 and 2.3; on the contrary, the developed countries (which include, among others, Australia and New Zealand) keep 44.8 sheep per 100 inhabitants against 10.8 in the tropics. Tropical Africa is particularly rich in livestock: 35 cattle, 27 sheep and 32 goats per 100 inhabitants. The situation is less favourable when one no longer considers the numbers, but the tonnages.

Meat and milk production

Table 1.5 gives the production of beef, mutton and goat, pig and poultry meat, as well as the production of milk, in the main areas of the globe. The tropical countries respectively produce 19 per cent, 22 per cent, 8 per cent, 20 per cent and 17 per cent of the world output and the developed countries respectively produce 69 per cent, 43 per cent, 59 per cent, 65 per cent and 75 per cent of the same products. The remainder comes from the non-tropical developing countries, that is to say essentially from China, Pakistan, Argentina, Uruguay, the Near East and from North Africa.

Table 1.5 Meat and milk production (1988)

Meat production*

	Beef and buffalo meat		Sheep and goat meat		Pig meat		Poultry meat	
	1 000 t	Percentage	1 000 t	Percentage	1 000 t	Percentage	1 000 t	Percentage
World	50 254	100.0	8 911	100.0	64 381	100.0	36 862	100.0
Tropical Africa	2 126	4.2	971	10.9	353	0.5	914	2.5
Tropical America	5 617	11.2	239	2.7	2 744	4.3	4 022	10.9
Tropical Asia and Oceania	1 690	3.4	722	8.1	2 341	3.6	2 334	6.3
Tropical countries (total)	9 433	18.8	1 932	21.7	5 438	8.4	7 270	19.7
Developed countries	34 582	68.8	3 803	42.7	37 828	58.8	24 029	65.2
Tropical developing countries	6 239	12.4	3 176	35.6	21 115	32.8	5 563	15.1

Milk production †

	Cow and buffalo milk		Small ruminant milk		Milk (total)	
	1 000 t	Percentage	1 000 t	Percentage	1 000 t	Percentage
World	526 619	100.0	17 316	100.0	523 935	100.0
Tropical Africa	6 996	1.2	2 945	17.0	9 941	1.9
Tropical America	31 504	6.2	527	3.0	32 031	6.1
Tropical Asia and Oceania	49 269†	9.7	1 754	10.1	51 023	9.7
Tropical countries (total)	87 769	17.4	5 226	30.1	92 995	17.7
Developed countries	378 007	74.6	5 870	33.9	383 877	73.3
Tropical developing countries	40 843	8.0	6 220	36.0	47 063	9.0

* Meat, expressed in carcass weight, originating from indigenous animals.
† Of which 24 765 produced by buffalo.
(Source: FAO, *Production Yearbook*, **42**, 1988)

Table 1.6 Participation of the principal regions of the world in the production of beef and buffalo meat and the production of cow and buffalo milk

	Beef and buffalo meat			Cow and buffalo milk		
	1970	1980	1988	1970	1980	1988
World	100	100	100	100	100	100
Tropical Africa	4.1	4.3	4.2	1.3	1.2	1.4
Tropical America	9.4	10.1	11.2	4.8	5.6	6.2
Tropical Asia and Oceania	2.5	2.5	3.4	5.7	7.0	9.7
Tropical countries (total)	16.0	16.9	18.1	11.8	13.8	17.3
Non-tropical developing countries	15.7	16.0	12.4	6.9	7.8	16.3
Developed countries	68.3	67.1	68.8	81.3	78.4	76.4

(Source: FAO, *Production Yearbook*, **42**, 1988)

In time, the contribution of the tropical countries towards world supplies of beef will increase slightly, considering that it went from 16 per cent in 1970 to 18.8 per cent in 1988. Furthermore, these same countries represent a greater and greater part of the world production of cows' milk (17.3 per cent in 1988, as against 11.8 per cent in 1970) (Table 1.6). This development is due principally to the slowing down of production in most parts of the developed world whereas many of the tropical countries are following a policy of encouraging their national production, a policy which is beginning to bear fruit. In the course of the last 15 years, whereas the milk production from the group of developed countries had a tendency to regress, that of tropical America increased by 2.9 per cent per annum, that of tropical Africa by 1.9 per cent and that of tropical Asia by 4.6 per cent (Table 1.7). As regards beef and buffalo meat production, it is in tropical Asia and Oceania that the highest rate of increase has been observed during the last 20 years, followed by tropical America. Globally production has increased more in the tropical countries than in the developed countries during this same period. However, it is notable that a significant part of the increase registered in tropical America is due to the exploitation of new pastures, whereas in tropical Africa and Asia, there has been something of a reduction in the areas of permanent pastures.

Table 1.7 Evolution of production over time (base 100: average 1969–1971)

| | Beef and buffalo meat | | | | | |
| | 1970[1] | | 1980 | | 1988 | |
	1 000 t	Percentage	1 000 t	Percentage	1 000 t	Percentage
World	39 952	100	46 758	117.0	50 254	125.8
Tropical Africa	1 662	100	2 006	120.7	2 126	128.0
Tropical America	3 773	100	4 739	125.0	5 617	148.8
Tropical Asia and Oceania	1 009	100	1 187	117.0	1 690	167.5
Tropical countries (total)	6 444	100	7 932	123.0	9 433	146.3
Developed countries	27 312	100	31 390	114.9	34 582	126.6

| | Cow and buffalo meat | | | | | |
| | 1970[1] | | 1980 | | 1988 | |
	1 000 t	Percentage	1 000 t	Percentage	1 000 t	Percentage
World	384 800	100	455 096	118.2	502 619	131.6
Tropical Africa	4 948	100	5 668	114.5	6 996	141.4
Tropical America	18 788	100	25 816	137.4	31 504	167.7
Tropical Asia and Oceania	22 011	100	31 800	144.4	49 269	223.8
Tropical countries (total)	45 747	100	63 284	139.7	87 769	191.8
Developed countries	312 932	100	357 146	114.1	387 007	123.6

1. Average 1969–1971.
(Source: FAO, *Production Yearbook*, **42**, 1988)

If one examines the annual production per animal by region (Table 1.8), one is struck by the very low yield from the tropical herds. This yield is noticeably inferior (1 as against 6.8) in the case of cattle, which only produce 12.6 kg per year of meat (carcass) as against 85.3 kg for their counterparts in the developed countries. The difference is noticeably less in the case of sheep and goat meat production (1 to 1.85), which leads us to suppose that sheep and goats are, in general, less affected by the tropical environment. The difference is greatest in the case of bovine milk production (1 to 8) or, in absolute values, 117 kg of milk per animal in the tropics as opposed to 932 kg of milk in the developed countries. It is the Asiatic cattle herd which has the lowest yield in meat (4.9 kg per year) as against 22.8 kg for the tropical American cattle herd. On the subject of milk production, it is the African animal which has the lowest yield (43 kg per year as against 144 kg per year for its counterpart in Asia). Sheep and goats produce less meat in tropical America (3.9 kg per year) and the most productive in tropical Asia. As a standard of comparison, the highest statistic for yield of beef is recorded in Belgium (102.6 kg), a country where animal production is carried on at a very high level of intensification. For France, the figure is 77.9 kg. Among the countries where beef production is still relatively extensive, examples are Australia (58.8 kg), Argentina (55.2 kg) and Brazil (25.3 kg). The comparison with Brazil, a tropical country, or sub-tropical in the southern part, gives an idea of the level which could be attained by cattle enterprises in the tropics.

On the subject of tropical bovine milk production, the progress realised in the area of applied animal genetics as well as in the nutrition of ruminants enables certain countries to obtain particularly high levels of milk production per animal per year: for example 5104 kg in Holland, 5312 kg in Sweden and 3875 kg in Belgium. Conversely, in Brazil, a country where there is still relatively little specialised dairying and where the majority of cattle is exploited mainly for beef, the figure is only 134 kg per animal per year.

The reasons for the mediocrity of the yields observed in the tropical countries are multiple and they are analysed in detail elsewhere. The principal

Table 1.8 Production per animal (kg per year) (1988)

	Cattle/buffalo meat	Cow/buffalo milk	Sheep/goat meat*
World	35.8	361.7	5.3
Tropical Africa	13.1	43.2	3.6
Tropical America	22.8	127.9	2.7
Tropical Asia and Oceania	4.6	144.3	3.7
Tropical countries (total)	12.6	117.1	3.5
Developed countries	85.3	932.2	6.5

* Meat expressed in kilograms of carcass.
(Source: FAO, *Production Yearbook*, **42**, 1988)

factors influencing yield are the low rate of exploitation of the herd (due to a high mortality rate, to a poor growth rate and to a very low calving rate) and the insufficient carcass weight. According to an FAO study (1979b), whereas the rate of exploitation of the cattle herd of the developed countries was 31.8 per cent in 1973, it was only 9.6 per cent in the same year for the developing countries overall. The mean carcass weights were 208 kg and 157 kg respectively. A study of Christiansen (1971) looked at the variations in herd yield so that one can compare one country with another and according to the quality of the stockmanship itself in the same region, which in this case was Latin America.

The genotype of tropical breeds is not generally the factor which limits beef production, at least with the modest level of environmental control which still prevails in the majority of tropical countries. The daily liveweight gain obtained in good rearing conditions (correct feeding, rigorous health control, good management) confirms this point. It is not the same in the case of milk production where cows of local breeds usually respond badly to improvement of the surroundings and rapidly reach their production ceiling.

Table 1.9 Productivity indices for beef cattle in some Latin American countries

Country Quality of stockmanship	Killing out percentage	Production ha/year (kg/carcass)	Production per animal present/year (kg/carcass)
Venezuela 1971			
(Western Llanos)			
Average husbandry	7.3	9.4	5.0
Improved husbandry	16.3	13.0	13.7
Intensive husbandry	22.4	190.3	19.6
Argentina			
(Province Buenos Aires)			
Average husbandry	30.0	90.0	18.0
Good husbandry	33.0	150.0	25.0
Uruguay			
Average husbandry	20.0	85.0	20.4
Good husbandry	29.0	140.0	33.6
Paraguay			
(Eastern Chaco)			
Average husbandry	17.0	18.0	25.7
Good husbandry	20.0	30.0	42.9
Brazil			
Average husbandry	13.0	11.0	11.0
Good husbandry	22.0	36.0	12.0
Dominican Republic			
Average husbandry	22.0	14.0	18.6
Good husbandry	31.0	120.0	41.4

(Source: Christensen 1971)

Supply, demand and trade

Supply

In the tropical countries, supply depends a lot more upon local meat and milk production than it does in the temperate developed countries. The availability of these two products, to the people, are very variable according to region and more so in one country than another (Table 1.10). As one could expect, tropical Asia comes very far behind the other groups for availability of beef per inhabitant: 1.2 kg per inhabitant per year, whereas tropical American and Africa respectively have availabilities of 14.6 kg and 4.6 kg and the developed countries as a group have 28 kg. For sheep and goat meat, the African consumer has 2.1 kg at his disposal as against 0.6, 0.5 and 3.07 kg per tropical American, Asian and developed country consumer. The availabilities of cows' milk varies from 306 kg per inhabitant in the developed countries to 15.1 kg for the tropical Asian countries, with an average of 39.4 kg for the tropical countries as a whole.

Table 1.10 Beef, mutton and cow's milk availability per inhabitant (kg/year) (1988)

	Beef/buffalo meat*	Sheep/goat meat*	Cow/buffalo milk
World	9.82	1.74	99.05
Tropical Africa	4.6	2.1	15.1
Tropical America	14.6	0.6	82.3
Tropical Asia and Oceania	1.2	0.5	35.6
Tropical countries (total)	4.2	0.86	39.4
Developed countries	28.0	3.07	306.0

* Meat expressed in kilograms of carcass obtained from local animals.
(Source FAO, *Production Yearbook*, **42**, 1988)

There is, on average, a difference in the proportion of different meat products between the tropical countries and the developed ones. Beef and pork together represent about three-quarters of the total meat produced in the developed countries as in the developing countries (essentially tropical).

Sheep meat represents 4 per cent in the developed countries compared with 8 per cent in the tropical countries, the corresponding figures for poultry meat being 24 per cent and 30 per cent.

Table 1.11 also shows that in the entire world, the proportion of poultry meat is growing rapidly, whereas that of sheep and pig meat is diminishing. The proportion of beef is diminishing in the developing countries but is still increasing in the developed countries.

Table 1.11 Relative production of different meats (percentage)

	Tropical developing countries			Developed countries		
	1962–1964	1972–1974	1988	1962–1964	1972–1974	1988
All meats	100	100	100	100	100	100
Beef and veal	40	36	39.1	39	41	34.5
Pig meat	38	37	22.6	37	34	37.7
Poultry meat	11	18	30.2	15	21	24.0
Sheep and goat meat	11	9	8.1	9	4	3.8

(*Source*: OAA/FAO, 1988)

Demand

Demand and real consumption essentially depend, in the tropics as in the temperate countries, upon the revenue per inhabitant. With this concept it is necessary to note that the price differences between the meat of different species are fairly variable according to region and country, which contributes to the orientation of the demand towards one meat rather than another. Thus poultry meat is in general more expensive in the tropical countries, where industrial rearing still only accounts for a modest part of the overall supply. For example, in the Ivory Coast, chicken cost 20–24 Francs/kg in 1977 as against 9–11 Francs/kg for off the bone beef.

The law of supply and demand contributes to render sheep meat more expensive than beef in a number of tropical countries.

The combination of the different factors such as average revenue, the availability of various commodities, relative price and eating traditions, leads to a great diversity of diets observed in the different regions. According to an investigation by FAO in 1971, the contribution of animal products (fish included) to the daily ration was as shown in Table 1.12

Table 1.12 Proportion of animal products in the ration

	Percentage of calories in the ration coming from animal source*	Percentage of proteins in the ration coming from animal source*
Asia	8.7	19.7
Africa	7.7	21.8
Latin America	19.3	45.5
Europe	32.6	55.4

* Fish included

Except in the traditional stock rearing regions (the Sahelian countries and the Llanos of South America, for example), the average consumer in the tropical countries is far from satisfied in his desire for meat and, even if this commodity is found in sufficient quantity on the national markets, his ability to purchase would not allow him to eat more.

The availability of animal products in the ration of inhabitants is given in Table 1.13.

Table 1.13 Availability of food per inhabitant (cal/day per inhabitant)

	Available food		Availability of animal products in ration
	1961–1963	1983–1985	1983–1985
World	2 316	2 665	350 (13.1)*
Developing countries (94)	1 957	2 424	176 (7.2)
Sub-Saharan Africa	2 045	2 051	102 (4.9)
Asia	1 856	2 380	137 (5.7)
Latin America	2 283	2 703	391 (14.4)
Developed countries	3 090	3 372	869 (25.7)

* percentage of total availability
(Source FAO, *Agriculture: Horizon 2000*, 1989)

During the period 1962–72, the availability of animal protein per inhabitant remained essentially the same in tropical Africa (9.4 g per day) and in Latin America (235 g per day) but rose from 6.5 to 7.3 g per day in the Far East and from 47.9 to 55.6 g per day in the developed market economy countries. The figures in Table 1.14, which only concern the consumption of beef, indicate that this quasi-stagnation of individual consumption in the tropical countries is equally observed for this commodity (beef) and that this situation continued in the period 1972–1977.

Table 1.14 Production, trade and consumption of beef in the tropical countries*
(carcass equivalent)

	Tropical Africa	Tropical America	Tropical Asia	Tropical Oceania
1972–1974				
Production (000 t)	1773	4178	1061	12
Balance of trade (000 t)†	− 36	− 184	70	37
Consumption total (000 t)	1737	3994	1131	49
Consumption per inhabitant (kg)	6.3	14.8	1.2	11.5
1975				
Production (000 t)	1748	4217	1097	12
Balance of trade (000 t)†	− 28	− 53	76	41
Consumption total (000 t)	1720	4164	1173	53
Consumption per inhabitant (kg)	5.8	14.8	1.1	12.0
1976				
Production (000 t)	1829	4356	1260	11
Balance of trade (000 t)†	− 20	− 105	85	44
Consumption total (000 t)	1809	4251	1345	55
Consumption per inhabitant (kg)	5.9	14.7	1.2	12.1
1977				
Production (000 t)	1866	4670	1139	13
Balance of trade (000 t)†	36	− 147	93	50
Consumption total (000 t)	1902	4523	1232	63
Consumption per inhabitant (kg)	6.1	15.2	1.1	13.5

* Trade in cattle on the hoof included here.
† Trade balance: signifies exports.
(*Source*: Division of Produce and Commerce, FAO.)

Trade

Overall, the tropical countries, which were net exporters of beef, were becoming slightly deficient in 1977 (Table 1.14). Asia and Oceania have been deficient for a number of years, whereas tropical Latin America is regularly in surplus. Tropical Africa became deficient considering that, after having exported 36 000 tones of beef in 1972–74, this region had to import 36 000 tonnes in 1977. Nevertheless, there are very noticeable differences between the climatic zones of the region: the Sahelian countries and East

Table 1.15 Production, supply and consumption of beef* in intertropical Africa (1974)

	Consumption per inhabitant (kg/year)	Supply per inhab. (kg/year)	Production Number of cattle per 10 people	Production kg carcass per animal per year	Imports (+) Exports (−) (in tonnes)
Sahalian countries†	7.3	7.9	7	11.5	− 83 000
E. Africa‡	6.6	6.8	7	10.5	− 49 000
C. Africa§	3.6	3.1	2	17.4	+ 26 000
Coastal countries of W. Africa¶	3.1	2.7	1	19.6	+ 49 000
Average for inter-tropical Africa	5.2	5.0	4	12.2	− 36 000

* Kilograms of carcass, offal not included.
† Sahelian and similar countries: Gambia, Burkina Faso, Mali, Mauritania, Niger, Senegal, Somalia, Sudan and Chad. ‡ East Africa: Burundi, Ethiopia, Kenya, Madagascar, Malawi, Mozambique, Uganda, Rwanda, Tanzania, Zambia. § Central Africa: Angola Cameroun, Congo, Central African Republic, Gabon, Zaire. ¶ Coastal West Africa: Benin, Cape Verde, Ivory Coast, Ghana, Guinea, Guinea-Bissau, Liberia, Nigeria, Sierra Leone, Togo.

(*Source*: Division of Produce and Trade, FAO.)

Table 1.16 Import and exports of different meats by various tropical regions (1977)

	Beef and veal t*	Beef and veal %*	Sheep t*	Sheep %*	Pig t*	Pig %*	Poultry t*	Poultry %*	Preserves t†	Preserves %†
Imports										
Tropical Africa	91 644	2.4	7 101	0.8	12 050	0.5	75 016	4.0	37 424	3.0
Tropical America	219 500	5.7	43 487	4.9	46 733	1.9	124 463	6.6	67 074	5.3
Tropical Far East	98 827	2.5	58 702	6.7	69 369	2.8	173 890	9.2	90 547	7.2
Total tropical		10.6		12.4		5.2		19.8		15.5
Exports										
Tropical Africa	20 399	0.5	170	0.0	95	0.0	291	0.0	8 149	0.6
Tropical America	158 725	4.1	223	0.0	9 856	0.4	215 981	11.7	99 252	7.8
Tropical Far East	33 433	0.8	6 250	0.7	1 027	0.0	111 313	6.0	21 039	1.6
Total tropical		5.4		0.7		0.4		17.7		10.0

* Values are for fresh, refrigerated and frozen meat (carcass equivalent)
† Values are for actual weight

% = Percentage of global trade.
(*Source*: Division of Produce and Trade, FAO.)

Africa were net exporters (1974), whereas the coastal countries of West Africa and those of Central Africa are more and more deficient (Table 1.15).

The participation of the tropical countries in world trade remains modest (Table 1.16): in 1987 they only took 10.6 per cent of world imports of beef, 12.4 per cent of those of sheep meat and 5.2 per cent of those of pig meat. On the other hand these same countries accounted for nearly 20 per cent of the imports of poultry meat. The same year, they participated in the world export of meat with 5.4 per cent for beef, 0.7 per cent for sheep meat, 0.4 per cent for pig meat and 17.7 per cent for poultry meat. The tropical countries were involved in 15.5 per cent of the imports and 10.0 per cent of the exports of meat preserves.

Although they may still be relatively low, the imports of meat into tropical countries constitute a new factor which will have to be taken more and more into account in the future, if the tendency towards the increase observed in the previous years is confirmed. For beef, the imports of tropical countries in 1987 represented 10.6 per cent of world imports as against 4.7 per cent for 1970. The part played by the tropical countries in world imports of sheep and goat meat, pig meat and meat preserves has remained just about constant in the course of the same period and that of poultry meat has moved from 15.2 to 20 per cent.

The multiplication coefficients only have an approximate value because the annual change in imports and exports is very irregular. They nevertheless allow conclusions to be drawn on trends: imports of beef are increasing faster than its export for all the tropical regions. Tropical America is developing its exports of pig and poultry meat considerably, but is reducing its exports of beef.

On the subject of production, consumption and trade in milk and milk products, the 1970s were marked by a decrease in the rate of growth in production at the world level and a supply which was generally greater than demand. However, in the tropical countries, this grew noticeably faster than production, although the latter had had an accelerated growth in relation to the preceding decade. These increased requirements led to an increase in imports of milk and milk products in almost all the tropical countries. In a general way, the price level of milk to the consumer considerably limits the demand for this product in the tropical countries. Nevertheless, consumption per head grew slightly in the majority of these countries. As in the case of meat, one notices great disparities from region to region. According to a study by the Division of Produce and Trade, FAO (1978), the following consumptions per inhabitant were observed in 1972–1974:

Africa	22.4 kg/year	Far East	30.8 kg/year
Latin America	81.8 kg/year	Near East	62.8 kg/year
Developed countries	201.2 kg/year		

World trade in milk and milk products is dominated by the European Economic Community (EEC) (10 035 000 t on average for the years 1972–

74), by Australia and New Zealand (5 685 000 t) and by imports within EEC (2 829 000 t by Italy and 2 674 000 t by the United Kingdom), those of the United States of America (1 475 000 t) and Japan (741 000 t). The whole group of developing countries imported, in the same period, an average of 8 345 000 t of milk and milk products, or about 46 per cent of world imports, Latin America along with the Far East being the principal clients.

Perspective of the future and long-term development of cattle production, consumption and trade

It is always particularly risky to make forecasts on the subject of the development of animal production and the consumption of animal products. In fact, predictions concerning production are often not very precise, notably in the developing countries and, taking account of their large coefficient of elasticity of demand for meat and milk, their consumption is very sensitive to changes in the purchasing power of the customer.

In the tropical countries, if the motivations remain the same, one can note a greater inertia and longer lead times in response to changes which occur in the factors of production or in the factors which affect consumption.

Developments: populations and GDP

In the publication, *Agriculture: Horizon 2000*, FAO presents the perspectives for the development of world agriculture and in particular deals with the case of 90 developing countries which represent 51 per cent of the world population, represent 70 per cent of all developing countries and which are, for the most part, situated in the tropics. In these 90 countries, one actually finds 78 per cent of the cattle, 59 per cent of the sheep and goats and 83 per cent of the pigs.

In the FAO forecasts, two scenarios have been envisaged. The first, an optimistic one, supposes that the developing countries will attain the general objectives of economic growth of the new United Nations international strategy for development, or 7 per cent per annum between 1980 and 2000, (6.8 per cent between 1980 and 1990, 7.2 per cent between 1990 and 2000). The second, less ambitious one, forecasts an annual growth of 5.7 per cent between 1980 and 2000 (5.6 per cent between 1980 and 1990 and 5.8 per cent between 1990 and 2000).

Table 1.17 gives, by region, the rates of demographic growth and growth in Gross Domestic Product (GDP) in the case of the less optimistic scenario discussed above.

Table 1.17 Rates of demographic growth and growth in Gross Domestic Product (GDP)

	Population Rate of growth			
	1963–1975	1980–1990	1990–2000	1980–2000
Developing countries	2.6	2.2	1.9	2.0
Africa	2.6	3.1	2.9	3.0
Far East	2.5	2.3	2.0	2.1
Latin America	2.8	2.7	2.5	2.6
Near East	2.7	2.7	2.4	2.6
Developed countries	1.0	0.7	0.6	0.7
World	1.9	1.8	1.6	1.7
	GDP Rate of growth			
Developing countries	3.2	5.6	5.8	5.7
Africa	2.1	5.3	5.6	5.4
Far East	2.1	5.7	5.8	5.8
Latin America	3.0	5.8	6.1	6.0
Near East	6.1	5.3	5.4	5.4
Developed countries	3.4	3.1	3.2	3.2
World		3.1	3.2	3.2

Values are percentages

Table 1.18 Average energy provision* and percentage of average requirements per person per day

	Total of 90 countries	Africa	Far East	Latin America	Near East
1961–65 Percentage	2111	2139	1990	2434	2285
Energy requirements	92	91	89	102	92
1974–76 Percentage	2179	2180	2023	2525	2562
Energy requirements	95	93	91	106	104
1990 Percentage	2381	2431	2285	2799	2828
Energy requirements	104	104	103	117	115
2000 Percentage	2499	2447	2336	2888	2860
Energy requirements	109	104	105	121	116

* estimate from 80 of the 90 countries
Energy kcal/day per person

Increase in nutritional requirements

The growth in demand will be due to demography (2 259 million people in 1980, 3 630 million in the year 2000) and due to purchasing power. It is accepted that for each unit increase in GDP, demand for animal products, which we are particularly interested in, increases by 0.48.

In the scenario envisaged, from a global point of view, in 1974–1976, the average ration for a person was 2179 kcal/day, or 95 per cent of the average requirement. In 1990, it should be 2381 kcal/day, or 104 per cent of average requirement and in 2000, the corresponding figures will be 2499 kcal/day and 109 per cent (Table 1.18).

These forecasts should be analysed by region because the situations are very different from each other and, within the regions, it is necessary to consider the states in which the mean annual income per head is less than 300 US dollars (1975): the needs which were covered were 86 per cent, or 1981 kcal/day per person in 1974–1976 and will be at least 96 per cent, or 2120 kcal/day per person by the year 2000.

In comparison, the developed countries had 3315 kcal/day per person available to them in 1980 and should have 3415 kcal/day available in 1990 and 3475 kcal/day in the year 2000.

In order to cover requirements, the annual rate of growth in crop production would have to be 3 per cent whereas that of animal production would be 3.7 per cent, or in total, a multiplication by 1.8 of the former and by 2.06 of the latter.

In the year 2000, animal production would represent 24 per cent of agricultural revenue as opposed to 20 per cent in 1980.

Development of production

In order to ensure that requirements are met, modifications of the role of the different species that supply the market should be encouraged. This development has already been appreciable for some years: greater increase in white meat consumption (pig and poultry meat) in relation to red meat (beef, sheep and goat meat) (Table 1.19).

Red meat, which represented 64.3 per cent (16.2 million tonnes) of total meat production in 1980, will account for no more than 55 per cent in the year 2000 (53.2 million tonnes) despite an increase in production of 80 per cent.

White meat will rise from 9 million tonnes (33.7 per cent) to 23.9 million tonnes (45 per cent), an increase of 165 per cent.

Milk production will rise from 97.7 to 186 million tonnes or an increase of 90.3 per cent.

Finally, it is poultry production which will have the strongest growth – from 4.7 to 14.2 million tonnes of poultry meat (202.1 per cent) and from 4.9 to 12.7 million tonnes of eggs (159 per cent).

These figures suggest the global increases in production which should be obtained, but the production as seen in the animal in the herd indicates the progress to be made.

Thus this production should rise from 15.4 kg in 1980 to 25.8 kg in the year 2000 for beef, from 3.9 kg to 5.7 kg for sheep and goat meat, and from 33.3 kg to 49.4 kg for pig meat, or annual increases of 1.06 per cent, 1.9 per cent and 2 per cent respectively.

In other words, accepting that the carcass weights of beef cattle rise from

Table 1.19 Forecast changes in animal production

	Red meat				White meat			
	1980	2000	Annual growth (%)	Increase (%)	1980	2000	Annual growth (%)	Increase (%)
Cattle and buffalo					Pigs			
Numbers	842	945	2.5	12.2	129	196	2.1	51.9
Production of meat	13.0	23.8	3.1	83.1	4.3	9.7	4.2	125.6
Production of milk	97.7	186.0	3.2	90.3	Poultry			
Sheep and goats					Numbers	2541	5190	3.6	104.2
Numbers	806	952	0.8	18.1	Production of meat	4.7	14.2	5.6	202.1
Production of meat	3.2	5.5	2.7	71.8	Production of eggs	4.9	12.7	4.8	159.0
Red meat	16.2	29.3	3.0	80.8	White meat	9	23.9	5.0	165

	1980	2000
Overall total (red meat and white meat)	25.2	53.2

Numbers expressed in millions
Production expressed in millions of tonnes.
(Source: FAO, Agriculture Horizon 2000, 1989)

Table 1.20 Past and forecast balances of food products of animal origin for 90 developing countries low hypothesis

	Year	Production	Imports	Exports	Trade (net)	Internal use	Rate of sufficiency
Beef, veal and buffalo meat							
Balance (past)	1975–79	12.2	0.7	1.4	0.7	11.5	106
Balance (forecast)	2000	23.8	1.8	2.4	0.6	23.2	102
Sheep and goat meat							
Balance (past)	1975–79	2.94	0.25	0.11	− 0.14	3.08	95
Balance (forecast)	2000	5.55	1.36	0.27	− 1.09	6.64	84
Pig meat							
Balance (past)	1975–79	3.93	0.04	0.03	− 0.01	3.94	100
Balance (forecast)	2000	9.65	0.06	0.18	0.12	9.53	101
Poultry meat							
Balance (past)	1975–79	4.37	0.24	0.05	− 0.19	4.56	96
Balance (forecast)	2000	14.18	0.07	0.29	0.22	13.96	102
Total meat							
Balance (past)	1975–79	23.44	1.23	1.59	− 0.36	23.08	101
Balance (forecast)	2000	53.2	3.29	3.14	− 0.24	53.33	100
Milk and milk products							
Balance (past)	1975–79	90.7	11.3	0.5	− 10.8	101.5	89
Balance (forecast)	2000	186.2	24.0	0.4	− 23.6	209.8	89
Eggs							
Balance (past)	1975–79	4.43	0.09	0.01	− 0.08	4.51	98
Balance (forecast)	2000	12.88	0.05	0.22	0.17	12.51	101

Values are in millions of tonnes.
(Source: FAO, Agriculture Horizon 2000, 1989)

137 kg to 156 kg as indicated by Hrabvoszky (1981), the yield would rise from 11.2 per cent to 16.1 per cent of herd numbers.

For sheep and goats, if the carcass weight rose from 12.5 kg to 14.7 kg, the yield would increase from 31.7 to 36.1 per cent.

For pigs, the corresponding figures would be 57 kg to 61.9 kg, 58.4 per cent and 79 per cent.

For poultry, the production per bird should rise from 1.84 kg to 2.73 kg as the average weight gain to aim for is in the order of 0.1 kg. It is necessary, therefore, that the yield increases by 168 per cent to 228 per cent.

Production and self-sufficiency

If one integrates consumption, imports and exports into the forecasts of predicted demand and self-sufficiency – (Table 1.20), one notes that for beef, buffalo meat and veal, self-sufficiency, which was 106 per cent in 1975–1979, will be no more than 102 per cent in the year 2000, i.e. an appreciable fall.

For sheep and goat meat, the situation is less favourable at 95 per cent in 1975–1979 and 84 per cent in the year 2000.

In total, for meat, self-sufficiency, which was 101 per cent in 1975–1979, will be no more than 100 per cent in the year 200.

For milk and milk products, the deficit will stay at 89 per cent despite an annual increase in imports of 11.3 to 24 million tonnes between 1975–1979 and the year 2000.

For eggs, self-sufficiency of 98 per cent in 1975–1979 will reach 101 per cent in the year 2000.

For the whole field of animal production, needs will theoretically be met at a level of 100 per cent, but the improvement of nutritional status will unfortunately be unequally distributed, for purely geographical reasons [distances of production zones from consumption zones, and climatic and economic conditions (greater demand in the zones of intensive development)].

Ways of increasing numbers

The figures do not give an indication of variations in production parameters, other than increase in numbers, growth of yield in number, and the improvement of production per animal.

Each of these objectives can be attained by different routes: the increase of numbers is linked to the fertility of the breeding stock and reduction of mortality; the increase in yield depends upon precocity, feeding conditions and the reduction of sickness. Increase in carcass weight is obtained by genetic improvement and by better feeding, which are the most important aspects of improvement.

It is for the animal scientist and the economist to make the choice according to the availability of the resources of labour, land, animals, capital, etc . . .

Means of increasing production

Increase in animal production is limited by increase in the availability of forage. FAO forecast that the areas devoted to the production of forage will rise from 27 880 to 32 620 million hectares from 1980 to the year 2000, the production (expressed in millions of tonnes) rising from 131.4 to 239.4, or an 82.2 per cent increase.

The use of concentrates is predicted to increase to 157 per cent (144.0 million tonnes) instead of 55.9 per cent.

From the structural point of view, a greater integration of livestock rearing and general agriculture should be encouraged. The numbers of cattle ought to rise from 159.3 to 184.8 million, or an increase of 16 per cent.

For investment purposes, the gross annual requirements for the livestock sector as such (increase in livestock numbers, development of pastures and of milk and meat production) should reach 10 108 million US dollars in 1990 and 13 838 million US dollars in the year 2000.

Conclusion

There is no single tropical environment, but a number of very varied situations. They sometimes present a certain number of common characteristics which contribute to create common constraints.

As a whole, the tropical countries have significant resources as regards livestock production and more particularly as regards cattle rearing. There are still abundant, if not excessive, rural labour force, significant cattle populations and vast areas of pasture, where it is often difficult, if not impossible, to envisage any enterprises other than livestock rearing. However the rational exploitation of these resources is still very patchy, although the techniques capable of resolving the problems of production are known today in the majority of cases. Productivity, whatever it may be on a per hectare, per head or per worker basis, has only progressed very slowly in the course of the last two decades.

As cattle production has not kept up with the rate of human population growth, there is a strong unsatisfied demand, in the majority of tropical countries, for milk and meat. However the actual consumption is seriously restricted by the low purchasing power of the majority of consumers, for whom retail prices are already too high. At the other extreme, the producer is often in a difficult position and the course taken, notably for beef, does not allow him to envisage the introduction of more intensive techniques. However these techniques are the only ones which would enable an increase in production when the limits of expansion of the pasture area are reached. In the face of this dilemma, the price of production hardly remunerative – the price to the consumer already too high, there only remains the hope that the national economies of the tropical countries will develop sufficiently fast to lead to an improvement of the living standards of their inhabitants so that they can satisfy their need for milk and meat.

It is difficult to envisage significant and lasting development of tropical animal production in the absence of a general economic leap in the tropical countries themselves. However, implementing improved systems of production will involve considerable investment, often beyond the scope of the small farmer. It will be important to assist these activities, at least during the initial stages, and to help them by reinforcement of the necessary support structures, notably in the areas of establishment, extension, veterinary assistance, agricultural credit, marketing and research. It is with this support that tropical livestock production can hope to reach its potential for production.

PART I

THE TROPICAL ENVIRONMENT

Introduction

Farm animal production in both the tropics and equatorial regions has the same aims as that in temperate zones: to convert cultivated or harvested natural products into either foodstuffs or raw materials for agro-industrial processes by using the animal as a converter.

The definition by Baudement, the first incumbent of the chair of animal science at the National Institute of Agronomy in France, which was founded in 1848 by the Count de Gasparin, is still valid today: 'farm animals are machines, literally they consume and produce'.

The term 'zootechnics', introduced by De Gasparin, is now little used but it does encompass the definition given by Sansom: 'the science of production and exploitation of the animal machine'.

There was a time when the terms 'problematical' and 'systems approach' were not invented, but the methodology indicated by Sanson outlined them: 'the exploitation of the animal machine shows the bringing into play of economic functions derived from normal physiological functions of a more or less highly specialised nature.'

To Baron, the animal scientist is 'an engineer of living machines; his task amongst other things is to examine procedures used by practitioners in order to formulate a scientific explanation and to dispose of irrational notions and habits resulting from observation only, which debase results and hold back progress.'

Claude Bernard considered animal science as 'experimental zoology' and Dechambre summed up Baron's ideas in 1928:

> the zootechnician must also be concerned with the economic consequences of the principles he has formulated. Farm animals, except for exotic breeds and those used for sport, are produced and exploited with the practical purpose of producing a definite output with a stated financial return. There is then a point in looking into the favourable circumstances in which this return can be maximised and consequently to take account of the economic parameters within which the animals are being raised.

Some examples will provide a good introduction to the description of animal production systems in the tropics.

To avoid errors of judgement and to understand the motivations of the stockmen, it is useful to describe the basics of the systems by which the stockman, starting with food resources and natural or cultivated forage, uses his animals to maximise his income. The term 'income' being considered in the widest sense; he obtains monetary income as well as capital appreciation from herd expansion or the purely subjective social benefit associated with the respect for one who owns many livestock.

There are many possible approaches to the description of production systems.

One can consider the animal as a system from which, starting with known inputs available to the stockman under given conditions, production value can be expressed in physical quantities (meat, milk) or in financial terms.

The animal can be considered as a subsystem in a larger organisation – the herd – which not only produces but also reproduces. Evaluation of production is more exacting than evaluation of inputs (basically foodstuffs), the later depends upon the exploitation of agricultural land or natural pasture. Finally, one can consider that the unit of production is made up by the herd and the land which it exploits.

Whatever the approach used, the objectives of production and the choice of means of production are the job of the stockman who takes account of the constraints imposed by the chosen system itself. Under the term 'environment' are gathered:

1. the physical and chemical conditions
   - climate, soils and water resources
2. the biological conditions
   - plant resources for food
   - disease and pests
3. cultural conditions
   - social structures of the stock rearers
   - involvement in the economic system.

All are likely to have an influence on the animals and on the human activities which affect their husbandry and exploitation.

Figure I.1 shows the complexity of the constraints to which the herd is subject and their interactions.

In order to look objectively at systems of production, it is advisable to describe:

1. the tropical environment in the wider sense;
2. the animal as an engine of production and the interaction of animal with environment;
3. the stockmen whose decisions determine the nature of herd exploitation systems;
4. the different types and techniques of animal husbandry.

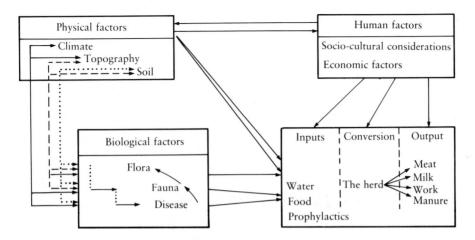

Figure I.1 Actions and interactions of factors upon animal husbandry

2
Climate

The fundamentals of climate

General

In the context of livestock rearing, climate must be considered for its effect on forage production, general agricultural production and on the animal itself. Certain factors favourable to plant growth may not be favourable to the healthy survival of the animals, for example high temperatures associated with high humidity.

Studies of tropical climate types follows two main streams:

1. Geographers have tried to define the characteristics of tropical climates in order to integrate them into a universal classification, grading depending upon the characteristics of a series of atmospheric conditions in their usual sequence: rain, temperature, wind etc.
2. Agronomists, foresters and ecologists try to connect climatic characteristics with the productivity of the biomass. As well as the purely atmospheric factors, they consider the inter-relationship between climate and the other components of the physical environment (vegetation).

Temperature, humidity, rainfall, wind and barometric pressure are the classic factors in the study of climate. From a biological point of view, it is suitable to introduce solar radiation and evaporation as well as the correlation between the different components of climate and between these and the soil.

Solar energy and climate

Fundamentals

The duration of daylight or absolute sunlight refers to the number of hours during which 'the sun shines', actually the period during which the solar radiation can be detected by light meters.

Relative sunlight refers to the relationship between the period of radiation and that of the daylight in the astronomic tables.

Heliographs, which record light, use the change of colour of light sensitive paper (Jordan's heliograph) exposed to direct light or after concentration by a spherical lens (Cambell Stokes' heliograph).

The measurement of total energy received at a point is made with a pyranograph which records variations of intensity of beams emitted by a thermopile (series of thermocouples) activated by the radiation received directly from space.

The measurement of energy intensity of the visible part of the spectrum is effected with photoelectric cells which can be connected to recorders. These cells can be used to measure the brilliance of a surface.

In meteorological records, the measures of energy are expressed in tens of joules per square centimetre (J/cm^2). For greater convenience in reports, larger units are used: watt-hour (Wh) or kilowatt-hour (kWh) per square centimetre or per square metre.

Nevertheless, in a number of works and in particular in those dealing with the reactions of animals to climatic factors, the results are expressed in calories. Table 2.1 gives conversion factors.

Table 2.1 Conversion of energy units

Energy units and equivalents.		Units as symbols
1 calorie (cal)	= 4.1868 joules	1 cal = 4.1868 J
1 therm (th)	= 10^6 calories	1 th = 10^6 cal = 10^3 kcal
1 joule (J)	= 0.2388 calories	1 J = 0.2388 cal
1 watt (W)	= 1 joule per second	1 W = 1 J/sec
1 watt-hour (Wh)	= 3600 joules per hour = 861 calories/per hour	1 Wh = 3600 J/h = 860 cal/h
1 joule per cm^2	= 0.2392 cal per cm^2	1 J/cm^2 = 0.2392 cal/cm^2
1 kilowatt–hour	= 3.6×10^6 joules = 860 kcal	1kWh = 3.6×10^6 J =860 kcal

Day length

Day length is virtually constant at the equator – 12 h. Elsewhere, the period varies according to season, the difference between short and long days increasing with latitude so that around latitude 20° N, day length varies from 10 h 50 min to 13 h 20 min, whereas at latitude 45° N it varies from 8 h 40 min to 15 h.

The total annual sunlight at Bangui (4° 22′ N) is 2331 h, at Quagadougu

(12° 22′ N) is 3303 h and at Nouakcott (18° 06′ N) is 2956 h; close to latitude 45° N at Grenoble, the corresponding figure is 2076 h (see Table 2.2).

Variations of day length are important in their relative values (lengthening days – shortening days). They affect plant vegetation and reproductive growth cycles and the sexual physiology of the animal.

Table 2.2 Total monthly periods of daylight and total monthly values for solar energy

Station	Bangui			Quagadougou			Nouakchott		
Geographic coordinates	4° 22′ N	13° 35′ N		12° 22′ N	11° 31′ W		18° 06′ N	15° 57′ W	
Month	Total monthly sunlight (1/10 hour)	Total monthly energy (kWh/m^2)	Daily mean	Total monthly sunlight (1/10 hour)	Total monthly energy (kWh/m^2)	Daily mean	Total monthly sunlight (1/10 hour)	Total monthly energy (kWh/m^2)	Daily mean
January	2455	89.97	3.00	29.40	180.27	6.01	2154	117.28	3.91
February	2103	125.30	4.18	2888	185.36	6.18	2512	136.86	4.56
March	1897	137.91	4.59	3085	212.13	7.07	2339	129.75	4.32
April	2266	164.83	5.49	2811	197.11	6.57	2858	177.08	5.90
May	2143	1378.02	4.57	2780	189.86	6.33	32.53	189.42	6.31
June	2026	130.94	4.36	2763	184.25	6.14	2461	149.53	4.98
July	1746	104.50	3.48	2632	187.28	6.24	2817	153.39	5.11
August	1729	143.08	4.77	2266	162.28	5.41	2631	158.92	5.30
September	1702	138.36	4.61	2417	187.83	6.26	2520	146.00	4.87
October	1595	156.16	5.21	2366	175.08	5.84	2438	167.03	5.57
November	1709	114.55	3.82	2992	177.00	5.90	2158	111.86	3.73
December	1942	106.44	3.55	3097	174.61	5.82	1421	150.14	5.00
Monthly mean	2331	154.90	4.24	3303	218.30	5.98	2956	178.70	4.89

Energy and solar radiation

On the day of the winter solstice, the incident energy received at the Tropic and the Equator varies between 0.6 cal/cm^2 per min and 1 cal/cm^2 per min respectively; while at the summer solstice, the greater value is observed at the tropic: 1.1 cal/cm^2 per min and at the Equator it remains at 1 cal/cm^2 per min.

The energy measurements recorded at the meteorological stations are used to draw up regional and world maps of incident radiant energy received from the sun, monthly and annually, expressed in kilowatt-hours per square metre (kWh/m^2) (Figure 2.1 and Table 2.2) or in kilocalories per second per square metre.

The areas which receive a mean monthly solar energy level of more than 2300 kWh/m^2 are largely deserts. The tropical areas receive a monthly average from 1860 to 2300 kWh/m^2, the equatorial areas receive from 1400 to 1860 kWh/m^2 and the temperate zones receive from 930 to 1400 kWh/m^2.

The different parts of the Earth do not receive the same amounts of energy and likewise, the amount of energy received varies with time. These variations cause the movement of considerable masses of air and water through their effect on winds, marine currents, rains and on evaporation of water from the sea, rivers, the soil, plant transpiration and from animals.

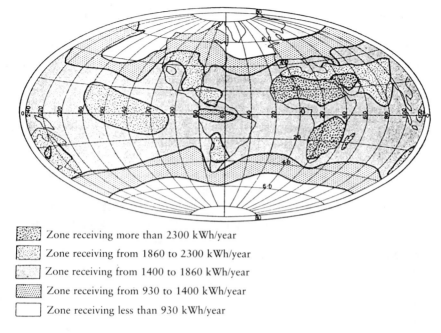

Zone receiving more than 2300 kWh/year

Zone receiving from 1860 to 2300 kWh/year

Zone receiving from 1400 to 1860 kWh/year

Zone receiving from 930 to 1400 kWh/year

Zone receiving less than 930 kWh/year

Figure 2.1 Distribution of solar energy on the surface of the earth

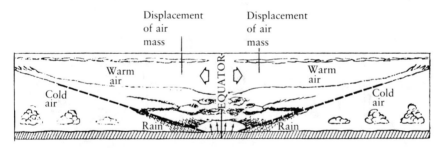

Figure 2.2 Principle of energy exchanges between the zones at the Equator and the zones at the tropics

Characteristics of solar radiation

Solar radiation has a wavelength across the range 0.2–5μm. The radiant power cuts off abruptly in the ultraviolet zone (0.1 μm), is maximum in the visible spectrum towards 0.5 μm and reduces progressively in the zone of heat radiation (infrared).

At the limits of the atmosphere, the energy given off by the sun towards the Earth is 1390 Wh/m^2, while that at the Earth's surface is no more than 970–1110 Wh/m^2 of which 7–10 per cent is obtained from energy already caught up in the atmosphere.

When the sun is at its zenith, outside the atmosphere the 1390 Wh/m^2 is made up of 8 per cent ultra-violet light, 41 per cent in the visible spectrum and 51 per cent infrared, while the corresponding figures for the 1000 Wh/m^2 received at the Earth's surface are respectively: 3 per cent, 42 per cent and 55 per cent. There is a shifting of the light waves of the spectrum towards the heat radiation end.

The radiation originating from the sun directly or from the atmosphere, which strikes the Earth's surface, is in part immediately reflected and in part absorbed; the absorbed portion is partially and slowly returned as heat.

This phenomenon is particularly well observed in the areas of the tropics having strong sunlight, the return of the heat happening during the night.

Plants, like the soil, absorb part of the solar and atmospheric radiation necessary for photosynthesis and reflect the infrared part of the spectrum.

This concept has a practical application in remote sensing for mapping vegetation types using photographic emulsions which are sensitive in infrared.

Figure 2.3 illustrates the exchanges of original solar energy which occur in the soil, near the soil and in the atmosphere.

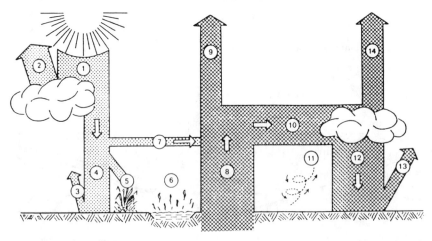

1. Direct solar radiation
2. Radiation reflected by the clouds
3. Radition reflected by the soil
4. Radiation absorbed by the soil
5. Radiation absorbed by photosynthesis
6. Radiation used for evaporation of water
7. Radiation absorbed by the atmosphere
8. Long-wave radiation emitted by the soil
9. Long-wave radiation emitted back to space
10. Long-wave radiation absorbed or reflected by the atmosphere and clouds
11. Energy used for the generation of winds
12. Long-wave radiation reflected by the atmosphere and clouds back towards the soil
13. Part of the latter radiation reflected by the soil
14. Radiation reflected by the atmosphere and clouds towards space

Figure 2.3 Illustration of energy exchanges

Temperature

Fundamentals

Ambient temperature is taken in the shade using a dry thermometer of the mercury or alcohol type.

Maximum and minimum temperatures are measured with special mercury thermometers with direct or recorded reading. Other types include electronic recording thermometers.

Temperatures are taken at fixed times: every 3 hours (6 a.m., 9 a.m., noon, 3 p.m., 6 p.m.) or only three times a day (6 a.m., noon, 6 p.m.).

Maximum and minimum recordings are evaluated, each 24-hour day, the difference between the two being the daily range.

Mean values are calculated each month, each year and over many years. They are used to produce isotherm maps (Figure 2.4).

Between the tropics, the mean annual temperature is between 22 and 29° C, the maximums are very high rising beyond 40° C and the minimums are rarely below 10° C.

The mean annual temperature is a function of latitude; near the Tropic of Capricorn (southern hemisphere) it is of the order of 22° C, slightly less than that for the Tropic of Cancer which is close to 24° C: for example 27.7° C at Tessalit situated at 20° 12′ N and near the Equator 24.7° C at Lambarene 0° 42′ S.

The difference between the warmest and coldest months increases with latitude. Near the Equator at Lambarene 0° 42′ S, the difference is 3.7° C, whereas near the tropic at Tessalit 20° 12′ N it is close to 15.5° C and at Quagadougu 12° 22′ N it is 7.6° C.

The variations between mean annual maximum and minimum temperatures (the maximum and minimum being taken from the same month) are more than 15° C near the tropics and are of the order of 5–6° C at the Equator.

The differences between mean monthly temperatures at noon and those at 6 a.m. vary enormously near the tropics – at Tessalit the difference is least in January at 8.3° C and greatest in March at 13.7° C. At the Equator, the difference is smaller and varies only a little – at Lambarene it is least in November at 4° C and greatest in March at 6.7° C.

Altitude has the same influence as distance from the Equator towards the tropics; above 800 m, the variation is in the vicinity of 1° C for every 180 m altitude. This can be noted at Nairobi, being 1600 m above sea level and latitude 1° 17′ S, the mean annual temperature is 17.5° C and the variation between maximum and minimum monthly temperatures is 3.9° C, a situation normally encountered at latitude 8° N.

Local conditions such as proximity to oceans, winds, cloud cover, rain etc. can noticeably modify the theoretical model of temperature variation.

Besides annual and mean monthly temperature, the degree of temperature variation in the course of the day is particularly important to the animal.

At Tessalit (20° 12′ N) with a warm dry climate, the difference between temperatures at noon and 6 a.m. (being 31.9° C and 21.6° C respectively on a mean annual basis) varies according to the month between 8.3° C in January and 13.7° C in April.

At Lambarene (0° 42′ S) with an equatorial climate, the corresponding figures are 27.9° C, 22.2° C (mean annual noon and 6 a.m. temperatures) and 4° C variation between noon and 6 a.m. in November and 6.7° C variation in July.

Temperature and biology

Certain information can guide the agriculturalist in his crop and animal production methods:

1. the probability and timing of temperatures of less than 0° C (slight in the tropics) or more than 40° C;
2. the sum of all the temperatures or of only those of more than 6° C (the minimum temperature for plant growth) during the whole year or during the period of possible plant growth.

The indices relating temperature with other climatic factors will be described later.

Maps

The recorded observations are used to make up isotherm maps. These are drawn by joining up with a continuous line, those stations where, in the same period, the characteristics of temperature have the same values (mean, minimum, maximum etc.) (Figures 2.4 and 2.5).

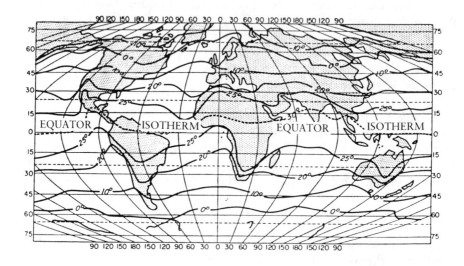

Figure 2.4 Map of annual isotherms (mean annual temperatures)

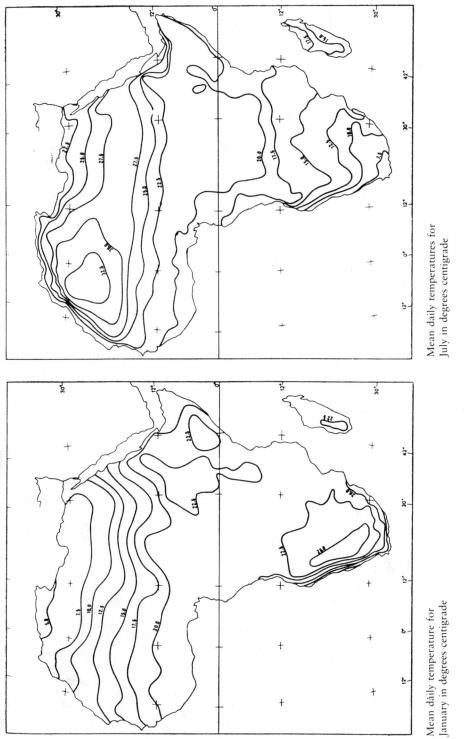

Mean daily temperatures for
July in degrees centigrade

Mean daily temperature for
January in degrees centigrade

Figure 2.5   Isotherm maps

Barometric pressure

Fundamentals

Barometric or atmospheric pressure is measured in millibars (mb) using a mercury or aneroid barometer; it is particularly used in weather forecasting. Two or three observations per day are sufficient.

The recorded observations, pin-pointed on the map, allow tracing of the 'isobars' by joining the points of localities in which the same pressures or the same mean pressures have been recorded at the same point in time, day, month etc. (Figures 2.6 and 2.7).

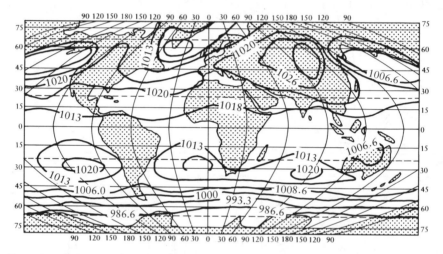

Figure 2.6 Isobar map for January (mean monthly)

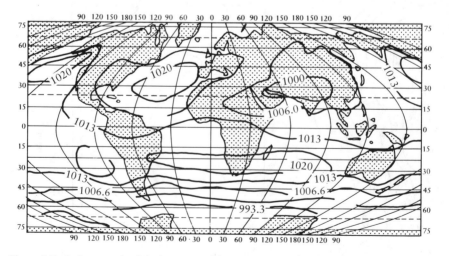

Figure 2.7 Isobar map for July (mean monthly)

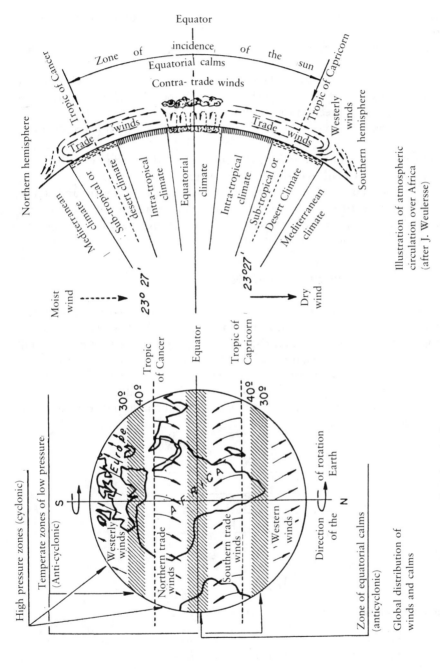

Figure 2.8   Global distribution of winds and calms

Characteristics of barometric pressure

Schematically, from the Equator towards the poles, one finds an equatorial zone of low pressures (anti-cyclones), a tropical zone of high pressures (cyclonic zones), a temperate zone of low pressures and a polar zone of high pressures (Figure 2.8).

Wind direction is represented in the form of a 'wheel' of winds whose spokes make an angle of 10° between each and are numbered clockwise from 1 to 36 starting from the direction of North.

Wind speed is expressed in metres per second (m/sec) or kilometres per hour (k/h).

Quantities of wind are indicated in metres per day; they are evaluated in stations provided with recording anemometers.

For clarity, on the spokes of the 'wheel of winds' (see above) and starting from the centre, there are vectors whose length is proportional to the quantity of wind recorded, the extremities of the vectors forming a polygon which can be marked with the prevailing winds.

Pressure variations throughout the day

In the tropics, barometric pressure varies following a regular wave form, with two maxima and two minima. From 4 a.m. to 10 a.m. the pressure rises, then drops from 10 a.m. to 4 p.m., rises again from 4 p.m. to 10 p.m., then falls from 10 p.m. to 4 a.m (Figure 2.9). The morning maximum is higher than that in the evening and the afternoon minimum is lower than that of the night, the range varying between 2.5 and 4 mb. This variation is distinctly felt by man and correlations have been observed with medical conditions (e.g. cardiovascular illness).

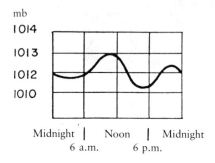

Figure 2.9 Day variations in atmospheric pressure

Pressure variations throughout the month

The variations between recorded minimum and maximum pressures during the same month are negligible at the equator and increase towards the tropics.

Winds

Fundamentals

Winds are generated by differences of barometric pressure occuring between different parts of the globe, differences having as their main cause the unequal distribution of solar energy and the rotation of the Earth. Wind direction is the result of the distribution of high and low pressures, of the force due to the rotation of the Earth (Coriolis force), of the land form and of the inertia of air masses.

Wind is measured with an anemometer, which can be permanently located at meteorological stations or be mobile for observation in the field.

Wind creation and direction

Theoretically, all the points on the Equator behave as centres of heat and there is a movement of air converging towards them in the lower regions of the atmosphere (the trade winds) and above them in the higher regions of the atmosphere there is an air movement in the opposite direction (contra trade winds).

As a consequence of the Earth's rotation, the air movements have deviated towards the right in the Northern hemisphere and towards the left in the Southern hemisphere (Coriolis force) (Figure 2.10).

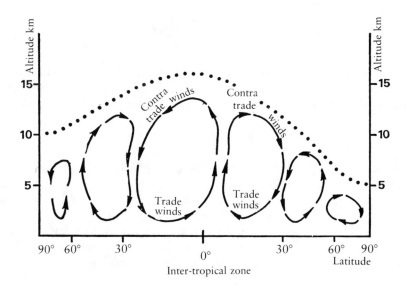

Figure 2.10 Air circulation by latitude and altitude

The heat at the Equator varies from one solstice to the other because of the movement of the Earth in relation to the sun, which brings about a shift in the system of trade winds and with it a change in rainfall patterns in much the same way as the relative position of oceans and continents modify the distribution of high and low pressure.

Humidity in the atmosphere

Humidity in the air has a direct effect on the rate of evaporation of water from the surface of the sea, soil and also on the transpiration of plants and animals.

Fundamentals

Absolute humidity of the air (f) is the quantity of water contained in the atmosphere; it is expressed in grams of water per cubic metre or the pressure of atmospheric water vapour itself at the observed air temperature.

Relative humidity (H) is expressed as a percentage and is the relationship between the preceding pressure (f) and the maximum pressure (F) of the water vapour which can be held in the air if it is saturated with water at the observed air temperature and barometric pressure.

$$H = 100 \times \frac{f}{F} \text{ per cent}$$

Saturation deficit, expressed in millibars, is the difference between the pressure of water vapour at saturation point (F) and the actual pressure (f) at the observed air temperature and barometric pressure.

$$D_s = F - f \text{ mb}$$

Dew point corresponds to the temperature at which water vapour held in the atmosphere begins to condense; the air is said to be 'saturated' because the pressure of the water vapour (f) at this point is then equal to the maximum (saturated) water vapour pressure (F) for that temperature.

Evaporation, which can be expressed in millimetres per 24-hour day, represents the height of water which would evaporate naturally from a still surface of pure water which is shaded from the effects of the sun, air and wind.

$$Evp/24 = mm$$

Measurement of the humidity of the air

Derivation of air humidity is achieved by measuring the difference between the temperature recorded on two identical thermometers, one of which is cooled by the evaporation of a thin film of water in contact with the bulb of the thermometer (wet thermometer) and which therefore registers a lower temperature than the second thermometer (dry thermometer) whose bulb is dry and uncovered. The lowering of temperature depends upon the rate of evaporation, which is itself a function of the hygrometric state of the air (i.e. how much water vapour it holds). (See Plate 2.1 – a wet and dry thermometer.)

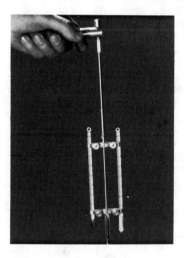

Plate 2.1   Wet and dry thermometer

The actual pressure of the water vapour (f) is given by the formula:

$$f = F - 0.00079 \, H \, (t - t') \text{ mm Hg}$$
$$\text{or } f = F - 0.00059 \, H \, (t - t') \text{ mb}$$

according to whether f is expressed in millimetres of mercury or in millibars. F is the saturation vapour pressure of air, its maximum water vapour holding capacity, at temperature t' and H is the barometric pressure at the observation site.

Numerical tables simplify the calculations (Table 2.3).

Measurement of evaporation

One method of measuring evaporation directly uses a calibration inside a glass tube of diameter 1.2 cm and height 26 cm, placed on a wooden tray and protected from animals by wire mesh. The tray must be placed in an open space and never shaded by nearby objects (trees, buildings etc.) (Figure 2.11). Evaporation from the blotting paper lowers the level of water in the reservoir, as recorded on the scale.

Table 2.3 Psychometric table. A table showing the hygrometric pressure in percentage terms as a function of the temperature difference between the dry and wet thermometer

t′	t−t′									
	0	1	2	3	4	5	6	7	8	9
40	100	94	88	83	78	73	68	64	60	57
39	100	94	88	82	77	72	68	64	60	56
38	100	94	88	82	77	72	68	63	59	56
37	100	94	87	82	77	72	67	63	59	55
36	100	93	87	81	76	71	67	62	58	55
35	100	93	87	81	76	71	66	62	57	54
34	100	93	87	81	76	70	66	61	57	53
33	100	93	87	80	75	70	65	61	56	53
32	100	93	86	80	75	69	65	60	55	52
31	100	93	86	80	74	69	64	59	54	51
30	100	93	86	79	74	68	63	59	54	51
29	100	93	86	79	73	68	63	58	53	50
28	100	92	85	78	73	67	62	57	52	49
27	100	92	85	78	72	67	61	57	51	48
26	100	92	85	78	72	66	61	56	50	47
25	100	92	84	78	71	65	60	55	49	46
24	100	92	84	77	71	65	59	54	48	45
23	100	92	84	77	70	64	58	53	47	44
22	100	91	83	76	69	63	57	52	46	43
21	100	91	83	75	69	62	56	51	45	42
20	100	91	82	75	68	61	55	50	44	41
19	100	91	82	74	67	60	54	49	43	39
18	100	90	82	73	66	59	53	48	41	38
17	100	90	81	73	65	58	52	46	40	36
16	100	90	80	72	64	57	51	45	38	35
15	100	90	80	71	63	56	49	44	37	33
14	100	89	80	70	62	55	48	42	35	32
13	100	89	79	70	61	53	47	40	33	30
12	100	88	78	68	60	52	45	39	31	28
11	100	88	77	67	58	50	43	37	29	26
10	100	88	76	66	57	49	41	35	27	24
9	100	87	75	65	56	47	40	33	24	21
8	100	87	74	64	54	45	37	30	22	19
7	100	86	73	62	52	43	35	28	19	16
6	100	85	72	61	50	41	33	25	16	13
5	100	85	71	59	48	39	30	23	13	10
4	100	84	70	58	46	36	28	20	10	
3	100	83	69	56	44	34	25	17		
2	100	83	67	54	42	31	22	13		
1	100	82	66	52	39	28	18	10		
0	100	81	64	49	36	25	15			

t′ = temperature recorded on the wet thermometer in ° C.
t−t′ = the difference in temperatures recorded on the dry and wet thermometers in ° C.

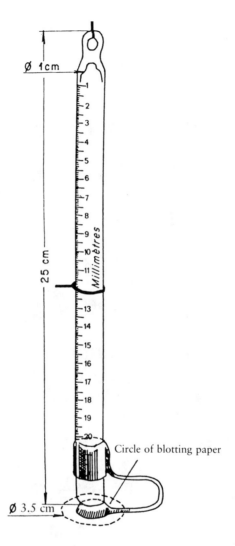

Figure 2.11 Piche evaporimeter

Characteristics of humidity in the tropics

The humidity of the air in the tropics varies considerably through the 24-hour cycle just as temperature varies; during the night the temperature can drop such that dew point is reached. This permits a number of xerophytic plants to survive in areas considered to be arid, particularly in proximity to seas and oceans, the dew being absorbed by the plants or by the soil (Table 2.4, Figure 2.12 and 2.13).

Table 2.4 Humidity – Evaporation (mean monthly)

	J	F	M	A	M	J	J	A	S	O	N	D
TESSALIT 20° 12' N 1° E												
Mean humidity (%)	31	21	23	19	19	20	20	30	24	25	21	20
Minimum relative humidity (%)	7	8	7	5	4	5	6	4	4	7	5	5
Maximum relative humidity (%)	75	51	72	38	73	55	73	92	77	70	58	58
Range (%)	68	43	65	33	69	50	67	88	73	63	53	53
Mean daily evaporation (%)	81	121	109	161	184	199	172	141	161	130	124	106
Maximum daily evaporation (mm)	137	153	172	228	297	308	242	304	298	189	176	195
Wind flow (m/min)												
OUAGADOUGOU 12° 22' N 1° 31' W												
Mean humidity (%)	30	25	22	34	55	66	71	79	77	72	44	30
Minimum relative humidity (%)	8	9	8	5	21	33	41	48	40	37	12	10
Maximum relative humidity (%)	88	59	86	90	98	100	100	100	100	99	95	74
Range (%)	80	50	78	85	77	77	59	52	60	62	83	64
Mean daily evaporation (mm)	86	102	112	100	69	44	37	25	27	30	68	83
Maximum daily evaporation (mm)	131	135	149	139	110	72	67	67	47	43	114	103
Total monthly evaporation (mm)	2 388	2 767	3 336	3 277	3 010	2 220	2 172	1 625	1 531	1 698	2 228	2 387
Wind flow (m/min)	1 220	793	1 197	1 853	2 022	1 978	2 380	1 164	886	916	839	1 064
LAMBARENE 0° 42' S 10° 13' E												
Mean humidity (%)	88	87	87	88	90	89	83	83	84	87	89	90
Minimum relative humidity (%)	57	53	54	50	63	57	63	64	49	54	59	60
Maximum relative humidity (%)	100	100	100	100	100	100	98	98	98	99	100	99
Range (%)	43	47	46	50	37	43	35	24	49	45	41	39
Mean daily evaporation (mm)	12	13	15	13	13	11	21	21	20	16	12	10
Maximum daily evaporation (mm)	20	20	25	25	24	19	29	31	34	29	18	19
Total monthly evaporation (mm)	545	?	1 340	763	909	772	867	737	1 167	721	786	670
Wind flow (m/min)	685	?	507	448	701	1 295	1 766	1 277	3 064	1 940	1 375	?

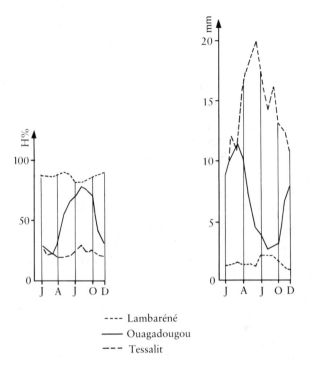

Figure 2.12 Mean daily relative humidity by month and mean daily evaporation by month (mm H₂O)

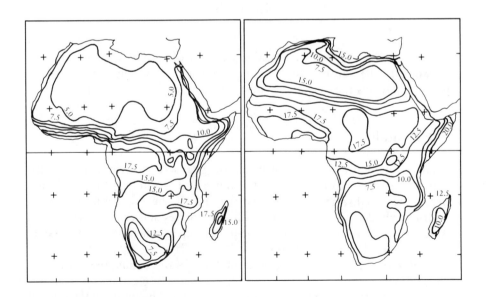

Figure 2.13 Mean levels of humidity in the air (g/kg) for January and July in Africa

Experiments conducted in Zaire at Kinsantu estimate that, in a zone where total rainfall is 1602 mm/year, the dew amounted for more than 187 mm, that is 11.6 per cent of the rainfall. Similar figures from 100 to 200 mm have been identified.

The quantities of water which evaporate from the surface of water depend upon:

- the temperature of the air in contact with the water,
- the temperature of the water at the surface,
- the relative humidity of the ambient air,
- the wind speed,
- the total radiation received,
- the salinity of the water.

From a biological point of view, evaporation is the result of the actions of wind and sunshine.

Daily evaporation is lowest at the Equator: 20–30 mm per day and may exceed 200 mm per day in the arid tropics. It is of the order 60–150 mm in those areas between the tropic and the Equator.

Again from a biological point of view, the humidity of the air has a direct effect on plants: along with temperature it regulates plant transpiration rates and evaporation from the soil surface; for animals it partly controls the mechanisms of temperature control, the dryness of the air accelerating water loss and perspiration.

Rainfall

As emphasised in the last section, this function of climate is of paramount importance to the agronomist and stockman; it controls the plant growing seasons and affects the availability of drinking water.

Fundamentals

Rainfall is commonly measured at meteorological stations using a rain gauge which in its simplest form consists of a funnel and a container. The collected water is measured, immediately after the end of the precipitation, into a measuring cylinder which is graduated in millimetres and centimetres.

Automatic rain gauges U.C.A can be used in areas where it is not possible to have personnel permanently on site.

Rainfall tables are often expressed in millimetres or centimetres of rain per 24-hour day.

The monthly or annual rainfall figures are calculated by totalling the rainfall figures for each day in the month or year (Table 2.5). These enable the

Table 2.5 Monthly rainfall figures from three sites: arid tropic, humid tropic, humid equatorial (mean over several years)

	J	F	M	A	M	J	J	A	S	O	N	D	Total
TESSALIT 20° 12' N–1° E													
Normal (1947–1970)	0.3	0.1	0.3	0.1	5.6	5.4	15.9	41.1	19.4	1.4	0.9	0.5	90.5
1976	3.4	0	0.1	0	14.4	1.0	14.1	29.8	18.3	2.2	0	0	82.4
OUAGADOUGOU 12° 22' N–1° W													
Normal (1956–1970)	0.2	2.3	7.5	20.9	87.8	125.9	177.7	262.3	158.2	27.6	2.6	1.6	874.6
1976	1.5	0	19.8	4.5	111.6	163.1	202.0	254.6	223.4	124.0	0	0	992.9
LAMBARENE 0° 42' N–10° 13' E													
Normal (1961–1970)	175.0	130.0	251.0	255.0	178.0	1.4	2.0	7.0	50.0	336.0	367.0	147.0	1 899.4
1976	165.8	261.7	224.0	295.0	147.0	0	1.2	9.3	45.3	256.2	325.0	215.2	1 945.7

Values are mm

construction of such products as rainfall charts (Figure 2.14) and isohyet maps (Figure 2.15).

For the agriculturalist, one must also record the following:

- mean precipitation for those days when rain falls,
- maximum precipitation on those rainy days,
- the mean number of rainy days per month, year etc.,
- the mean intensities, calculated by dividing the number of millimetres of water recorded after each fall of rain by the duration of these precipitations,
- the variation between years.

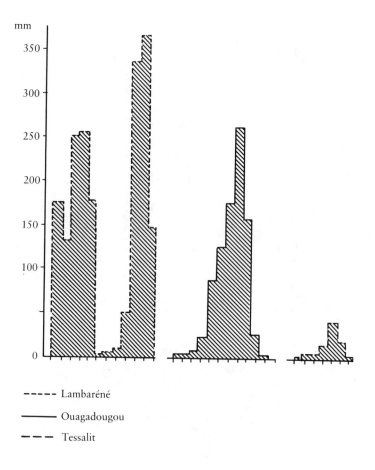

----- Lambaréné

——— Ouagadougou

— — — Tessalit

Figure 2.14   Monthly rainfall figures (average calculated over 23 years)

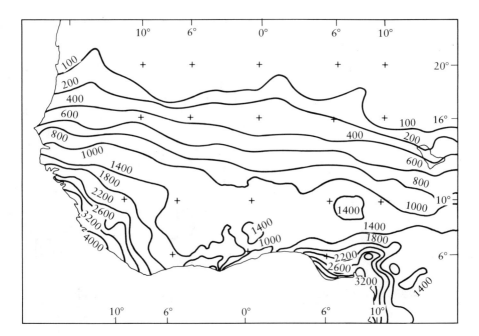

Figure 2.15 Annual rainfall in West Africa (mm)

Rainfall characteristics in the tropics

The rainfall patterns in the tropics depend upon latitude, mountains and the proximity of oceans. They are classified according to the chronological incidence of wet and dry seasons, but not by the stability of annual rainfall figures.

The tropical rainfall patterns are characterised by a long dry season, possibly up to 9 months, and a rainy season; the latter being proportionately shorter than and having less rain than falls at the Equator.

The equatorial pattern is associated with those areas where it rains all year round with maximum precipitation at the equinoxes and minimum precipitation at the solstices.

The subequatorial pattern, in between the two previous zones as far as latitude is concerned, has two rainy seasons which last: one from 30 to 60 days and the other from 15 days to a month.

Geographically the distribution of pattern types is almost symmetrical in relation to the Equator but reversed as regards their behaviour: when at 15° N it is the dry season, at 15° S it is raining (Figure 2.16).

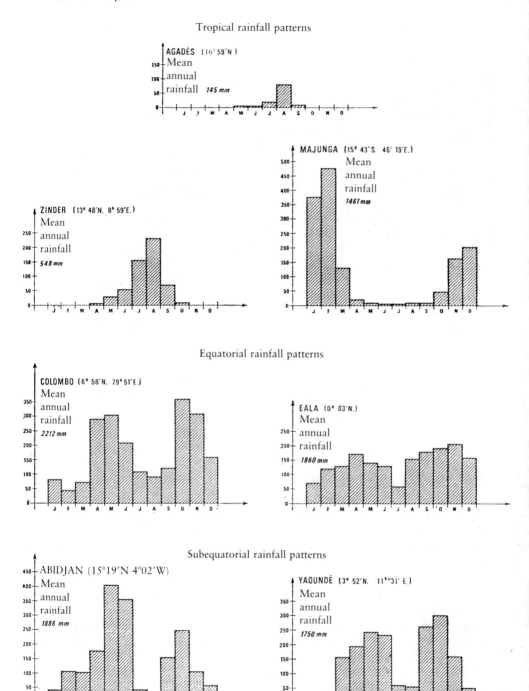

Figure 2.16 Rainfall histograms for weather stations within the tropics

Categorisation of climate from an agronomic point of view

Different indices

Analytical presentation of climatic factors is essential but is inadequate to describe the interactions between factors.

Numerous authors have tried to calculate indices or create graphs by combining basic climatic factors. Only those indices which appear in works concerning the tropical regions will be considered.

de Martonnes dryness index

$$i = \frac{\text{mean annual rainfall}}{\text{mean annual temperature} + 10}$$

This gives information used in geography.

Aubreville's classification

Aubreville introduced classification of climates as a function of monthly and annual rainfall indices:

Humid month	> 100 mm rainfall
Intermediate month	30–100 mm rainfall
Dry month	< 30 mm rainfall

The climate at a particular station is characterised by three numbers. The first indicates the number of 'humid months', the second the 'intermediate months' and the third 'dry months'.

Gao: 1–1–10.   Libreville: 8–1–3.

Among the climates it distinguishes as a function of rainfall the following types:

- very dry – less than 400 mm rainfall
- dry – from 400 mm to 1200 mm
- semi-humid – in the same range as 'dry'
- humid – more than 1000 mm without a real dry month
- highland – having the characteristics of 'humid' but affected by altitude

The author who formulated this classification, introduced into it the effects of the fundamentals on temperature and flora.

Climate and soil water

Evaporation – Evapotranspiration

Definition

The previous schemes only bring in atmospheric factors without consideration of the biosphere.

Many approaches have been envisaged to link climatic factors with agronomic factors. As plants can only grow and reproduce if the resources of usable water and temperature are sufficient, these two factors have been taken into consideration when categorising the soil climate (edaphic climate).

In the tropics, with rare exceptions, temperature is always more than 6–10° C. As this is considered the minimum temperature for plant development, it is not necessary to look at the bottom end of the temperature scale but only at the top end, when it is more than 40° C.

The usable resources at root level depend on the difference that exists between the external inputs (apart from irrigation these are from rainfall, dew and the water table) and the losses due to evaporation at the soil surface and to retention by the plants. The soil, depending on its type, only intervenes to reduce the losses by infiltration and to increase retention.

Although this idea of water balance is easily understood, its mathematical expression is considerably less easy, for it depends upon a number of factors, some of which are difficult to measure.

Actual evapotranspiration, expressed in millimetres of water, can be measured experimentally, but the technique draws more from research than from practice. Therefore researchers have developed empirical formulae which allow estimation of a probable theoretical value of 'potential evapotranspiration' for a period of time, for a station or given region, which give information about the water balance without the soil characteristics being taken into consideration.

Estimation formulae

Among the available formulae which estimate evapotranspiration, are those of Blaney and Criddle, and Turc.

Blaney and Criddle's formula

$$\text{potential evapotranspiration} = \frac{K}{100} (45.7\ Tc + 813)\ P$$

Where potential evapotranspiration is measured in millimetres per month.

K = coefficient individual to each region
Tc = mean daily temperature for the month
P = percentage daylight for the month under consideration (this is a function of latitude).

It is usable for the dry Mediterranean, sub-arid and arid zones. It has the disadvantage of using data which are difficult to determine.

Turc's formula

$$\text{Evapotranspiration} = (1g + 50) \times \frac{t}{t + 15}$$

In which:

$1g$ is the mean monthly value of total daily solar radiation (cal/cm^2 per day),
t is mean monthly temperature in ° C.

It is applicable in the temperate and Mediterranean zones. For the dry zones, it is convenient to introduce a corrective term if the relative humidity (H) is less than 50 per cent.

$$\text{Evapotranspiration} = \left[(1g + 50) \times 0.40 \times \frac{t}{t + 15} \right] \left[1 + \frac{50 - H}{70} \right]$$

Graphs

Beside the formulae, there are charts which allow one to visualise the variations of the water balance and the duration of periods favourable to plant growth.

Water balance graph

The graph (Figure 2.17) shows the beginning and end of rains, monthly rainfall indices, the mean monthly values of potential evapotranspiration and the values corresponding to half the potential evapotranspiration. This graph allows characterisation of climatic variations.

The rainy season (a1–c1) lasts from the beginning to the end of the rains.

The humid period corresponds to that during which the precipitations are more than half of the evapotranspiration a2–b1 and b2–b'2 when the soil is short of water but the plants can develop.

Period b2–c2 shows the beginning of the dry season with reducing soil water reserves.

Figure 2.17 was drawn for the station of Bamako (12° 39′ N 8° W) with

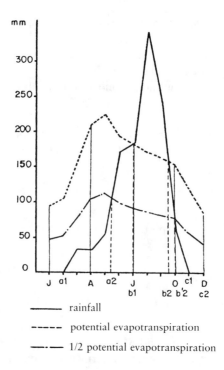

　　　　　rainfall

- - - - - potential evapotranspiration

—·— 1/2 potential evapotranspiration

Figure 2.17　Graph of water balance, Bamako (Mali) latitude 15° N

mean annual precipitation for the years 1931 to 1960 of 1099 mm and mean annual temperature during the same period of 28.1° C. Potential evapotranspiration has been calculated by Blaney and Criddle's formula, then plotted on the graph with the monthly rainfall curve and, again using the same coordinates, the 50 per cent potential evapotranspiration curve has been superimposed on the same graph.

Gaussen's rainfall/temperature chart

Gaussen and his school, following Demangeot, found a convenient definition for dryness: 'In a country without frost, it is a dry month if, in the course of which, the precipitations expressed in millimetres are less than double the mean daily temperature, expressed in degrees centigrade.'

Thus, a month during the course of which the mean daily temperature is 25° C is dry if total rainfall is equal to 40 mm and humid if the rainfall is equal to 60 mm

Table 2.6 and Figure 2.18 have been drawn up for the stations of Abidjan and Gao; the first being in a humid equatorial climate having only three dry months and the second in a Sahelian sub-desert climate having 10 dry months.

Each station is characterised by a rainfall/temperature chart in which the temperature scale is double that of rainfall (Figure 2.18); to reduce the size of the charts, a logarithmic scale is used.

Table 2.6 Elements of the calculation of Gaussen's rain/temperature chart

	J	F	M	A	M	J	J	A	S	O	N	D	
ABIDJAN													
R mm	28	40	118	156	384	590	180	29	52	206	194	110	2087
t° C	26.9	27.8	28.3	28.2	27.9	26.1	25.5	24.6	25.3	26.4	27.4	27.3	26.8
PE	73	73	79	82	69	53	53	48	51	59	78	76	794
GAO													
R mm	0	0	1	1	6	27	75	110	36	5	0	0	261
t° C	22.3	24.8	28.8	32.03	34.4	34.5	32.0	29.7	31.4	31.7	28.2	23.7	29.5
	Dry months				Humid months					Dry months			
PE	141	165	213	220	246	229	211	177	183	182	147	141	1832

R mm : monthly rainfall index in millimetres
t° C : mean annual daily temperature in ° C
PE : potential evapotranspiration in millimetres
dry months : R mm < 2 t° C
humid months : R mm > 2 t° C

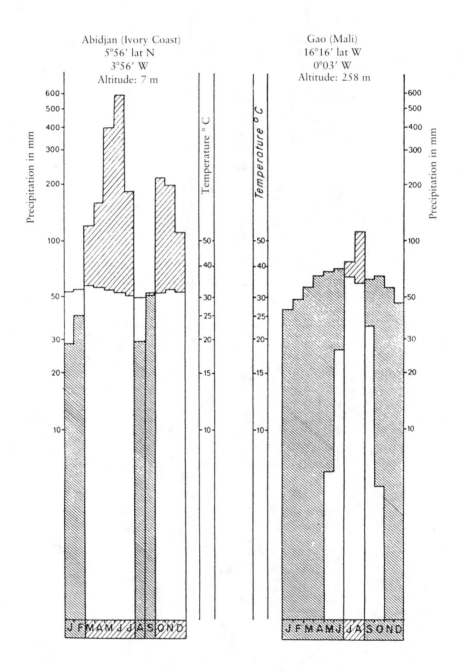

Figure 2.18 Gaussen's rainfall/temperature chart dry months R mm $\geqslant 2t\,^\circ$ C

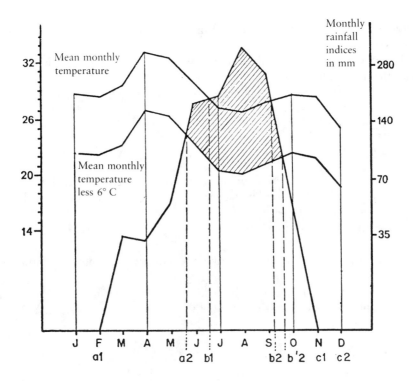

Figure 2.19 Euverte's graph – data from Bamako (Mali) (1953)

Euverte's graph (Figure 2.19)

Euverte, taking account of the fact that requirements for water are an exponential function of temperature* – they double when temperature increases by 6° C – proposed the use of a 'hydrothermic table' which links monthly rainfall indices, temperature and potential evapotranspiration.

The correlation of the temperature scales and rainfall index scales takes account of potential evapotranspiration:

- 14° C corresponds to 35 mm of water and
- 20° C corresponds to 70 mm of water.

The values of rainfall indices are plotted on a logarithmic scale; those of temperature on an arithmetic scale, their correlation taking account of the foregoing values.

The active period for vegetation corresponds to the points where the rainfall

---

* $\log PE = 0.841688 + T \times 0.05017167$
  $PE = 6.94525 \times C\ 0.0501/7167\ T° C$

curve is above the curve for temperature minus 6° C, which is in fact half of potential evapotranspiration.

This graph approximates the curve of water balance, which has been plotted with the data from one station (Bamako).

The information relates to humid and sub-humid periods which are shown by letters on the graph.

Climographs

In a climograph, each period of time considered is characterised by a point having as coordinates two climatic factors, then the points are plotted in the chronological order of their observation.

There are climographs giving:

1. as coordinates, the monthly rainfall indices and mean monthly day temperatures;
2. as coordinates, mean monthly day humidity or mean monthly day saturation deficits against mean monthly day temperatures (Figure 2.20).

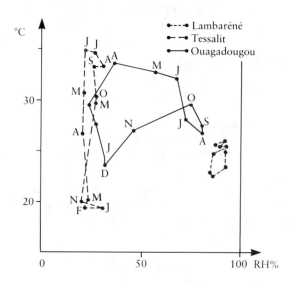

Figure 2.20 Climograph of relative humidity (mean monthly) in relation to temperature (day mean monthly)

Climographs allow more easy comparison of the climates at different stations; they are, above all, useful at a time when species of plant or animals, adapted to the climate of a particular region, are moved to another region; if the climographs are analogous, the transfer is more often than not successful. They are used in the ecological study of animals (see Chapter 3).

Exceptional years

When describing climates from the agronomic point of view, one refers to mean annual or mean monthly temperatures, rainfall and humidity. By the very nature of the calculation of these mean values, the information relating to the hazards of exceptional years or series of years is neglected.

This fact is regrettable, for there is an under-utilisation of recorded data. The calculation of rainfall medians using limited series of observations is more reliable than the calculation of means because the distribution curve is usually not symmetrical.

This is so in the area of Mopti (14° 30′ N 4° 12′ W) in the typical tropical climate, where mean annual rainfall is 500 mm, the rainfall index is:

- 1 year in 2 less than 500 mm (Sahelo–Soudanian climate type);
- 1 year in 5 less than 350 mm (Sahelian climate type);
- 1 year in 10 less 280 mm (pronounced Sahelian climate type);
- 1 year in 20 less than 100 mm (Sahelo-desert climate type);
- 1 year in 100 less than 100 mm (desert climate type).

The biomass, in the course of the exceptionally dry years, will be reduced and the animals of the region will find difficulty in obtaining a maintenance ration of food.

Just as important as the duration and intensity of showers of rain is their frequency. If at the beginning of the rainy season, the rainfall is normal, all the annual plants will germinate but they only develop if the showers are regularly spaced and of sufficient intensity to maintain the humidity of the soil, otherwise the young shoots will wilt and disappear before having flowered and produced seed; the following year, the plant cover of annual species will be practically non-existent and as a result, for the animals, there will be a prolonging of the famine period beyond the end of the dry season.

These concepts of exceptionally dry years or of irregular rainfall have not often been taken into account in development plans which predict numerical growth in herd sizes. When exceptional situations have arisen, no corrective measures could be applied since they had not foreseen that such disasters would be possible.

Aridity – the UNESCO cartographic representation

In 1979 the United Nations Educational, Scientific and Cultural Organisation (UNESCO) published a 1/25 000 000 scale map showing the world distribution of arid regions with explanatory notes in which it was proposed to categorise arid zones using five seperate criteria:

1. the relationship between mean annual rainfall and mean annual potential evapotranspiration;
2. mean temperature of the coldest month;
3. mean temperature of the warmest month;
4. the length of dry periods;
5. rainfall patterns.

On the map, each criterion is represented either by colour, hatching or by cartographic symbols.

The ratio of rainfall to potential evapotranspiration (R/PE) has been preferred to the difference between them (R − PE) because in regions having climates with greatly contrasting seasons, it presents a good biological correlation; it is very representative of the relationship between actual evapotranspiration (ETR) of a soil/plant system and the maximum evapotranspiration (ETM) in the absence of water constraints (ETR/ETM). Besides, it largely encompasses the production of dry matter by the plant cover.

The calculations of evapotranspiration values have been carried out for 1600 stations from data supplied by Organisation Mondiale de Meteorologie (= World Meteorological Organisation) (OMM), using Penmann's formula which takes account of solar radiation, atmospheric humidity and wind.

According to the value of the relationship R/PE, unesco distinguishes:

- hyper-arid zones,
- arid zones,
- semi-arid zones,
- sub-humid zones.

From an agricultural point of view:

Hyper-arid zones (R/PE < 0.03) correspond to deserts with minimal and very chancy rainfall; one does not come across any perennial vegetation with the exception of bushes in river beds and ephemerals, which can develop in favourable years. Grass production and agriculture are generally impossible. Variability of rains between years can reach 100 per cent.

Arid zones (0.03 < R/PE < 0.20) have sparse vegetation which, according to the region, comprises bushes and small woody succulents with thorns or without leaves. Very extensive nomadic herding is possible but not rain-fed farming. The annual rainfall index varies between 80–150 mm and 200–350 mm, and the variability of precipitation between years can be between 50 and 100 per cent.

Semi-arid zones (0.20 < R/PE < 0.5) include steppes, savanna and tropical thickets. In good livestock rearing regions, rain-fed agriculture is possible but risky in its results due to rainfall variability. In the tropical latitudes which interest us here, rainfall index varies between 300–400 mm and 700–800 mm when most of the precipitations occur in the summer, and between 200–250 mm and 450–500 mm when most of the precipitations occur in the winter. The variability of precipitations between years ranges from 25 to 50 per cent.

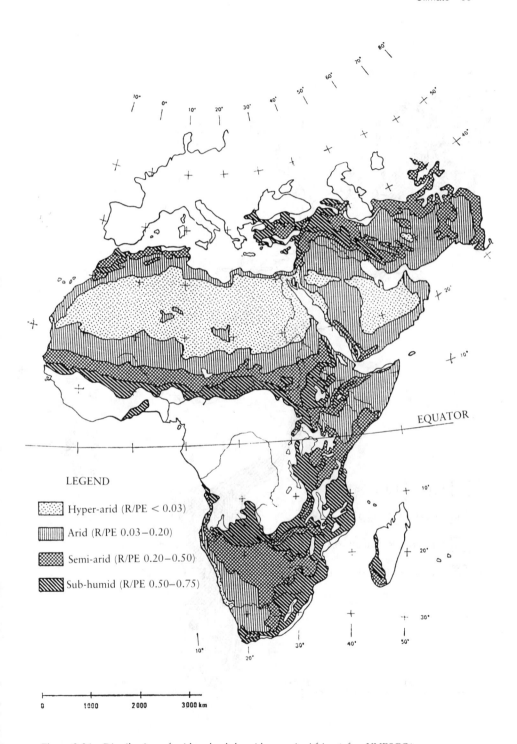

Figure 2.21 Distribution of arid and sub-humid zones in Africa (after UNESCO)

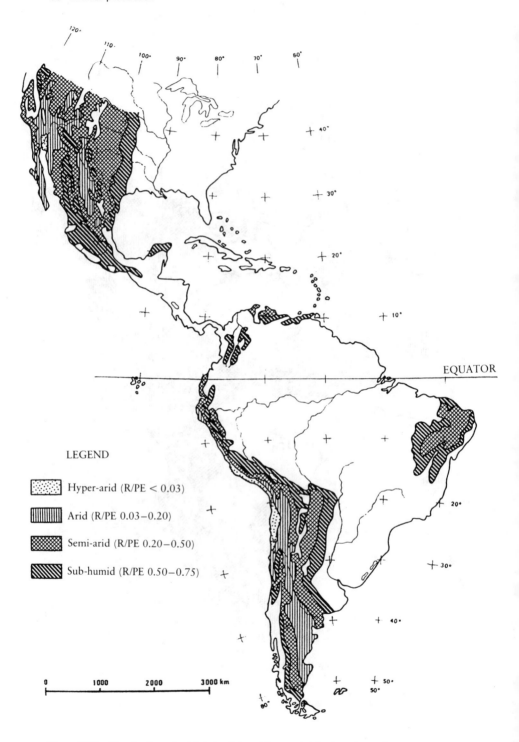

Figure 2.22 Distribution of arid and sub-humid zones in the Americas (after UNESCO)

Sub-humid zones (0.50 < R/PE < 0.75) include certain types of tropical savanna and agriculture follows normal modes of exploitation. The variability of precipitation between years is less than 25 per cent.

For the livestock producer, the UNESCO map has the advantage of presenting, in a stylised way, the environmental conditions which the animal must endure. It allows comparisons between systems of production in regions which are separated by great distance but of which the cartographic characteristics are similar. Figures 2.21 to 2.24, taken from the UNESCO map, give a stylised representation of four typical arid zones as defined above for the areas in the tropics.

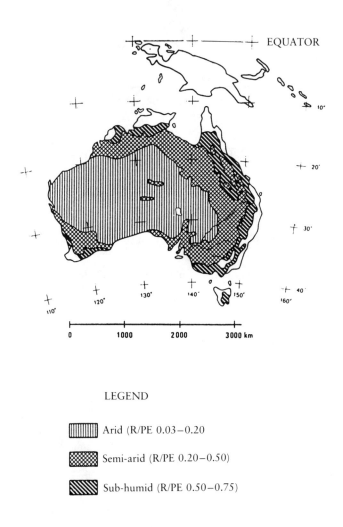

LEGEND

[⫼⫼⫼] Arid (R/PE 0.03−0.20

[▨▨▨] Semi-arid (R/PE 0.20−0.50)

[⧄⧄⧄] Sub-humid (R/PE 0.50−0.75)

Figure 2.23 Distribution of arid zones in Australia (after UNESCO)

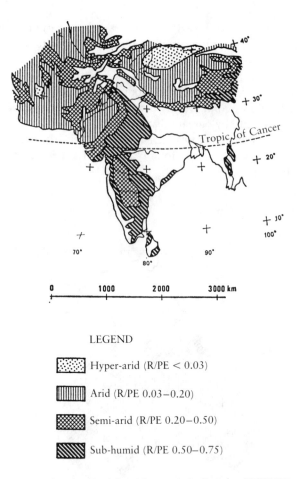

LEGEND

▦ Hyper-arid (R/PE < 0.03)

▥ Arid (R/PE 0.03–0.20)

▨ Semi-arid (R/PE 0.20–0.50)

▧ Sub-humid (R/PE 0.50–0.75)

Figure 2.24   Distribution of arid and sub-humid zones in India (after UNESCO)

3

Animal production and climate

Climate acts directly upon animals; solar heat, humidity and dryness of the air, its temperature and the intensity of winds upset or facilitate the physiological processes that contribute to temperature regulation and affect hunger, thirst, reproduction etc.

Climatic factors control the vegetative cycles of forage crops, the choice and production methods of forage species, harvesting dates and particularly the resources and accessibility of drinking water. Climate, therefore, determines the system of exploitation of pasturelands and herd management.

Some consideration of physiology will allow understanding of the response mechanisms of the animal to the extreme conditions of the environment and the animal's adaptation to such climatic factors.

Biological constants of domestic animals

One cannot study the relationship between the animal and its environment without knowledge of the physiological constant states maintained by self-regulating processes of the animal: body temperature, respiration rate and heart rate.

Body temperature

Domestic animals are homothermous – their temperature remains constant or nearly constant irrespective of the environment in which they live, otherwise, as is well understood, excessive variations are lethal.

Body temperature is the best indicator of the good health of the animal and its variation above and below normal is a measure of the animal's aptitude to resist hardship factors of the environment.

Each species has an individual normal temperature but the body temperature of domestic homeotherms is between 36.5 and 42° C (Table 3.1), while

Table 3.1 Normal temperatures of domestic animals
in tropical climates (° C)

Domestic animals	Minimum	Maximum
Ruminants		
Zebu*	37	41
Humpless cattle	37.5	40
Buffalo	38	39
Sheep	38	40
Goats		
Other domestic animals		
Horse	37.5	38.5
Donkey	37.5	38.5
Camel*	36.8	38.8
Pigs	38.5	39.5
Poultry	40	42

* On cold mornings the temperature of the Zebu can fall to 36° C and in the warm weather can rise to 41° C: that of the camel can fall to 35° C and rise to 40.5° C under the same conditions.

they live in environments whose temperatures vary between − 40° C and + 50° C.

A normal body temperature in an environment of extreme heat or cold is an indication of good functioning of the vital organs and of good acclimatisation to the environment. In young animals the temperature is higher by 1–1.5° C than that of adults.

When the animal's activities follow the normal rhythm of day and night, its temperature varies according to a regular cycle; it is higher in the evening around 6 p.m. than it is in the morning around 6 a.m., the difference varying with species but it is generally from 1.5° C to 2° C (nycthemeral rhythm).

The internal temperature of the body is higher than that of the skin and the extremities, cooling being achieved by movement of heat towards the body surfaces and transfer into the surroundings. Even without blood circulation there would be transport of heat by conduction, although the conductibility of tissues varies: if that of adipose (fatty) tissue is taken as unity, then that of skin is double and that of muscle is triple. Tissues play a part as insulators, adipose tissue being the best.

Blood circulation is the main means of heat transfer and its effectiveness is a function of the relationship between the central volume of blood and that of the blood in the exterior parts of the body.

Respiration rate

Respiration rate can change very rapidly and, at the extreme, in a matter of minutes. It is directly influenced by the animal's activity and by environmental conditions.

The size of the animal is related to the respiration rate, the latter being inversely proportional to the volume of the animal.

In comfortable temperatures (see p. 79) the rates shown in Table 3.2 are observed.

Table 3.2 Respiration rates – complete cycles
(inhalation and exhalation) per minute

Domestic animals	Young	Adult	Old
Zebu		22–40	
Humpless cattle		22–58	
Buffalo	25–29	24–25	
Sheep/goats	15–18	12–15	
Horse	10–20	9–18	8–15
Camel	10–12	5–9	
Pigs		13–15	
Poultry		14–26	

The volume of air inhaled as a function of weight (W) gives:

the residual volume $= 24.1 \times W^{1.13}$ ml
the volume of flow $= 7.69 \times W^{1.04}$ ml
maximum capacity $= 56.7 \times W^{1.03}$ ml
dead space $= 2.76 \times W^{0.96}$ ml

Definitions

residual volume : air which cannot be exhaled
reserve volume (VR) : air which can be exhaled by a forced exhalation
complementary volume : air which can be inhaled by a forced inhalation
flow volume : air inhaled and exhausted at the time of normal breathing
total capacity : reserve volume + complementary volume + flow volume

Thus for a bovine animal of 250 kg (one tropical livestock unit):

total capacity $= 16.7\,l$ ml
flow volume $= 2.4\,l$ ml

Heart or pulse rate

Heart rate which is expressed in beats per minute is, like the respiration rate, inversely proportional to the weight (W) of the animal, $238 \times W^{-0.25}$, see Table 3.3. It can alter rapidly due to external factors such as temperature or due to intense activity by the animal itself. The amount of variation is as much as 30–40 per cent.

The rate is observed directly by counting the beats of the heart by listening to it or by feeling, with the index finger, the pulse of arteries at particular points on the body. For the horse these can be the cannon bone or between the angle of the lower jaw and the lower incisor region (facial artery). For the camel and cow it can be underneath the root of the tail (coccygial artery). In the cow, with each beat of the heart the jugular groove bulges visibly with each wave of blood flow (i.e. with each heart beat), so enabling one to count the beats at a distance from the animal.

Table 3.3 Heart beats per minute

Domestic animals	Young	Adult	Old
Ruminants			
Zebu	70–100	59– 62	
Humpless cattle		58– 64	
Buffalo	69– 60	58– 60	56
Sheep/goats	90–100	75– 85	60–65
Other domestic animals			
Horse	50– 70	36– 40	32–38
Camel	45– 60	30– 50	
Pig	100–110	60– 80	
Poultry		130–160	

Table 3.4 Number of red and white blood corpuscles in domesticated animals

Domesticated animals	Number of red cells per mm^3 (millions)	Number of white cells per mm^3 (thousands)	Blood cell volume (Haematocrit value)
Cattle			
adult	5– 8	5–12	30–40
young		12–15	
Sheep	9–12	8–11	27–37
Goats	11–18	7–20	23–33
Pigs	5– 8	10–20	39–57
Horse	5–11	5–15	30–40
Camel	9–11	7–15	

Blood

The number of red blood corpuscles (erythrocytes) and white corpuscles (leucocytes) of animals in good health varies between species (Table 3.4), between individuals and in the same individual according to its condition and health.

Parasitism and under-feeding cause anaemia which reveals itself in a reduction of the red blood cell count and a reduction of the haemoglobin contained within each blood cell.

Bacterial and viral illnesses affect the number of white corpuscles and the ratio between the different types of white corpuscles. The volume of blood cells (haematocrit value) is calculated as a percentage of the total blood volume and this is determined by centrifuging or precipitating a given volume of blood, which has been treated so that it will not clot, under standard conditions.

Among the white blood cells, are many types identified by their cytological features and by differential staining. In healthy animals, the percentages of the various types vary little (Table 3.5), but in sick animals the percentages are greatly modified and this feature can be used for disease diagnosis.

Table 3.5 White blood corpuscles (percentage of total blood volume)

Domesticated animals	Granulocytes – polynuclear			Mononuclear	
	Neutrophils	Basophils	Eosinophils	Lymphocytes	Monocytes
Cattle	36	0.75	6.5	50	6
Sheep	35	0.4	0.5	52	2
Goats	33	0.8	3.0	60	2
Horse	58	0.6	4.0	35	4
Donkey	3				
Camel	54.5	–	3.7	41.8	–
Pig	30	1.2	2.0	60	3.5
Chicken	35	3.0	5.0	60	2

Urine

The quantities of urine excreted from the body varies according to climate and its composition depends on feeding, drinking and climate: warmth and humidity have a substantial influence (Table 3.6).

Table 3.6 Urinary data

Domesticated animals	Quantity excreted in 24 h (litres)	Density	pH
Cattle	4.0–15	1.025–1.045	7.8–8.4
Sheep	0.5– 1.3	1.015–1.070	5.3–8,6
Goats	0.5–1.5	1.015–1.070	
Horse	3.0– 6	1.020–1.060	6.0–8.4
Camel	0.5– 6	1.045–1.056	
Pig	2.0– 4	1.005–1.016	5.4–7.0

Heat regulation

Definitions

At birth, the animal's characteristics are an expression of its own genotype influenced only by the nutrients supplied by its mother during gestation and the conditions of that gestation.

After birth, the fulfilment of the genetic potential will depend on the feed, including energy sources available to the young animal.

Besides the nutrients with which it will build and maintain its body, the animal must obtain nutrients of a catalytic nature and energy containing nutrients. These must be in a physiologically usable form for chemical and biochemical reactions necessary for vital cell and organ activities, namely digestion, absorption, transportation, movement, production and reproduction etc.

In 1879, Berthelot stated two theorems which are the fundamentals of the modern theory of animal temperature regulation: the first concerns the living organism only giving out heat; the second concerns the organism expending energy.

1. For a period in which a living creature has no other source of energy than its food, in which it does no work, at the end of which it is in the same state it was at the beginning, the heat which it develops is equal to the difference between the energy content of its food (oxygen and water included in this category) and that of its excretions (water and carbonic acid included).

2. The quantity of heat developed by a living creature which carries out work, but still without an extra source of energy other than its food and without suffering any appreciable change in its chemical constitution (perhaps calculated by the difference between the energy content of its food and that of its excretions) is reduced by an energy figure equivalent to the work accomplished.

Berthelot's two theorems present a total energy balance for the intake of food.

The validity of these principles has been demonstrated by conducting calorimetric tests on a man at rest and at work over a period of 93 days. By direct measurement of energy in the form of heat and work produced by the subject in a calorimetric chamber, 2.716 kcal were recorded. Measuring the heat of combustion of the food and the excreta in a bomb calorimeter, it was recorded that 2.719 kcal of energy were used by the man – almost exactly corresponding to the figure above.

Between the food which the animal consumes and the use of the nutrients in building the body and the use of energy required for body functions, there is a long chain of chemical and physico-chemical processes which all produce waste: faeces, urine and heat, which must be eliminated from the body.

It has also been shown that for an ox which receives a ration of hay and cattle cake of which the energy value is 29 538 cal (combustible energy), the energy is used as shown in Table 3.7.

Table 3.7 Energy balance

Constituents (g)		Taken in (cal)	Given out (cal)	Percentages
6 988	hay	27 727		
400	linseed oil cake	1 811		
16 619	faeces		14 243	
4 357	urine		1 210	59
142	methane		1 896	
37	losses from the skin		88	
	heat emission		11 493	38.9
	weight gain		608	
		29 538	29 538	

The *energy of conversion* refers to the energy loss which is dissipated in the form of heat and corresponds to the consumption of food, its digestion and its use. Also used is the term *extra heat*, which is in fact a loss and which must be deducted – this can range between 20 and 40 per cent of the food or ration and here it is 38.9 per cent.

Table 3.8 uses the figures from Table 3.7 and introduces two other definitions and shows the value relationship between the different categories of energy.

Table 3.8 Relationships between the different energy categories

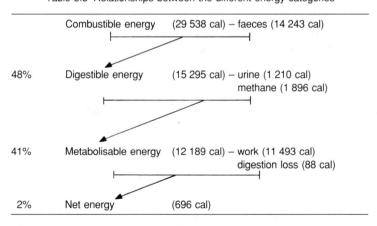

Thus of the 3 800 cal in 1 kg of hay (combustible energy) consumed by a ruminant, only 1445 cal or 38 per cent will be usable by the animal for its maintenance, growth, reproduction, production and ultimately for laying down of reserves (retained energy) (Table 3.9).

Table 3.9 Energy losses

Energy (cal)		Per cent	Means of loss	Loss (cal)	Loss as a percentage of combustible energy
Combustible energy	3 800 cal	100			
			Faeces	1150	30.3
			Urine	35	0.9
			Gaseous fermentation (methane)	320	8.4
			Conversion energy (heat)	850	22.2
Net energy	1445 cal	38			
			Total	2355	62.0

In practice, the calculation of net energy, starting with combustible energy is carried out with the aid of tables which give the values to use for each food and each species.

Heat production – volume – body weight

It is interesting to find the relationship between weight, surface area of the animal and the heat which it produces.

On first consideration, one can assume that the heat emitted into the surroundings is proportional to the surface area of the skin and the heat which the animal produces is proportional to its volume or to its weight.

Using 26 groups of mammals ranging from a mouse to a cow, research has established that the value of metabolisable energy at rest (M) over 24 h and expressed in kilocalories, for an animal of W kilograms liveweight, followed a regression curve according to the formula:

$$\log M = 1.83 + 0.756 \log W \pm 0.05$$

In practice one uses weight to the power 0.75 which is designated metabolic weight.

$$M \text{ kcal} = 70 \times \text{weight kg}^{0.75}$$

or approximately:

$$M \text{ kcal/hour} > 3 \text{ cal} \times \text{weight}^{0.75}$$

For a ruminant weighing 250 kg (one tropical livestock unit), the metabolic weight is equal to $250^{0.75}$ or 62.87 kg and the metabolisable energy at rest for 24 h is 4400 kcal.

External sources of heat

The animal living in the open air, at pasture for example, receives a continuous flow of energy originating from:

- radiation from direct sunlight;
- energy absorbed by the atomosphere and clouds and then re-emitted in a longer wave-length;
- energy reflected by the soil and plant cover;
- energy absorbed by the soil and plant cover and then re-emitted either by conduction or convection;
- heat energy carried by the winds.

This is demonstrated in Figure 3.1

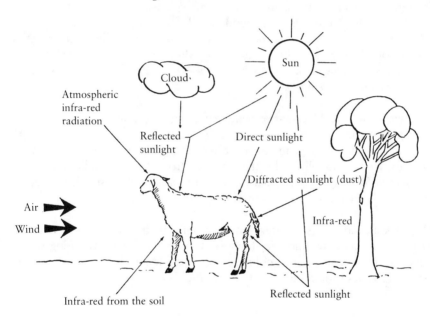

Figure 3.1   Sources of radiant energy

At latitude 40° N, in 24 h an animal receives about 2000 cal/cm^2 of its body surface and this is divided up as shown in Table 3.10.

Table 3.10 Energy received at the soil

Source of energy	Intensity (watts per cm^2)		Energy cal/cm^2 per min	
	Noon	Midnight	Noon	Midnight
Direct sunlight	0.077	0	1.1	0
Energy reflected by the atmosphere	0.014	0	0.2	0
Heat emission from the soil	0.048	0.035	0.7	0.5
Heat emission from the atmosphere	0.085	0.028	0.5	0.4

There are no precise measurements of the same order for the tropical regions, except those which concern total radiation which includes direct sunlight and energy reflected by the atmosphere; it is of the order of 0.091–0.109 watts/cm^2 as against 0.091 watts/cm^{2}in the example in the Table 3.10.

One can estimate that an animal, in the course of a day in a tropical region, receives from 2000 to 2500 kcal of energy each 24 h from the environment, which is added to some 4500 kcal from metabolism, giving a total of 7000 kcal which it must dissipate.

Physiological classification of climates

The warm blooded animal always loses 20–40 per cent of the potential energy of its ration and in addition, in the tropical regions, it must lose the energy received directly from the surroundings by radiation, convection and conduction. The possibilities for heat loss will depend upon the characteristics of the surrounding air and this is shown by Max Sorre who classified climate by the role which the animal's physiological mechanisms must play in order to ensure its constant temperature:

1. *Thermogenic* or cold climates: heat regulating mechanisms must make up for the tremendous heat losses.
2. *Thermolytic* or warm climates: heat regulating mechanisms must remove the heat from metabolism plus that received from the surroundings.
3. *Temperate* or warm climates: heat equilibrium is easily assured, regulation being made alternatively by thermolysis or thermogenesis.

This classification does not take into account all the situations an animal must face; thus, as in thermolytic climates, there are cold periods during which the animal must counteract cooling. Notwithstanding this reservation, the intertropical zones should be classed among the thermolytic climates.

Constant temperature and climate

When a population of homeothermic animals lives in the same surroundings and suffers the same climatic conditions of temperature and humidity, the population adapts itself to this environment by a series of physiological reactions which tend to reduce heat loss to a minimum to ensure constant temperature. This is defined as follows for such a population:

1. *Zone of thermal comfort*, which corresponds to the temperatures and humidities at which the energy losses needed to ensure constant temperature are minimal and the animal is not manifesting any defensive reactions against heat or cold.

2. *Thermoneutral zone* in which physiological defences against cooling or warming do not involve a notable increase in energy loss in order to maintain body temperature at its normal value.

Figure 3.2 gives a stylised account of the animals' response to the hostile influences of heat and humidity.

On the subject of regulating mechanisms, the temperature of the air has a direct influence on warming or cooling the animal. The humidity, or rather the saturation deficit of the air, affects the efficiency of the homeothermic processes.

Body temperature has a tendency to decrease when the heat losses exceed the heat produced by metabolism, at which point starting at the *lower critical temperature* there is an increase in heat production until a maximum (*metabolic summit*) is reached. If in spite of everything, the losses exceed the lower critical temperature, the body cools (*hypothermia*) and death occurs due to a cessation of enzyme activity and due to toxication.

When the reverse happens, the organism warms up starting at the *upper critical temperature*, heat loss accelerates and if it cannot stop the heating up, the body temperature rises rapidly (*hyperthermia*) and death occurs when it reaches 42–42.5° C.

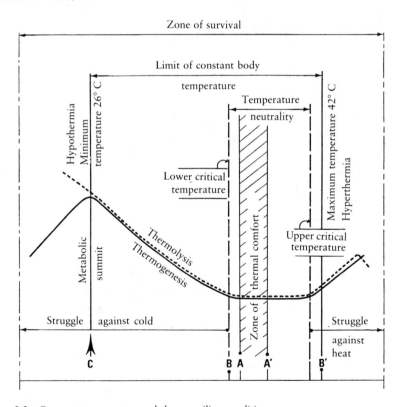

Figure 3.2 Constant temperature and the prevailing conditions

Death from hypothermia is slower than that from hyperthermia – one can keep animals alive when lowering their temperatures from 38° C to 21–22° C.

For the animal adapted to the tropical Soudanian climate, data of saturation deficit as a function of temperature, shows the optimum conditions (zone of comfort) for normal heat regulation (Figure 3.3).

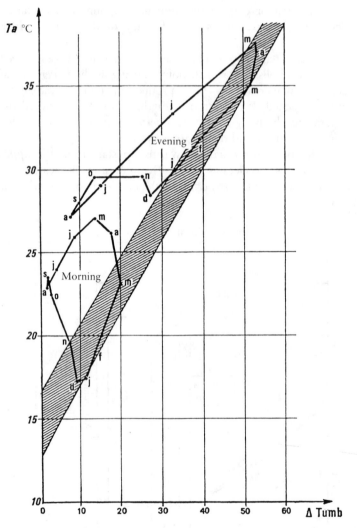

Δ Tumb: saturation deficit expressed in millibars
Ta ° C : ambient temperature expressed in ° C
Climograms of prevailing conditions for the morning at 8 a.m. and the evening at 6 p.m.
Shaded area: zone of comfort

Figure 3.3 Definitions of a zone of thermal comfort for cattle adapted to a Soudanian climate

Thermal balance

Table 3.11 illustrates the different paths of heat production (thermogenesis) and heat loss (thermolysis), which must be in equilibrium. However, part of the heat can be momentarily held on the body surface.

Table 3.11 Pathways of thermogenesis and thermolysis

Heat loss (thermolysis)

Protection against the heat

The skin and hair, fleece or coat constitute a first defence against direct or indirect radiation.

The insulation effect is predominant in woolly sheep whose fleece can, on the surface, reach a temperature of more than 60° C without the animal being uncomfortable; in cattle and sheep with short, glossy and shiny coats, a large part of the radiation is reflected; this is so in the case of white Zebus in Australia, which have a shiny coat reflecting 0.40 cal/cm^2 per min whereas Aberdeen Angus cattle with shaggy hair only reflected 0.10 cal/cm^2 per min (MacFarlane, 1956).

However, while 20 per cent of radiation is reflected, the rest is not totally absorbed by the skin, but by the coat and the energy is emitted by convection in radiation of a longer wavelength.

The protective mechanism may not be beneficial when it reduces the possibility of heat exchange between the body of the animal and the surrounding air. This is so in the case of shaggy haired animals.

The role of hair and skin colour is debatable. Nevertheless, it must be noted that pigmented skins are less sensitive to infra-red radiation and less subject to burning than are those having areas with no pigmentation, such as albinos.

Pathways of heat loss

Protection against radiation is purely physical; the loss of internal heat and of that received from the surroundings takes many paths which one ought to define for instruction purposes, but which are intimately linked:

1. Mechanical – by faeces and urine
2. Physical – by radiation, convection and conduction
3. Physiological – working by complex mechanisms which end in the removal of heat through the skin, via respiration and through the first paths above (i.e. digestive), water being the vector.

The distinction often used between *tangible losses* which relate to losses that can be measured by direct calorimetry (radiation, convection, conduction) and *intangible* or latent losses by transpiration and perspiration, does not help the understanding of the phenomena, other than the fact that the animal controls only the first path.

Mechanical removal by faeces and urine

As well as the potential energy of the constituents of urine and faeces which comes from what remains of the gross energy furnished by the food, the excrements remove the heat which was necessary to raise the temperature of the food mass, from what it was when consumed, to the temperature of the body itself.

An ox, which produces 20 kg of faeces and 6 litres of urine in 24 h in surroundings which have a temperature of 20° C, eliminates with them 370 kcal not including their potential energy.

Physical removal

Losses by radiation

All bodies, whose temperature is different from absolute zero, emit energy in the form of radiation, the intensity of emission depending upon the absolute temperature and the capacity of the surface to emit heat.

This latter characteristic is very close to unity, being 0.95 for a glossy shining coat.

$$R = \epsilon \, \sigma \, T^4$$

σ being a constant:

$$\sigma = 8.2 \text{ cal} \times 10^{-11} \times \text{cal cm}^{-2} \text{ min}^{-1} \text{ k}^{-4}$$

This is applicable to an ox with a glossy coat having a body temperature of 38° C which emits 0.4 cal/cm² per min.

Losses by convection

When a body is immersed in either air or liquid, energy exchanges (C) take place at the surface of contact from warmer (T_w) towards colder (T_c); they depend upon the surface of the body (S) and on the coefficient of convection which depends upon the nature of the surface of the solid body.

$$C = S \, (T_w - T_c)$$

This formula has universal use but its application poses several problems because the coefficient of convection is not known precisely.

Starting with the theoretical calculation it has been shown that the losses from convection in calm air are negligible compared with those from radiation.

The rapid replacement of air in contact with the coat clouds the true losses by convection, but in tropical conditions it remains negligible, of the order of 0.06 cal/min per cm² for a temperature in the region of 25° C or hardly 2 per cent of the heat of metabolism.

Losses by conduction

The losses are due to direct transfer of energy from the warm body (T_w) to the cold body (T_c) at the point of contact of the surfaces; the intensity of exchange depends upon the surfaces in contact and the conductibility of the bodies involved.

So an animal lying on a bed of wood will lose heat less than one lying on a concrete surface. According to Rückbüsch (1977), the heat loss on a bed of wood at 20° C is equivalent to the loss on a concrete floor at 30° C: a bed of straw 2.5 cm thick reduces the losses of heat associated with concrete floors by 41 per cent.

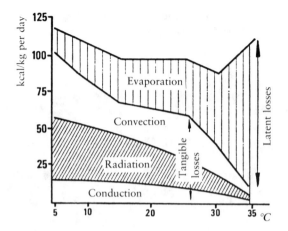

Figure 3.4 The effect of ambient temperature on heat loss. The relative importance, in the pig, of heat loss by conduction and convection (tangible losses) and by vaporisation of water (latent losses) as a function of ambient temperature variations from 5–35° C (after Rückbüsch)

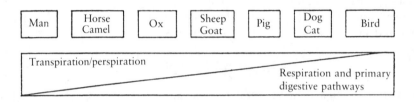

Figure 3.5 Relative importance, according to species, of the pathways of thermolysis

Relative importance of the different physical pathways of heat loss

At the lower temperatures, heat loss is carried out particularly by convection, conduction and radiation; at the higher temperatures beyond 30° C it is done mainly by evaporation at the surface of the body (Figure 3.4).

Physiological loss (latent heat)

Thirty per cent of heat is eliminated by evaporation of water via the skin, via respiration and via the digestive tract.

The importance of these three mechanisms varies with species; Figure 3.5 shows the relative roles of the skin pathway and respiration pathway in warm blooded animals according to species.

At the surface of the skin, heat elimination by sweat and transpiration is permanent.

In sweating, there is emission of sweat from glands which specialise in this function; certain animals however, the pig and dog in particular, lack them. These glands are innervated by the parasympathetic system.

In transpiration, the water diffuses passively across the integument; it exists in all species and is particularly important in those species lacking in sweat glands. In the pig, it represents 35–65 per cent of losses by evaporation.

Each gram of water which arrives at the surface of the body removes as many calories as there are degrees between the temperature of the food ingested and the body temperature, or 17 cal for an ambient temperature of 21° C. But, further, it will remove the heat derived from the body of the animal which will act with the ambient heat to vaporise the water so removing 575 cal per gram.

This cooling mechanism will be even more effective when the vaporisation is made directly from the skin, when the saturation deficit of the atmosphere is raised and when the air in contact with the skin is quickly renewed.

If the coat is too thick, the heat of vaporisation is then only derived from the surrounding air and it does not participate in heat loss.

It is estimated that according to the condition of the animals and to the characteristics if the surrounding air, 25–60 per cent of the heat is removed through evaporation from the skin surface of animals which perspire.

It is convenient to note that the sweating and transpiration remove, with water, the electrolytes Na^+ and Cl^- in significant quantities. There is a continuous exchange between the blood and the extracellular environment for the replacement of lost water and, to maintain a constant concentration of Na^+ ions in the blood, a diet rich in this element is necessary.

The distribution of rock salt to the herd, transhumance on the salty lands of the Sahel, the cures from traditional medicines (*yaeres* in Cameroun) show that herdsmen have, for a long time, had a very precise understanding of the need for salt in their animals. Perhaps they had noticed first that wild animals, at certain periods of the year, gather on the salty lands (namely the migration of the wildebeest in East Africa).

The heat removed via the respiratory pathway corresponds to that which is necessary to warm up and humidify the air that is breathed in; the effectiveness of this mechanism depends on the temperature and humidity of inhaled air and on the importance of pulmonary ventilation (Table 3.12).

Table 3.12 Characteristics of air breathed

Component	Ambient	Body	
Temperature	17° C	38° C	38° C
Oxygen	20.8%	14.0%	15.4%
Nitrogen	79.2%	80.4%	79.2%
Carbon dioxide	0.03%	5.6%	5.4%
Water vapour	20–95%	100.0%	99.0%

Mechanisms of heat regulation

In an animal adapted to climatic conditions, the regulatory mechanisms intervene without visible signs; cardiac and respiratory rhythm, behaviour of the animal etc. remaining normal. When heat production is insufficient or excessive, reflex and hormonal mechanisms set in motion organic reactions which act together and supplement each other to establish effective heat control.

Everything happens as if the regulatory mechanisms were linked to a 'reference temperature' so that any divergence from it will lead to a compensatory reaction.

Augmentation of heat loss

Hyperthermia can result from an increase in the internal production of heat: such an increase in internal heat production can be brought about by intensive feeding or feed rich in heat producing contents, by greater muscular activity, but also by a lack of effectiveness of the heat loss mechanisms under the influence of organic inhibitions or from temperature and humidity conditions of the environment.

The animal combats hyperthermia by an increase in heat loss: augmentation of the sweating process, of the ability to emit heat via the skin and fleece, by an intensification of the water losing process through respiration and through the digestive tract, by panting and eventually by a massive secretion of saliva which is no longer swallowed but foamed at the mouth; in exceptional circumstances the problem can be assisted by a complete breakdown of the metabolism with the emission of diarrhoea.

The increase in water vaporisation through the skin and of sweating is produced by an increase in water supply to the skin resulting from dilatation of the blood vessels and surface capillaries. This reaction is due to a preventive defence reflex having its origin in the layer of the nerve endings in the skin and equally due to a reaction of the central nervous system (hypothalamus) to the increase in temperature of the blood.

This vasodilatation causes a rush of blood to the periphery of the body and, at the same time, an increase in blood circulation; there is a very real dilution of the blood by plasma and water in the muscular and conjunctive spaces; its density and the proportion of proteins and red blood corpuscles fall. If sweating is very considerable and quick, this phenomenon of dilution can be masked. Research has shown that the rush of blood to the periphery of the body could be 50 times the normal value.

As the intensification of the sweating increases the loss of Na^+ ions, it can bring about a mobilisation of K^+ ions in the intercellular spaces and cause pathological phenomena: heat stroke, contractures, muscular cramps, loss of co-ordination of movement etc.

The increase of heat removal by the respiratory pathway is brought about primarily by vasodilatation of the capillaries of the mucous membrane in the upper respiratory tract and is similar to the vasodilatation in the skin; if the congestion is too great it can cause nose bleeding (epistaxis).

Acceleration of the breathing rate which is motivated by the heat sensors in the skin, then has its effectiveness reinforced by the congestion of the nasal tracts; this phenomenon has been considered as an internal cooling process.

The increase in the breathing rate accompanies a reduction in the depth of inhalations, the air inhaled circulating quicker in the nostrils, pharynx, large bronchii, bronchioles and sometimes in the buccal cavity.

In the alveoli the residual air increases, it is saturated with humidity and the temperature there is the same as that of the blood in circulation, which explains pulmonary congestion in cases of heat stroke.

In carnivores such as pigs and birds which lack sweat glands, the upper digestive tracts (mouth, salivary glands and tongue) play a more active role in the elimination of surplus heat than they do in cattle.

This acceleration in ventilation was described by Richet in 1858, by the term 'heat polypnoea' (panting); the maximum respiration frequency is inversely proportional to the weight of the animal and reaches 200 inhalations per minute in the cow, 250 in the calf, 350 in the sheep and 440 in the lamb (Rückbüsch, 1977).

Panting does not remove salts as in sweating and transpiration; it contributes its full effect by an anatomical process which, in carnivores and ruminants, assures irrigation of the central nerve areas with blood cooled to the same level as that cooled by the upper respiratory and digestive tracts.

Other means of heat loss

Besides the previous phenomena which are controlled by nervous reflexes and are rapid responses to abnormal situations, more complex phenomena are initiated because the animal subjected to uncomfortably warm conditions restricts its movement, grazes less and, if the possibility exists, drinks more.

At the same time, one notices a reduction in the amount of water removed by faeces and urine, the latter being more concentrated.

In lactating females, milk production drops and its composition changes.

Water requirements

Water requirement varies with humidity and temperature. Both of these environmental factors influence heat regulation by animals and the water content of the forage consumed.

A group of Sudanese Peul Zebus and a group of N'Dama humpless cattle, kept permanently on the same natural pasture, were allowed to drink *ad libitum* each day (Bamako, Mali): we observed during the rainy season, when

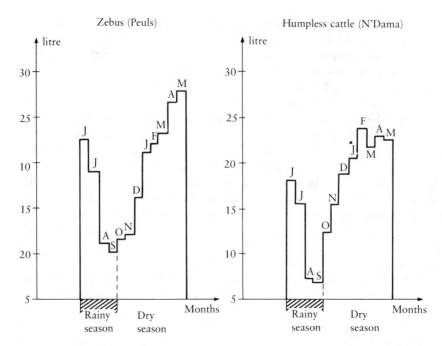

Figure 3.6 Mean daily water consumption

the temperature was low, the relative humidity high, and the water content of the forage high, that an increase in the external temperature brought about an increase in consumption of water while an increase in the relative humidity had the opposite effect; if the humpless cattle and Zebus both react in a way very close to that of temperature, the humpless cattle follow a path of reaction very distinctly linked to the variations in relative humidity (Figure 3.6).

During the dry season, when the temperature is average and the relative humidity is low, the variations in temperature have a very weak effect and are identical in the two groups, whereas the reactions to variations in relative humidity are very distinct and more intense in the Zebus than in the humpless cattle.

At the end of the dry season, at the beginning of the rains, the Zebus and humpless cattle react in different ways. The variations in temperature have a very weak effect on the humpless cattle, negligible on the Zebus, and the correlation between water requirements and variations in humidity is greater in the Zebus than in the humpless cattle.

If one considers water requirement as a measure of the intensity of action of the thermoregulatory mechanisms, it appears that in Zebus as in humpless

---

Figure 3.7 (opposite) a) Water consumption per kg of metabolic weight in a group of Zebus and a group of humpless cattle

b) Water drunk + water contained in the ration on a basis of 2.5 kg dry matter/100 kg liveweight

a.

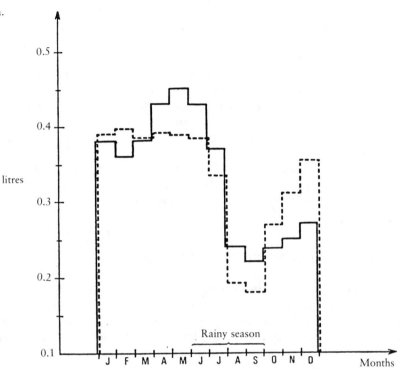

------- Zebus

------- Humpless cattle

b.

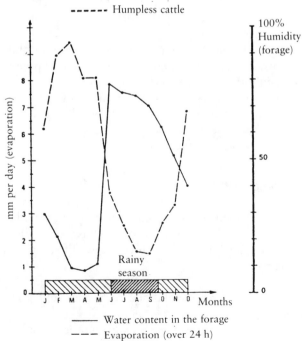

------- Water content in the forage

--- Evaporation (over 24 h)

cattle, it might be, above all, the level of relative humidity which influences their action, and when the temperature reaches a level close to that of the body, for the same variation in relative humidity, the response in Zebus is much stronger than it is in humpless cattle.

The comparison of partial correlation coefficients (water needs and temperature at constant relative humidity) show that the humpless cattle stand high humidity better than the Zebus. This conclusion is confirmed by the geography of domestic animals, Zebus live in the Sahelo–Sudanian zone (very dry for 9 months in 12) and N'Dama cattle live in the Guinean zone which is humid for 8 months in 12.

In Figure 3.7, the curves relate the quantities of water consumed to the metabolic weight. The differences in behaviour are best demonstrated in Figure 3.6 where only the mean daily water consumption values are shown.

More complex mechanisms of heat regulation

The co-ordination and regulation of the vital functions, of which constant temperature control is only one example, are controlled by the central nervous system (brain and spinal cord) with nerves to and from it, the sympathetic and parasympathetic nervous systems and finally the endocrine glands and their hormones, the three systems having organic and functional liaison.

So the central nervous system, which receives information from the sense organs, responds to stimuli in a co-ordinated fashion and it is possible to identify in the brain the precise locations of the nerve centres responsible for maintenance of these functions. Apart from this, all the endocrine glands are activated by sympathetic and parasympathetic nerve fibres which, if they are stimulated, excrete chemical mediators, which activate or inhibit interactions between the central nervous system, hypothalmus and hypophysis which take their control mainly from the endocrine functions.

Figure 3.8 shows the influence of external factors via the hypothalamus on the brain on production (milk, meat etc.). It will be helpful at this stage to recall the properties of the endocrine glands concerned with heat regulation; the pituitary, the thyroid and the adrenals.

The roles of the pituitary

In the course of development of the embryo, the pituitary develops starting with the mesoderm and encephalic nervous tissue; at the last stage of development, one can distinguish three very different histological and physiological parts:

1. The anterior lobe secretes metabolic hormones and gonad stimulating hormones.
2. The posterior lobe hormones have a neuro-motor action.

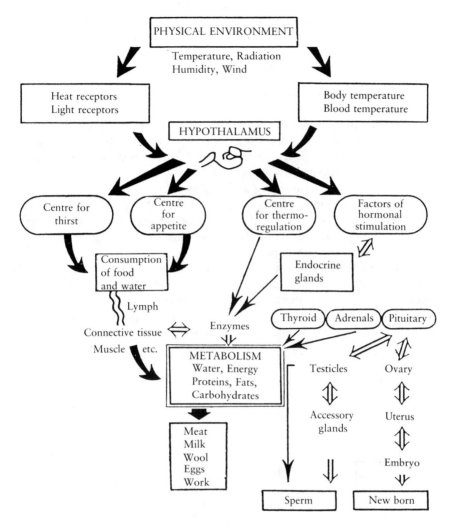

Figure 3.8 Diagram of interactions between the physical environment and production by the animal

3. The intermediate lobe secretes a hormone acting on the production of pigments.

Alone, the metabolic hormones of the anterior lobe act directly in heat regulation, namely:

1. somatotrophic hormone (STH) or growth hormone which has a direct action on the cells of the organism;
2. thyroid stimulating hormone (TSH) which controls the secretion of thyroxin by the thyroid;
3. adrenocorticotrophin (ACTH) which controls the secretion of cortical hormones by the adrenals.

Among the hormones of the posterior lobe, only vasopressin is involved and this acts on blood pressure and particularly on the elimination of water by the kidneys.

Roles of the thyroid

The thyroid gland, besides the hormones which it secretes (thyroxine and di-iodothyronine) directly controls cellular metabolic activity and also plays a role in morphogenesis, growth, activities of the nervous system, lactation, egg laying and wool production (Figure 3.9).

The thyroid secretes thyroxine all the time, the regulation of this activity being assured by the anterior lobe of the pituitary and TSH acting as mediator; when the proportion of thyroxine falls in the blood, excretion of TSH increases and this determines an increase in thyroid activity, the reverse happening when the proportion of thyroxine increases.

As long as the ambient temperatures remain in the neutral zone, the hypothalmic centres simply assure the co-ordination of the centres of the mesencephalis acting on the automatic life processes.

Reinforcement of the action of heat loss and heat production only occurs when the cutaneous mechanisms, transpiration and sweating, are incapable of

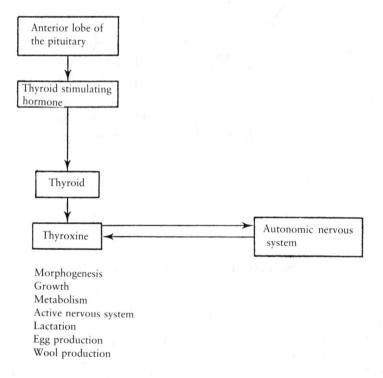

Morphogenesis
Growth
Metabolism
Active nervous system
Lactation
Egg production
Wool production

Figure 3.9 Principal actions of thyroid hormone

maintaining the temperature of the blood at the reference temperature. When this happens the hypothalamus is triggered into action by messages received through the nerve pathways from the skin sensors, these being de Krause capsules for cold and de Ruffini corpuscles for warmth. The hypothalamus can equally react directly to variations in blood temperature as has been shown experimentally, an increase determining an acceleration in pulmonary ventilation and a lowering of body temperature; a decrease has the opposite effect (Table 3.13).

Table 3.13 Heat regulation by hypothalamus – breathing rate and body temperature changes

Body changes	Temperatures and rates		
Warming of the hypothalmus			
hypothalmic temperature	39.1° C	39.2° C	39.8° C
respiration rate*	18– 20	70–83	88–100
body temperature (rectal)	39.1° C	39.3° C	39.2° C
Cooling of the hypothalmus			
hypothalmic temperature	40.4° C	39.0° C	39.2° C
respiration rate*	95–100	62–76	40– 48
body temperature (rectal)	39.2° C	38.9° C	39.1° C

* complete cycle per min

The skin receptors first determine the reflexes originating in the medulla which, via the ortho- and parasympathetic fibres, then induce a modification of the blood demand in the capillaries of the peripheral parts of the body by:

1. a reduction of the demand by vasoconstriction in the case of cooling (sympathetic);
2. increased vasodilation in the case of warming (blockage of the sympathetic mediators).

When there is warming, the sympathetic fibres which activate the sweat glands secrete an enzyme which produces a chemical mediator – bradykinin. This induces sweating, but also, as it diffuses into the conjunctive areas, causes vasodilation of the capillaries.

If, at one time, these reflex phenomena were considered as the only pathway of thermoregulation, it was demonstrated that their action was of short duration and that in fact, it was above all the cerebral centre which intervened the reactions starting to operate in sequential order:

1. intensification of changes in blood demand;
2. inhibition or acceleration of sweating;
3. eventual acceleration of breathing;
4. modifications of the heat producing mechanisms;
5. modifications of food movements within the body and its related functions.

The intensification of blood demand is brought about by the sympathetic nervous system.

The increase in sweating is initiated by central hyperthermia, but it can be inhibited by a very low external temperature; research has shown that, in man, sweating was independent of surface temperature when this is higher than 33° C.

For surface temperatures of less than 33° C, there is an inhibition of sweating. Intense muscular work can raise internal temperature, but if external temperature is low, there sweating is inhibited.

Increased breathing rate is initiated by excitation of hypothalmic regulating centres (see above).

Adaptation to climate

If the animal is permanently subjected to a warm climate, it will have to adapt physiologically to the environmental conditions. The first modifications concern the distribution of water in the blood and diffusion spaces; the return to a normal proportion of proteins is sufficiently quick but it is slower for the red corpuscles.

Adaptation is more or less complete in the horse; one can note seasonal variations in the above characteristics whereas such a phenomenon is not apparent in cattle.

It is not possible to determine the aptitude of a breed of animal to subsist in a tropical climate. It is obvious that species and breeds of animals have different reactions which one can often put down to anatomical or physical characteristics.

The list of examples here is far from exhaustive.

1. In cattle, humpless breeds and Zebus react differently in a warm and dry climate.
2. In Zebus subjected to dry (humidity < 20 per cent) and warm (more than 30° C) climates, one can observe body temperatures of 40° C or even 40.5° C; when subjected to cold (8–12° C) and dry (humidity < 40 per cent) weather, it is not rare to observe hypothermia (36.5° C) in the same animals. When the weather is warm and humid, heat loss is less efficient in Zebus than in humpless cattle.

It was found that the incidence of sweat glands per unit surface area was higher in Zebus than in humpless cattle, which explains the large variations in body temperature and the efficiency of their cutaneous heat loss.

The difference in reactions to climatic conditions between indigenous pure bred animals and their crosses with exotic breeds, shows that the adaptation to climate is not a simple adjustment.

The remarkable adaptations of buffalo to warm humid climates and that of camels to Saharan climates are in favour of this hypothesis.

For cattle, one can cite the success of the transfer to equatorial Africa, with a warm humid climate, of the breeds N'Dama, Baoule and Lagune from Ivory Coast and Benin, whose climates are very similar to those of the receiving areas.

The characteristics favourable to acclimatisation are firstly those which allow normal functioning of heat loss, those concerning the coats are important; short, shiny and glossy hair is more favourable than long, shaggy hair.

Shaggy coats have an uneven surface, they reflect radiation less, they form a barrier to heat diffusion by convection and conduction and, above all, form a mat which opposes swift evaporation of sweat.

The nature of coats is a genetic characteristic, from a general point of view, and it has been proven that tolerance of tropical climates is very much linked to genetic factors.

As long ago as 1932, the Jamaica Hope breed (the result of a cross between the breed Criollo and European stock) was described as being perfectly adapted to the Bermudan climate.

In 1944, research showed that the Holstein and Jersey breeds reacted differently to climate. Comparing the reactions of Sudanese Zebus with their F_1 and inter-cross F_2 with Montbeliarde and Charolais bulls, reared since birth in a Soudanian climate, we have found that the Zebus are characterised by a large amplitude of variation in body temperature, their morning temperature being lower than the other groups and their evening temperature being higher than that of the F_1 and F_2 Zebus $\times$ Montbeliarde, but lower than that of the F_1 Zebus $\times$ Charolais.

For low ambient temperatures, the temperatures of the F_2 Zebus $\times$ Montbeliarde are higher than those of the Zebus but less than those of the F_1 Zebus $\times$ Montbeliarde. When the ambient temperatures are high, the influence of Zebu blood intervens; the temperature of the F_2 is less than that of the Zebus, but higher than that of the F_1, showing evidence of a very great tolerance to high ambient temperatures.

These observations are only a small sample of new research on climatophysiology conducted throughout the world in order to find 'the breed' which can, by its qualities of adaptation, accommodate itself to all situations.

An examination of a number of publications dealing with the subject reveals two main trends in the research.

1. One group shows the results taken in controlled environment rooms on a relatively modest number of animals and which give useful information on the thermoregulatory mechanisms, due to the possibility to control the factors of climate and food intake.
2. The others treat the observations made on animals living in open intensive or extensive rearing conditions and subject, at the same time, to the effects of all the climatic factors.

From the point of view of development operations, the latter publications are more interesting, particularly when they take account of the problems of failures. Because of the complexities of the heat regulation mechanisms which influence purely nervous reflex phenomena, as well as the major changes in the liquid content of the blood, and the changes in distribution and elimination of water, it is not surprising that transfers of animals from temperate to tropical areas are carried out with more failures than successes.

It appears then that the successful conclusion of a development programme cannot be achieved in another zone except in one where the climatic conditions are similar or artificially made similar, or when the breed of animal transferred has been experimentally proved to possess a genetic potential to allow it to adapt.

Climate and morphogenesis

It was seen in Chapter 2, that climographs drawn using the mean daily temperature and relative humidity for each month, allow comparison of climatic conditions of different stations. They can be used to form a picture of the physiological qualities of a climate.

In associating breeds of animals from tropical regions with the climograph of the original home of the breed, we have noticed that Zebus are found in regions for which the major part of the climograph are in the warm, dry parts, while humpless cattle are found in regions where climographs are situated in the warm, humid parts of the diagram.

Also, comparing the size of animals with the appearance of the climograph, one notes that animals of large stature occur in regions whose climograph are of large area and conversely that animals of small stature are found in zones with a climograph of small areas of land.

As long ago as 1847, Bergmann observed that, among the varieties of a warm blooded species, the smallest are those which live in zones where the mean temperature is highest.

In 1877, Allen announced the following rule: 'in homeothermic types in a given area, the relative importance of projecting parts and groups of exposed parts of the body decreases with the mean temperature of their surroundings.'

Schreider combined Bergmann and Allen's rules. Among apparent homeothermic breeds and species, the surface of the body increases in relation to its volume and weight in climates which impose, for at least a part of the year, the necessity for the use of heat loss mechanisms.

The reverse tendency is observed in climates favourable to heat loss.

The roles of heat and ambient humidity are now better known, and the works of Hammond on morphogenesis in domestic animals allow better understanding of the respective roles of the physical environment and feeding. In morphogenesis, it is then possible to state the following:

1. A warm humid climate, characterised by a climograph with small area and in which heat loss is difficult, induces thyroid activity in animals which are

subject to a reduction of heat production; as thyroid activity controls fetal and postnatal growth, it is then not surprising to observe that animals of small stature are found in warm humid zones.

2. Purely hormonal action is re-inforced by poor milk production by the mothers which is again controlled by thyroid hormone.

3. When there is a transfer of animals from a temperate zone to a tropical or equatorial zone, one observes, over generations, a modification of the harmonic relation between weight and stature and above all between height of the withers and height of the breast bone; there is an increase in the relationship of surface area to weight and this is particularly evident in milking breeds.

Meanwhile, these phenotypic modifications reduce none of the genotypic qualities; this is seen in the populations of animals of the N'Dama and Lagune breeds descended from animals transferred from West Africa to Zaire which, finding favourable conditions, have a better conformation and greater weight than those cattle in the indigenous home of their ancestors.

4

Animal production and water resources

Nature of the resources

General

The development of livestock rearing could not be considered without water supply. Access to sources of drinking water has caused struggles for their possession since time began.

For 50 years or more, numbers of wells and drillings have been made in the intertropical zones, and it is now possible to take courses on the design of new schemes and the management of old ones.

Water requirements

As has been shown, cattle must be watered at least every second day, but they must, according to season, consume 10–40 litres of water. Similarly camels, if they are only watered every 5–6 or even 8 days, drink 100–150 litres at one time. Also, when one speaks of water supplies, it is not only the individual animal that is considered but the herd and this introduces effective constraints: access facilities for the herd, means of delivery of the water, demands on the well and water quality.

Drinking from open running water is easier, quicker and far more effective. This is unfortunately not the rule in tropical zones, especially when they are arid and herdsmen must largely take water from wells and bore holes by hand or with bullocks, donkeys or camels because mechanical means of lifting from deep wells are relatively few in number.

Watering a herd of 50 cattle from a 25 m well at 20 litres per animal corresponds to a work equivalent of 490 000 joules, or at least 5–8 h work for a man on his own. The herdsman is far from idle and there is no need to dwell on the stockman's interest in water supplies.

Origin of water resources

The resources come from:

- surface water,
- ground water.

Surface water is formed from waters which have flowed, for example pools, lakes, rivers and streams.

Ground water originates from the infiltration of rainfall which takes place at the same place as the precipitation or after the water has flowed for some short or long time.

So the reserves of ground water can be supplied by infiltrating water which exists below ground at the time when flows are in spate. Other parts of the African continent receive part of the waters of the River Niger.

Fossil reserves are known, into which water infiltrated at a time when the land was being formed and were closed by earth movements. They are not re-stocked with water (Sahara).

The flowing of water reduces the quantities which can infiltrate particularly in arid zones where, over 1 km of free flow, losses by evaporation are 100 litres/sec, or 360 m^3/h.

In such an area, it is estimated that in crossing its inland delta, that is the area between Segou and Timbouctou, the Niger loses half of its water by evaporation and this amounts to 30–40 billion m^3 a year or more than 1000 m^3/sec.

The speed and importance of infiltration depends on the nature of the soil and its substrata, permeable soils and rock allowing water to pass quickly while porous rock assures retention.

The characteristics porosity and permeability are linked.

Porosity is due to spaces existing between the constituent elements of the rock and what they are filled with; it can reduce or even suppress permeability if the spaces are so fine that the phenomenon of surface tension opposes the movement of water (clay, closely packed very fine sand). However rocks which are impermeable by nature (igneous rocks, granites, calcareous rocks, lateritic pans) can become permeable because of fissures, fractures and cavities which have been created by erosion or earth movements.

Infiltrated water gathers in aquifers which are categorised according to:

- their depth (deep, shallow);
- the nature of the ground in which they form (alluvial, aeolian deposits, granite troughs etc.);
- their situation with respect to other horizons and to the soil (covered or uncovered);

- the possibility of their exploitation (ground water, artesian, subartesian);
- their composition (fresh, brackish, magnesium or iron containing).

These systems of classification supplement themselves as one looks further into the subject.

Surface water

Among surface waters one can distinguish:

- permanent sources;
- temporary sources.

Permanent sources

Permanent sources in rivers, streams, and lakes allow easy drinking, the water is of good quality; at the time of their formation they can contain clay but not in quantities dangerous to the animal.

During transhumance, the herd goes to the permanent sources when the drop in water renders pasture accessible until it is again submerged.

Drinking places contaminated by sediment when they reach their low water mark can be a source of parasitic infestation by strongyles (red worms), schistosomes and fluke.

Temporary sources

In this category one must put wadis, gulbis, marigots etc., in fact torrents which only carry water during short periods of the rains, and pools that form in depressions left after water has ceased flowing. The latter disappear in the dry season because of evaporation which can be more than 3 m per year while precipitation in the area is no better than 400–500 mm.

Pools form because when depressions are sealed by pulverised clay originating in the washings from disturbed ground.

The waters in temporary pools are generally little silted up, the particles remaining in suspension; the water is no longer usable for humans because it causes intestinal problems but it can be drunk by animals.

Pools are used for drinking right through the rainy season and are only abandoned when they turn into a quagmire.

Underground water

General

The sources are classed according to their depth as shallow or deep. Among them, some are free, others are captive (Figure 4.1).

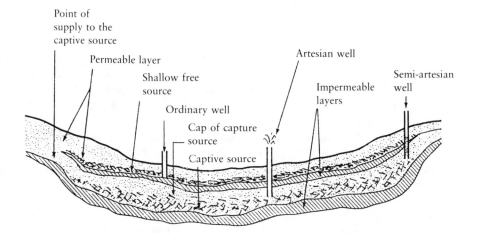

Figure 4.1 Diagram of ground water and captive sources

Free sources are fed directly by infiltration which fills all the ground which they occupy and no other impermeable layer separates them from the surface of the soil. Known as ground water sources, they are also called, the well layer (Φρε in Greek).

Captive sources are contained between two impermeable layers, their supply coming from their edges or from the parts where their ceiling is in contact with a layer which is not completely impermeable.

In artesian wells or bores, the water gushes out of the ground as soon as the cap of the source is pierced; this phenomenon occurs when the side of the source is higher than the level of the ground at the point of digging.

Wells or boreholes are sub- or semi-artesian when the side of the source is intermediate between that of the ground level and that of the cap of the source; water climbs up the bore hole above the point of entry into the source but does not reach ground level.

Shallow sources

These arise from infiltration of rainwater, from water flowing over the surface and from the flow in water courses, which are stopped by the first impermeable layer they meet.

Their depth varies from several metres to around 30 m. Their importance depends on the nature of the geological formations which enclose them and most are found in sand and alluvial rocks of relatively recent formation.

One can distinguish:

- aeolean sand layers;
- layers at the bottom of pools;
- alluvial layers;
- layers of breakage of old bedrock.

Aeolean sand layers

On the shores of oceans and on the edge of deserts, there are vast areas covered with barely stable sand, which has been carried and reshaped by the wind. Their thickness can reach many tens of metres. They generally lie above old bedrock formations.

Rains, which fall there infiltrate very rapidly and stop at the first impermeable layer whose depth varies with the relief of the bedrock formation and their final level varies from several metres, in the intermediate troughs, to 20–30 m in areas of sand plateaux.

The wells which are sunk there have yields from 1 to 50 litres per second; they are very important in Sahelian Africa because they can be dug out by craftsmen and sited in areas suited only to grazing where rainfall is insufficient for agriculture.

Such sources are found also in Ethiopia and Kenya in the Rift Valley.

Sources in the base of pools

These sources are common in all the areas where relief is not very pronounced such as plateaux and plains; flowing waters do not find outlets to permanent water courses, gathering in depressions whose bases have become sealed by very fine elements such as clay and fine sand which have been washed there.

Below this impermeable bed, there can be a much coarser substrate which holds a layer fed by moving water which has infiltrated through the slope of the depression where the flow breaks down the seal.

These sources in the base of pools are lenticular and are exploited by holes which the stockmen hollow out themselves and whose depth is only a few metres, their yield being very low perhaps $4-5 \text{ m}^3$ per day.

Alluvial sources

Recent or ancient alluvial lands are, by reason of their texture (sand and gravel), favourable to the retention of water. When the rainfall and the relief of the bedrock which support the alluvial material allow, the reserves which form there are significant and easily exploited.

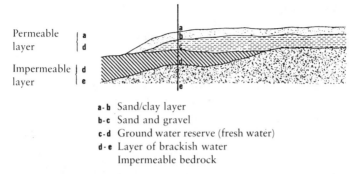

Permeable layer | a, d

Impermeable layer | d, e

a-b Sand/clay layer
b-c Sand and gravel
c-d Ground water reserve (fresh water)
d-e Layer of brackish water
    Impermeable bedrock

Figure 4.2   Diagram of coastal resources

Coastal sources of this type, situated near deltas (Figure 4.2) close to the sea, pose problems as regards their exploitation. In effect, as in all deltas, the water level of the water course is above the surrounding ground level and the alluvial source, situated below the bed of the river, is fed by rainfall and infiltrations which take place during flood when the river breaks its banks. However, sea water permeates into the edges of the alluvial coastal ground where it establishes a delicate balance with the fresh water, the latter occupying the upper and the brackish water occupying the lower layers.

If the zone of fresh water is no longer fed due to insufficient rainfall, restricted flooding or water control being too effective, then the brackish water has a tendency to rise with the consequential sterilisation of the soils.

These coastal sources are exploited by small wells in the dry season, when the animals stay on the coastal pastures at a time when their salt content is highest.

In the interior of the continent, alluvial sources situated in inland deltas (Niger, Mali, Nile or Sudan) only differ from coastal sources by the absence of the interference of brackish water, otherwise their water supply and exploitation are identical.

Sources in ancient valleys are of a different nature. The alluvial materials were deposited there in a time when the water courses were permanent, their volume considerable and erosion very intense. The valley bottom was progressively filled and when the volume of flow fell, the valley dried out, the reserve was no longer fed, other than by infiltration of rain water through the sides of the basin, and the river disappeared into the sands.

The depth of the source steadily reduces from the head of the valley (25–30 m) towards where it joins up with the river bed (1–3 m). These reserves flow out very slowly towards the foot of the valley where often they can be seen emerging. The retention abilities are exceptional and they correspond to the variations of the relief of the bedrock which accordingly constitutes a truly 'subterranean dam'.

These sources, which one finds in all of pastoral Africa (Niger, Sudan, Ethiopia), are exploited by traditional or concrete wells and their size is such that, in certain regions, it is possible to obtain a supply of 40 m³ per hour without significantly affecting the stability of the reserve.

Near where the reserve reaches the surface, it can become brackish due to salinity of the land, caused by the deposition of dissolved salts after evaporation of water which has reached the surface of the soil by capillary action.

These alkaline salt deposits become the object of exploitation of 'natron' which stockmen buy for distribution to their animals.

The salts are obtained by evaporation of waters which have been in contact with saline soils (Dallol Bosso, Dallol Maouri).

Sources in areas of breakdown of ancient bedrock

Whereas alluvial sources occur in ground whose constituents come from erosion of other formations, sometimes very distant from their present site, breakdown sources are found in ground originating on site from the transformation of rocks which, normally, are hardly favourable to water retention and which have become permeable or water bearing, either as a result of physicochemical modification or by fissure or fracture due to earth movements.

This is the case with ancient rock formations (granites, shales, gneiss, volcanic formations) which form the impermeable substrate and the case with more recently compressed grit-stone, compact limestone material with dolomite and finally lateritic formations (ironpans and *bowals* (semi-desert plateau with ironstone crust)).

It is not possible to categorise the nature of the resources and the means of exploitation; however in heavy rainfall areas, the structure modifications having been intense and continuing to be so, the reserves there are more important than in the case of granite substrates where the quantities of retained water are very significant but which are difficult to exploit, the permeability being low.

In low rainfall areas, the reserves of this type are often deep (25–30 m) and the yield dubious.

The subject of lateritic pans and of areas in the process of laterisation merits interest only because of the land surfaces they occupy.

Without discussing the mechanisms which initiate lateritic formation, it is accepted that movements of the water table play a basic role.

In places these formations reach tens of metres' thickness. On the surface the ironpans are by nature impermeable, but are rendered permeable by fissures and fractures. Pools and water holes form in the rainy season and these allow exploitation of plateau pastures (Guinea).

When pan formation has not reached its final stages, the permeability is very high due to fissures, fractures and, above all, to cracks which exist between the granular elements of the rocks which are undergoing the process of laterisation.

In the rainy season, lateritic formations are rapidly filled with water, but in the dry season there is little retention; the water quickly passes to the lower levels and it is not rare to see wells at depths of 10–15 m which overflow in the rainy season and are completely empty in the dry season.

Exploitation of such reserves depends upon local conditions and above all on relief; natural sites exploited by the use of cisterns can allow extension of the period of grazing on plateaux (Cameroun, Ivory Coast).

Deep sources

By deep sources, one means those whose water level is more than 40 m below ground level. Here are found both free and captive sources and among the latter are artesian and semi-artesian.

Deep wells are found in sedimentary basins and their exploitation is achieved with wells up to 80 m deep, although the record depth of 190 m has been reached in Mauritania by boring.

The main sources in tropical Africa

It is unnecessary to describe in detail all the sources in the tropical regions. However, it would seem useful to describe the main water systems which one might meet, because they impose techniques of exploitation and delivery and, as such, systems of animal husbandry.

Deep sources in West Africa

The deep sources are a paradox of the Saharan and Sahelian regions of West Africa. The form of system which the sources take are: Continental intercalary (primary material, Silurian sedimentation), Maestrichian clays and sands (secondary material of the middle Cretaceous period), Palaeocene limestone (tertiary material), and finally terminal Continental (tertiary, quaternary and recent material) certainly represents one of the biggest reserves of subterranean water in the world. The map in Figure 4.3 illustrates such sources.

Terminal continental resource

This takes up an area of about 500 000 km². Although its depth is often as much as 100 m, this is the first water bearing level (water table) which wells reach in the Sahelian pastoral zones of Senegal, North East Mali and Niger.

Its source of water is rainfall and from the River Niger which, from Koulikoro to Ansongo, plays the role of reservoir for collection of waters from the region.

From the works of Auvray de Palaudi, Archambault estimates that if one thousandth of the water absorbed each year by the inland delta infiltrates into the reserves, this would represent 50 million m³ or 1.7 m³/sec.

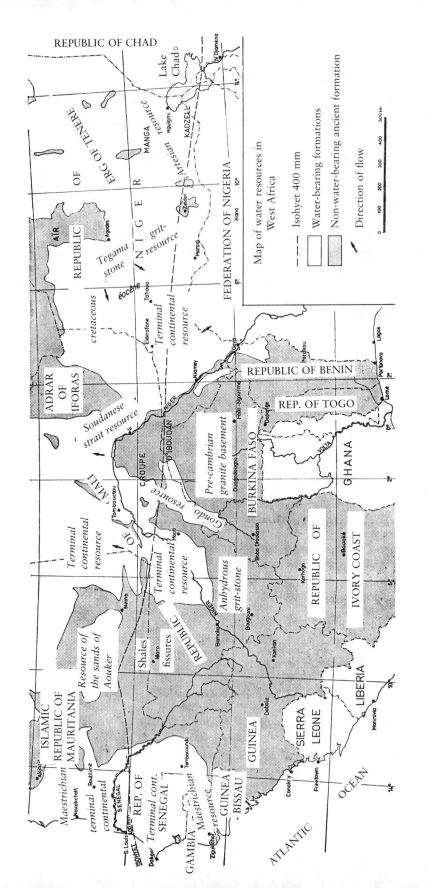

Figure 4.3   Map of subterranean water resources in West Africa (Map by L. Maurier in the work of J. Archambault, 1960)

The supply varies with the quality of the wells from 30 m³/day in the area south of the Mauritanian basin to 180 m³/day in the Senegal basin and almost 3000 m³/day in the Mali basin.

Maestrichian sand resource

The Maestrichian sand resource is limited to the Senegalo–Mauritanian basin (Figure 4.3), covers more than 100 000 km² and its reserves are estimated at 5 000 billion m³. This is a captive source whose water level varies between 100 and 200 m below ground level and its depth of water from 200 to 450 m.

This source is exploited by boreholes of which some are semi-artesian. With bores assisted considerably by gravity and by the relative height of their perimeters, yields of 10–15 m³/min are obtained.

Continental intercalary resource

This is a free or captive resource according to region. It is practically continuous from Chad to Mauritania, it covers an area of the order of one million square kilometres, 2500 km from East to West and is close to 1000 km wide in places.

Individual sectors are identified as Mauritanian, Malian, Niger and Chadian, which have their own characteristics as regards the origin of the waters which feed them, but their exploitation remains the same and is by wells when the static water level is not deeper than 70 m and by boreholes when it is deeper.

In the Niger sector, the resource is fed by the flows from Aïr, the static water level is between 410 m and 340 m near to Adrar Dutchi, the resource is captive and it is exploited by artesian wells. Where it is semi-artesian they use boreholes which maintain the static level (50 m). Where it is exploited by the wells which only use the upper part of the reserve, yield can reach 180 m³/day in Senegal but only 30 m³/day in Mauritania.

In the Niger sector, the terminal continental formations are more complex. There are many shallow sources and, below, at least two levels linked hydraulically, with free sources above. The yields there are considerable, being 250–300 m³/day for the middle layer and from 150–1200 m³/day for the lower level.

Deep sources in Central and East Africa

As shown in Figure 4.4 one finds some of the same types of source in Central and East Africa as have already been met in West Africa, also found are those which lie on old geological formations.

The sources are classed as:

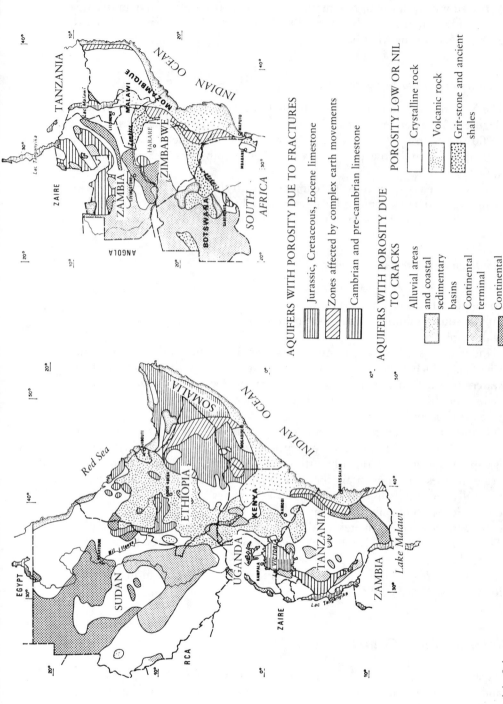

Figure 4.4 Subterranean water resources in Central and East Africa

Aquifers with porosity due to fractures

These are found in limestone (Cretaceous, Eocene, Cambrian and Pre-cambrian) and those areas affected by complex earth movement. They are associated with the formations most frequently found in the Horn of Africa (Somalia, Ethiopia, Kenya), but also appear in a more limited form in Tanzania and Mozambique. In these areas, the resource is generally very deep, the supply of most wells low and the hardness of the water high.

Aquifers with porosity due to cracks

These are alluvial areas and coastal sedimentary basins, terminal continental formations and continental grit-stone. These formations are important on both sides of the Equator; in Sudan on the one hand (Nubian sandstone, terminal continental) where it covers half of the country and in Botswana on the other. In these regions the water is generally deep (60–120 m). The Nubian sandstones are fed by infiltration of the waters of the Nile, notably near to Khartoum.

Formations with little or nil porosity

These are crystalline rock, volcanic rock, gritstones and ancient shales. These formations are found in the high regions of Ethiopia, Kenya, Tanzania and as far as Zimbabwe. In these areas, the waters can stay in the fractures of the bedrock; the yield of the wells is low or moderate. The presence of water in abundance on the surface indicates low reserves below ground.

Exploitation of water resources

Areas of surface water

Water courses

The only problem presented here is that of access to the water supply and maintenance of it for stock rearing purposes since, when large hydro-agricultural schemes are set up and irrigation schemes occupy the banks of streams and rivers, herds can no longer be taken there because of the damage that they can cause, not only in the growing season but also during the rest of the year (demolition of bunds and drains etc.)

When the setting up of a scheme by the Government of Niger encroached on Mali on the banks of the River Niger, the herds were driven back outside the development area, but after use it became apparent that the presence of

Plate 4.1   Sansanding dam on the River Niger (Mali)

Plate 4.2   Well with concrete curb and boughs supporting pullies

the animals was desirable for their contribution to fertilisation and improvement of the soil; watering places were established and access tracks marked out.

On the other hand the areas, whose agricultural schemes would have been too costly, have seen their pastoral vocation realised and specific schemes have been developed.

This conclusion takes into consideration all hydro-agricultural development whose establishment would involve closing off water access to the animal because it is often the only means of getting value from areas unsuitable for

Plate 4.3   Stockman watering stock individually

irrigation and intensive agriculture, as well as being the only way of using the unused parts of the crop (haulms etc.) and by-products of the harvest from irrigated areas.

Temporary water courses

Their exploitation can be improved, in certain cases, by creating water retaining structures in the form of small bunds whose siting will be selected to avoid silting up or to allow washing out of the build-up of silt.

Natural pools

Temporary pools dry out more or less as a function of the intensity of evaporation of open water, of infiltrations, and often of the transpiration water taken up by the roots of the vegetation that develops there.

Animals drink directly in natural pools but when the water level falls, the animals' excrements transform the pools into putrid quagmires. This is why stockmen dig water holes near such pools and lift the water, which has been naturally filtered and is therefore cleaner.

The improvement of pools aims to extend their duration by increasing their retentive capacity; many methods are possible such as deepening them, raising their edges and cutting down infiltration or evaporation from their surfaces.

The deepening of pools has been used with greater or lesser degrees of success. The base of pools is impervious due to sealing by fine particles which have been brought there by erosion and when digging, one finds a succession of beds of coarse then fine particles. If the erosion has been intense or historic, the impermeable layer is very thick and one can then dig into it, but digging can bring the base of the pool into contact with underlying permeable material, into which the water can disappear; one can thus end up far from the intended goal.

If the pool sits on a captive source of water, digging can increase the duration of the free water, but it is preferable to leave exploitation to the water hole method which provides clean water and limits evaporation.

Infiltrations will be limited by applying coats of puddled clay to the base of the pool. When there are stones close by, a stone lining can have a favourable effect and in temperate countries plastic linings are used for the same effect. Their laying down is a delicate affair, they must be welded together at the joins, covered over with earth and the need to avoid trampling by livestock must be recognised.

Protection against evaporation from the surface can be achieved by application of liquids, which form monomolecular films (long chain saturated alcohols). However, heat reduces the cohesion of the films which are easily broken up by the wind. At best, evaporation is reduced by 20 per cent, but it is necessary to renew the film fairly often.

Polystyrene balls, used for the same purpose, have reduced evaporation by 50 per cent on small surfaces but they are not adaptable to large surfaces because they are very sensitive to the wind.

The above methods aim to increase the quantities of water available. The improvements can also have as their objective a better quality of water by repelling the animals whose defecations are a considerable source of pollution and contamination and which have direct access to open water.

Access to open water being interrupted by thorn hedges to form a small enclosure, drinking is carried out at a water hole connected to the base of the pool by a pipe or, if the relief of the ground permits, at a trough. It should be made by hand, a job not always acceptable to the stockman.

Artificial pools

When the lie of the land is suitable, water storage for the herd can be constructed, its volume depending upon rainfall and the surface area of the depression.

For a herd of 500 head, it is necessary to provide $10 \, \text{m}^3/\text{day}$, or $1200 \, \text{m}^3$ every 3 months, being the time taken by a herd to graze the dry pastures within its walking distance from the artificial pool and after the natural pools have dried up. Taking account of infiltrations and evaporation, one must reckon on a minimum usuable volume of $2000 \, \text{m}^3$.

If one notes that, in an area where the rainfall is 500 mm, half a million cubic metres of water fall on one square kilometre, one can see that the choice of reservoir site and soil and sub-soil quality are most important considerations.

Many construction techniques are possible.

1. The pool can be dug and the spoil used to form an embankment on the downhill part of the slope. This technique assumes an impermeable subsoil and soil (fine clay).
2. The pool can be formed by a dam placed perpendicularly at the lower end of a depression.
3. The reserve can be fed by capturing part of the flow of a temporary water course.
4. Finally with the technique of hill lakes, a thalweg is crossed by an earth embankment, the water flow of the slope being collected by drains. One can, without too much terracing, collect reserves of 5000 to 10 000 m^3 if one takes the trouble to construct at the head of the valley (cf. Madagascar, Cuba, Burkina Faso).

All the works should be provided with a reservoir calculated to be large enough to avoid overspill of water across the crest of the retaining embankments. It is considered necessary to have a section of 1.5 m^2 per square kilometre of basin.

Whatever the techniques adopted, the reservoir ought to be equipped with a drinking trough so that the animals do not have direct access to the open water:

- a water hole linked by pipe to a catchment in the open water;
- a drinking trough with a sluice gate if the site allows positioning of the trough at a level below the level of the bottom of the reservoir;
- a drinking trough fed by a siphon which goes over the top of the dam and is stopped by a tap (Brazil).

Water collection

In areas of low rainfall, where the rains are rare but heavy, it is advantageous to stock-pile water in cisterns situated at a low point, the water being collected on a surface stabilised by a bed of concrete or an emulsion of tar, and the water being retrieved by a pump or by gravity.

This technique can be applied in areas strongly laterised and with good slopes (*bowals* (semi-desert plateau with ironstone crust)).

Exploitation of subterranean water

Subterranean waters can only be exploited directly in places where the resource emerges on the surface. They can only be reached by hydraulic works, water-holes, wells and boreholes which penetrate into the aquifer.

Exploitation of shallow resources

Exploitation is by water-holes or wells. The construction techniques of the latter are more elementary: digging by hand with a lining made of wood and straw for traditional wells, otherwise boring with mechanised equipment and lining with concrete or steel.

Water-holes

These are used for sources very close to the surface of the ground – at most 5 m deep, sources at the bottom of pools, at the bottom of wadis or alluvial sources; these are simple holes whose walls quickly erode away and which last hardly more than one season; their diameter varies from 1 to 2–3 m.

Their yield is as low as $1-5 \text{ m}^3$/day in certain regions, but increased yield is achieved by digging horizontal tunnels into the water bearing layer.

Water-holes are dug by the stockmen who use them and there is a need to keep digging them all the time that they are in use.

Water is usually extracted with a calabash, this having been filled at the bottom of the hole and then passed to another person who empties it into a wooden bucket from which the animals drink one after another.

In Ethiopia, where the water-holes in places are more than 10 m deep, many stockmen climb down into the hole and remove the water by making a human chain and passing wooden gourds; their work, whose speed is remarkable, is kept in rhythm by singing.

Traditional wells

Stockmen have, for a long time, dug wells in order to exploit shallow water sources. Except in exceptional cases, these wells are no deeper than 20 m and their diameter is generally 1 m to at the most 1.2 m.

They are dug with pick and shovel. As it progresses the well builder descends, he lines the walls with green straw from millet, sorghum or maize placed according to its type, and holds this in position with supple unpeeled branches placed according to their diameters. These branches are tied together with thongs made from bark stripped from trees or shrubs of the Euphorbiaceae family, or better still from baobabs if they are available.

These wells do not penetrate very deep into the water bearing layer and their yield is generally low.

When the ground dug into is solid, the lining can be dispensed with and the depth can reach as much as 60–80 m.

Traditional wells do not have curbed tops, the opening being covered with a deck of round cut timber with a square or triangular hole framed by very hard acacia logs over which pass ropes by the stockmen to pull the water containers up.

The wells are the property of the graziers who have the use of the surrounding pastures. The cost of building them is paid for by those who use them. In certain regions, well builders belong to ethnic groups or particular castes (Haddad in Chad).

Modern wells

If, by modern wells, one means those whose lining is made of strong materials, one can class among them those which are sunk by hand by the Moroccans in Tombouctou and whose linings are made from fired earth; and those in which the sinking is made by hand and whose lining is made by plastering and pounding of cement mortar against the walls of the well which have first been covered by wire netting or concrete reinforcing mesh.

The simplest technique to use in ground consisting of sand or running sand is undercutting in which rings drop by gravity as the removal of material proceeds (Figure 4.5).

When the ground is firm and the water bearing layer not too deep, the well can be dug, then the rings lowered and finally the space between the lining and walls filled with sand and gravel.

There are now mechanical means of well digging which avoid the constructor spending long times in the well and, above all, which allow sinking into the water bearing layer as far as 5 m without having to pump.

The wells most frequently constructed have a diameter of 1.8 m, interlocking lining rings of 15 cm thickness and 75–100 cm height which are reinforced with mesh of 0.4 cm diameter; at the lowest point the rings are anchored by feet laid outwards in a star shape.

Water collection equipment

The delivery of wells is a function of the length of the part of the well which penetrates the water bearing layer. Due to the materials of this layer lacking cohesion, a water collection structure is the most delicate part to construct; it must allow water to reach the well while, at the same time, avoid entry of fine materials into the base of the well from the surrounding water bearing layer. So the filtering medium maintains a cohesion essential to the rigidity of the works.

A classic arrangement involves closing the end of the shaft with a slab, the rings which are in contact with the water bearing layer being pierced by weep-holes of 14 mm diameter and surrounded with gravel. This apparatus is unfortunately difficult to maintain if, for any reason, it silts up.

A second method (Figure 4.6) involves sinking an impervious ring 1–2 m into the water bearing layer, ensuring its firmness by anchoring with feet placed in a star shape, then lowering a 'sieve ring' or 'screen' made of many rings of diameter less than the lining, which are pierced by weep-holes and held solidly to each other by metal struts and precast to this effect, the base of the lowest ring being closed or pierced with small holes.

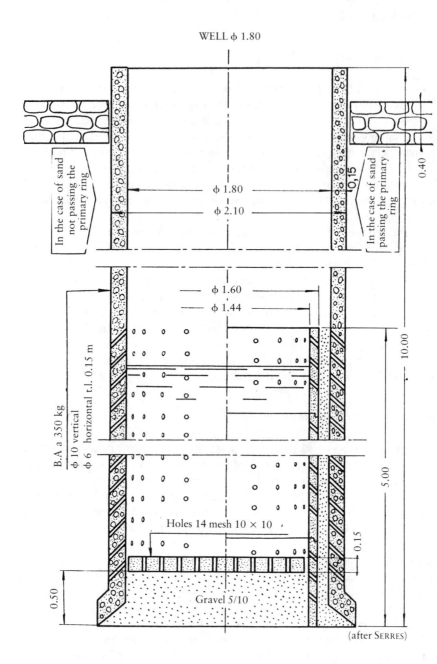

WELL ф 1.80

ф 1.80
ф 2.10

In the case of sand not passing the primary ring

In the case of sand passing the primary ring

0.40

0,15

ф 1.60
ф 1.44

B.A a 350 kg
ф 10 vertical
ф 6 horizontal t.l. 0.15 m

10.00

5.00

Holes 14 mesh 10 × 10

0.15

Gravel 5/10

0.50

(after SERRES)

Figure 4.5 Well of diameter (ф) 1.8 m (undercutting)

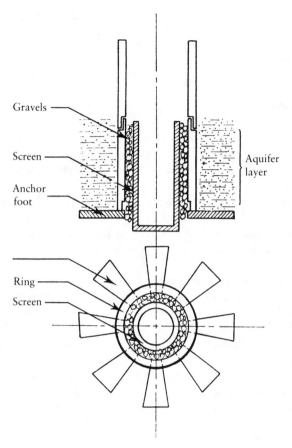

Figure 4.6 Well with self-contained screen

The space between the lining and the screen is filled with gravel to give the apparatus a certain rigidity.

The yield of the wells is increased by 'stretching' the gravel infill. The fine elements of the water bearing layer near the well are flushed out by intense pumping, the gravel placed between the lining and the screen replacing them; vibration can accelerate the descent of the gravel.

With use, the filtration rings have a tendency to drop and so each year they must be checked. To compensate for erosion, it suffices to fix a new ring on the screen and top up the gravel between the lining and the latter.

The screen must always rise 1 m or better 2–3 m up the lined part of the well in order to maintain its rigidity and to avoid leaning over or even rocking.

In strongly supplied sources where the arrival of the water by pumping is rapid, slowing down is achieved by an annulus of gravel placed inside the ring (15–20 cm) and held by a cement or metal collar. In Chad, they use double walled rings leaving an empty space of 5 cm for filling with gravel.

A well which supplies 1.5 litres/sec or 5 m^3/h is excellent. Supplies of 0.5–

1 litres/sec or $1.8-3.6$ m³/h are average; 0.3 litres/sec or 1 m³/h amounts to a feeble supply (fissured rock source) but sometimes it is necessary to be content with this.

Surface structures

Surface structures have as their primary goal the protection of the edges of the well to ensure durability, to facilitate lifting of the water, to reduce losses, to ensure watering of the animals in the minimum length of time and in the best conditions possible.

The curb protects the well from water flowing back in; for shallow wells, where lifting is carried out by hand, a curb of 50 cm height will serve as support; it will be edged with a concrete ring of about 2 m width sloping towards a peripheral channel which carries the water to the drinking troughs.

When the well is deeper, and lifting is carried out by animal traction, it is necessary to reserve positions around the ring where forked boughs, which support the pullies, will be set (Plate 4.2). Tradition dictates that each stockman has his own pulley, rope and bucket.

For a well of 1.8 m diameter, it is necessary to anticipate the siting of six such forks. Moreover, the ring will be high and bordered by raised ground which allows the draught animal to gain momentum at the start of its lift.

All types of drinking trough have been tried, but when lifting is carried out by hand, stockmen prefer to water their animals one after the other from the bucket.

When lifting is carried out by animals, the stockmen prefer small drinking troughs of a few metres to very large ones and this is because they can keep an eye on the stock drinking.

The approaches to the drinking troughs should be strongly paved to avoid their erosion by trampling and water flows.

Surface structures should not be constructionally linked to the well lining because, if as a result of infiltrations, they start to subside, they ought not be able to cause damage to the lining.

Exploitation of deep sources: boreholes

By borehole one means the drilling of a hole of small diameter which can penetrate the earth for many hundreds of metres. The yield from pumps which can be installed, or from artesian springs which may be struck, can be considerable and up to 2000 m³/h, for the bore may reach deep into the aquifer.

The realisation of such works requires heavy equipment and specialised personnel, thus it is appropriate to include them in a list of required regional equipment.

Borehole construction

Water boreholes have profited by oil exploitation. A drill bit, turned by a motor, bores a hole in the ground into which tubes, whose diameter reduce from the head to the base of the hole, are lowered; for a depth of about 200 m, the upper tubes have a diameter of 45 cm while the one which penetrates into the water bearing layer is 20 cm.

Stainless-steel screens, perforated with fine holes (0.25 mm), are lowered into the bed of the aquifer to avoid silting up of the bore.

Around the screen, quartz gravel of 1–3 mm diameter, is placed to a thickness of 5 cm. This gravel which forms a filtration medium, should reach a level 5–10 m above the screen (Figure 4.7).

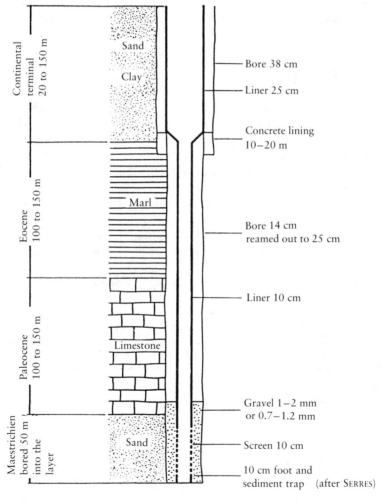

Figure 4.7   Bore for exploitation of Maestrichian source. Test yield 50 m³/h. Working yield 20 m³/h.

Some boreholes are 'improved': by actively provoking the source by pumping or by injection of compressed air, the positions of sand layers are flushed out. Thus a cavity is created, which may reach tens of cubic metres and which is filled from the surface, via the space between the bore wall and the lining, with graded gravel. The speed of the small trickles of water is slow, there is now no sand barrier, the water collection surface corresponds to the surface area of the gravel filter medium and the flow is increased considerably. In sands of good or average permeability, yields reach $50-200$ m^3/h as opposed to $5-20$ m^3/h without 'improvement'.

For the exploitation of fairly shallow sources in thin water bearing layers, horizontal catchments are used. A watertight liner, with openings in its base which are closed by gates, is lowered as far as the water bearing layer. Screens of lengths maybe reaching 80 m are driven through these orifices into the water-bearing layer; such installations have given yields of 250 m^3/h or 1100 litres/sec.

Exploitation level

In free sources, pumping draws (pulls down) at the base of the water bearing layer whose yield depends upon the depth of penetration of the catchment into the layer, but when the source is artesian or semi-artesian, as soon as the drill bit pierces the ceiling of the layer, water rises up the tube if the engineer has not taken care to introduce 'mud' into the bore in order to equalise the pressure with the source.

This is the case in Niger, with bores sunk into the intermediate Continental source at $130-250$ m deep, where the wells are artesian and the natural static water level is positive; in the Continental terminal case the natural static water level is between $40-90$ m deep while the ceiling of the source is some 200 m deep.

Table 4.1 gives the characteristics of several boreholes.

Table 4.1 Characteristics of some boreholes

Country	Location	Ground	Depth of bore (m)	Static level (m)	Yield (m^3/h)	Note
Niger						
	Yelou	Continental Hamadie	129	10	149	artesian
	Kizamou	"	251	14.7	170	artesian
	Koutoumbu	"	152	16.7	200	artesian
Senegal	Amali	Maestrichian sand	209		30	
	Linguere	"	300		119	
	Vendou Kotar		260		10	
	Loumbel		316		70	

In subartesian boreholes, a technique of exploitation (bore-wells) is recommended which applies when lifting of water can be carried out by hand or by animal traction (natural static level less than 40 m deep). A well, which receives the water from the borehole, is sunk and everything happens as if the pipe of the borehole was widened to the diameter of the well from 45 cm to 1.8 m.

The well plays the role of a cistern and should be covered. Two techniques are possible: the well is sunk to about 5 m below the natural static water level, the borehole is built by the side of the well, to which it is connected by a horizontal pipe, or better still the borehole is sunk in the middle of the well-cistern; when the water bearing layer is struck the water rises spontaneously into the well-cistern.

The obvious inconvenience of the system is that both a well and a borehole have to be dug at the same time, but economies are made with regard to heavy pumping equipment for the borehole, and as the yields required are reduced, one can use pipes of 10–13 cm instead of 20–25 cm; overall one can economise by 30 per cent on the cost of a borehole.

Finally, if lifting is carried out by hand there is no additional pressure on the grazing, the herd numbers being limited by the amount of water which can be lifted manually or by animal traction.

This technique permits rehabilitation of boreholes sunk to depths of 60–80 m and whose yield was becoming inadequate.

Surface equipment associated with boreholes

It is difficult to categorise all associated equipment which has been built; Figure 4.8 illustrates typical equipment used in Niger.

Lifting water

Traditional techniques

Manual lifting

This is used whenever water is drawn from less than 10 m but is rarely seen when the lift is 15 m or more.

It is practised with the aid of a bucket, leather container or one made from rubber (from a thin tyre or lorry inner tube), attached to a ring of wood; it measures from 30–40 cm in diameter and can contain 10–20 litres of water. This is lowered down the well by a rope, usually made from hide, which is attached to the container on three points of a circle.

The water is emptied into a drinking trough made from puddled earth, a wooden bucket, a calabash or a bowl (Plate 4.3).

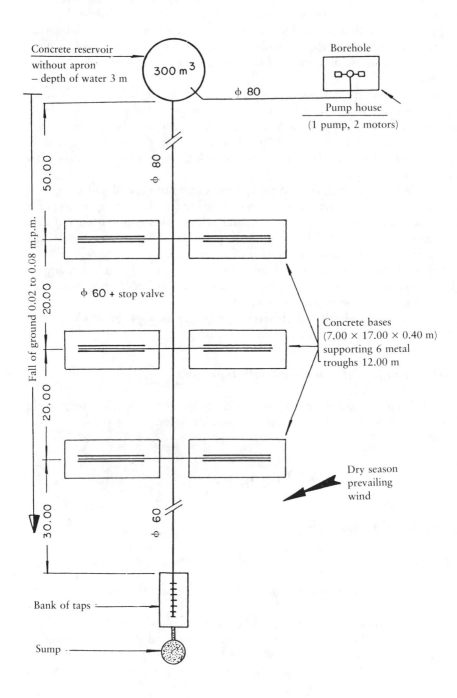

Figure 4.8 Pumping station of the Nord-Tahoua type

The supply is relatively small; three persons working at the same time in a relay can lift 2 m²/h.

The use of pulleys makes things easier but does not accelerate the work and only tends to be used for depths lower than 15 m.

Lifting with animal traction

When the water is more than 15 m deep, it is lifted by animals. Bulls are most frequently used; camels and donkeys are used to about equal extents and horses are only used occasionally.

The containers hold 30–40 litres of water and are lifted by ropes which pass over pulleys fixed on to forks, of which there might be two or three for traditional wells, four for concrete wells of 1.4 m diameter and up to six for those of 1.8 m diameter.

The animals pull one after the other in rotational succession and are led by a child who starts them pulling at the required time and brings them back to the well again in order to lower the container. A man near the well empties the container into the drinking trough.

The containers may have an automatic emptying arrangement which is very common in India but not so common in Africa (Figure 4.9).

For a well of 40 m depth time requirements are:

- 50 sec to raise the container;
- 3 min to handle on the surface;
- 30 sec to lower the container;
- 1 min to fill the container at the bottom of the well,

or a total of 5 min 20 sec, nearly 6 min.

For a well of 70 m depth, the total time for one operation is about 8 min.

If four animals each pull 40 litres 10 times in an hour, the delivery of the well should be 1600 litres/h.

If the well cannot supply this quantity of water, lifting should be stopped.

It is estimated that in 8 hours lifting, 20 m³ of water can be extracted per day. If the wells are shallower (20 m), 3 m³/h or 30 m³/day can be extracted.

Modern techniques

Lifting water is a hard task for the stockmen who have sought to make the job less arduous or indeed to avoid it altogether.

While in the Mediterranean areas, the Middle East and India, mechanical means of delivery have been developed – carousel driven lifting, battery pumps, chain pumps, water mills etc. – it has not been the same in Africa

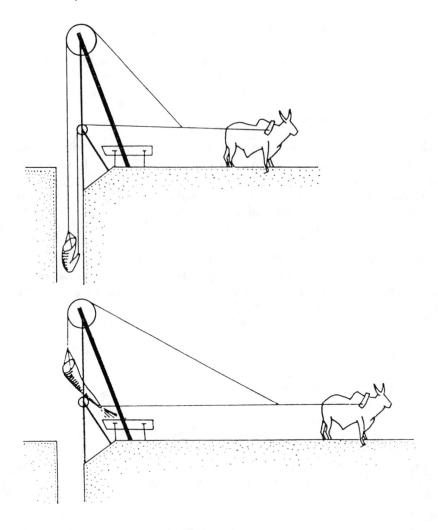

Figure 4.9 Container with automatic emptying

where a number of efforts have been made. The failures have basically come about because of rapid wearing out of moving parts by sand or the inapplicability of the supply of the machinery to the needs of the stockman and psychological factors cannot be eliminated (the herdsmen draw the water they need when they need it).

Mechanical equipment requires, for its adoption and maintenance, the existance of a technical infrastructure in the community and some form of financial appreciation: why pay when you can do the work yourself? Furthermore, drawing water by hand or by animal traction does not involve breakdowns!

Hand pumps

The supply required for animal watering, except perhaps in a small poultry farm, does not allow the use of hand suction pumps and those which deliver according to demand at a drinking bowl or ballcock.

Wind pumps

These are largely used in North and South America, they are not useful for shallow or average depths.

The regime of winds in the tropics permits use of wind pumps and gives very satisfactory delivery rates. Thus a borehole situated in the east of Mali, having a static water level at 43 m with 4 m of bend to deliver into a reservoir 5 m below the ground (manometric height 52 m) has achieved the following daily deliveries using a wind pump:

6 January	
to	31.0 m³/day
15 March	
to	23.5 m³/day
31 March	
to	13.0 m³/day
1 April	
to	30.0 m³/day
28 June	
to	15.0 m³/day
30 December	
to	19.3 m³/day
25 January	

The wind pumps were working away all through the dry season driven by winds of 3 m/sec and turning from 7 a.m. to 11 a.m. and 4 p.m. to 8 p.m. In December and January they also turned at night.

To obtain good results with a wind pump, the following are necessary.

1. Choose a robust and proven material.
2. Show preference for models whose mechanisms are contained in a watertight housing.
3. Choose a model adapted to the winds prevailing at the site of the bore; poor winds are unable to overcome the inertia of the system if the capacity of the pump is too great such that any gain in delivery is lost in time of pumping.
4. Ensure that the right model is adapted to the source; to take account of the inertia of the body of water to be lifted at too great a depth, the capacity of the pump should be established before finding itself buried in the ground.

5. Make provision for a storage reservoir of 3 days' water requirements to provide for the periods of peak demand in the middle of the day and of the season.
6. Choose the site judiciously to avoid areas of wind turbulence.
7. Do not put the tower above the well or the well/bore hole, in order to allow direct pumping up to the container.
8. When the equipment is in place, ensure maintenance at least twice a year, particularly to check the system of propeller feathering before the onset of the period of rains and tornadoes.
9. Last but not least, before installing the windmill, define the rules with the users and appoint two or three persons to be responsible for repairs, which can be foreseen, in case of serious breakdown.

Lifting by engine

Lifting by engine can be carried out starting from open free water, the water being delivered into a reservoir.

Generally used for boreholes, engines drive a centrifugal pump of the cellular type with a number of stages.

There are installations where the engine is connected to an electrical generator and the pump driven by the electricity is immersed in the bore.

Slow engines of the marine type using diesel oil are preferred to those using petrol. The power developed is from 20 to 30 hp for two cylinder models and 30–50 hp for the three cylinder ones.

Engines of 6–8 cylinders are not used exclusively for livestock purposes.

The power to be used is calculated according to the height of delivery, the capacity of the engine and turbines, and the supply programme desired. Evaluation of the latter is made according to the characteristics of the water bearing layer of the bore or well, bearing in mind that there should not be a significant lowering of the static water level of the source.

Use of solar energy to pump water

The increase in oil prices has accelerated the adoption of solar power for uses normally associated with diesel and petrol engines.

The intertropical zones have more than 3000 h sunlight, the surface of the soil there receiving 700 W/m^2.

This energy, falling as it does in a non-continuous fashion, can only be used if its use is adapted to this non-continuity. Pumping of water into storage is one possibility.

In solar pumps (Plate 4.5), the actual pump part of the apparatus does not differ at all from other pumps driven by electricity or fuel.

Solar pumps are driven by motors whose working principles are very different; in the first group, heat radiation is converted directly into mechanical energy; in the second, light energy is first converted into electrical energy.

Plate 4.4   Wind pump (Guilleminot design)

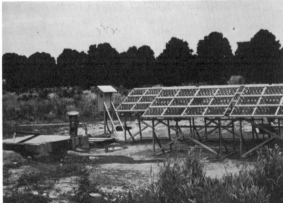

Plates 4.5 and 4.6   Pump using energy collected by a bank of solar cells (Guinard design)

Thermodynamic cycle

The principle of the cycle is simple. In the process of transfer of heat energy from a warm source, obtained by capturing solar energy, to a source cooled by water pumped from the well, part of the energy is converted into

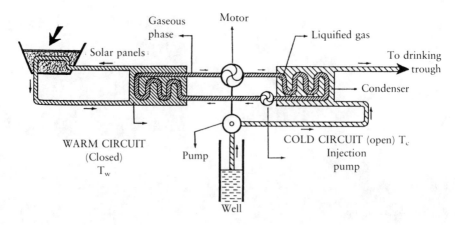

Figure 4.10 Solar pump working on a thermodynamic cycle

mechanical energy to drive the pump directly or via the intermediary of a generator.

The conversion is brought about by the change of state from liquid to gas under pressure, by the heat of the warm circuit, then by the expansion and liquifaction of the gas in a chamber cooled by the cold circuit.

The liquefied gas is re-introduced by a small pump in the exchanger circuit (Figure 4.10).

Table 4.2 Characteristics of Sofrete solar energy pumps
Ambient temperature > 25° C. Water temperature < 28° C
Mean radiation 700 W/m²

Surface area of collectors	63 m²	77 m²	112 m²	1700 m²	3000 m²
Delivery per hour	3 m³	5 m³	7 m³	210 m³	420 m³
Period of working per day	4–6 h	4–6 h	4–6 h	5–6 h	6–6 h
Minimum daily yield for 4 hours exposure to sunlight and lifting 30 m	12 m³/day	20 m³/day	28 m³/day	1000 m³/day	2000 m³/day

The fluid which changes from liquid to gas alternatively is either butane or freon.

Pumps of this type are already installed in Africa for ambient temperatures of more than 25° C, a well water temperature of less than 28° C and solar radiation producing 700 W/m² over 4–6 h. It is possible to deliver 12–2000 m³/day with a lift of 30 m according to the surface of the solar collectors (Table 4.2).

The only criticism one can make about these pumps is their relative bulk and their low delivery in relation to the energy gathered by their collectors:

less than 0.6 per cent for small pumps and 1.6 per cent for the biggest.

In spite of the progress already made, other improvements will be forthcoming. They will involve:

1. efficiency of the collectors (estimated improvement: 30 per cent);
2. direct use of the fluid in the collectors (10–20 per cent);
3. blade motors (100 per cent);
4. delivery pumps (5–10 per cent).

Photoelectric cycles

Solar energy is converted by collectors into electric current using photovoltaic batteries (Plate 4.6).

These batteries use the property of certain semiconductor crystals of, when subjected to a flux of light, creating an electrical potential difference in themselves. Connecting a number of cells in series, then in parallel, allows increased intensity and voltage of the current and enables feeding directly to the storage accumulators and electric motors for, among other things, lifting water.

In this system there are no moving parts; the 'cells' which produce the electricity from sunlight are incorporated in resin or glass. The cost of manufacture is still high, but recent developments should lower costs.

Types of pump

The choice of pump is governed by the depth of the source and its yield.

When the source is less than 7 m deep, suction pumps can be used. Deeper than this, either hydro-ejector pumps which, by a relatively simple mechanism, use part of the water delivered to drive the water from the source by gravitational fall; or immersion pumps are necessary.

The latter contain an immersed electric motor and a centrifugal pump (Figure 4.11) coupled to it. The equipment is suspended in the well or borehole by delivery piping to which is attached an electric cable.

Recently, a manufacturer has patented a method whereby the energy produced on the surface by an engine is transferred by compressed air to the level of the immersed pump. The compressed air works a filtration system and delivers the water from the well (Vita patent).

When one is dealing with a permanent fall of water, a 'water ram' can be used; it sends only part of the water up to a higher level. The fall of water should to be at least 0.8–1 m. The minimum supply should be at least 15 litres/sec, or many times more than the required delivery volume, and finally the delivery height should be less than twenty times the height of the fall of water.

Once the ram has been installed, it is not necessary to inspect it nor does it

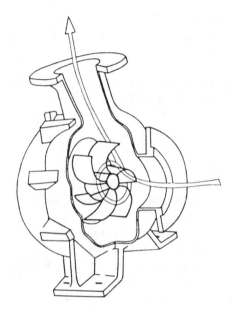

Figure 4.11 Principles of the centrifugal pump

require energy. It is an ideally adapted piece of equipment for ranches situated in mountainous areas where there are good flows of water.

The choice of pump requires precise study of the nature of the water resources and cannot simply be made 'from the catalogue'.

Quality of drinking water

Chemical composition

Animals are less exacting than human beings when it comes to the quality of drinking water, but, unless really fresh water is available in sufficient quantity, well and borehole water is used for humans, other animals and even for irrigation and so account should be taken of quality.

It will be usable if its salinity does not lead to functional problems and if it does not contain germs or parasites.

Mineralisation is measured by the weight of dry residue per litre obtained by evaporation at 110–180° C.

Conductivity, the reverse of resistance, increases rapidly with the content of dissolved salts and it gives an idea of the chemical purity of a water.

Ammonia, nitrite and nitrate content gives an indication of the amount of biological degradation of organic material in the water.

From a *nutritional point of view*, the ions Ca^{++}, Mg^{++}, Na^{+}, SO_4^{--}, Cl^{-}, CO_3^{--}, and often the ions Fe^{+++}, Fe^{++} and dissolved CO_2 are involved.

Alkaline earth metal content is expressed as *degrees of hardness*, which in fact defines the softness or hardness of the water and is linked to the capacity of the water to the capacity of the water to lather (Table 4.3).

Table 4.3 Characteristics of water according to degree of hardness

Degree of hardness	Characteristics of the water
0– 6°	very sweet
6–12°	sweet
12–18°	moderately sweet
18–25°	slightly hard
25–50°	hard
Above 50°	very hard

Chemically pure water lathers when an alkaline washing soap is poured into it (soft water); if it contains alkaline earth metals, the soluble alkaline soap is transformed to insoluble alkaline earth soap (scum) and the water does not lather (hard water). It will only lather when all the alkaline earth metals have been precipitated.

One degree of hardness corresponds to 10 mg of lime dissolved per litre.

From a nutritional point of view, it is considered that drinking water should have less than 1 g of dry residue per litre.

Between 1 and 2 g, the water is said to be saline and the animals should become accustomed to it. Waters containing bicarbonate of soda are perfectly agreeable to animals. Waters containing sodium carbonate cause diarrhoea at concentrations above 2 g/litre. Waters containing sodium sulphate have the same effect at concentrations above 4 g/litre.

Water containing calcium carbonate is more dangerous for the equipment than for the animal. In sources under pressure, rich in carbonic gas, calcium carbonate is dissolved and on pumping, the carbonic gas separates off, the calcium carbonate is deposited on the screens, in the pipe-work and valves which all become scaled with the result that output is reduced.

It is agreed that drinking water should have a degree of hardness of less than 30° but this value is often exceeded (Table 4.4).

Table 4.4 Water quality as a function of chemical composition

	Pure	Drinkable	Suspect	Poor
Nitrites	nil	nil	traces	measurable
Nitrates	nil	nil	traces	measurable
Ammonia	nil	nil	up to 0.002	above 0.002
Organic material (oxygen demand)	< 0.001	0.001–0.003	0.003–0.004	> 0.004
Sodium chloride	T < 0.027	0.027–0.066	0.066–0.165	above 0.165
Degree of hardness	< 6°	< 30°	> 30°	> 50°

Water borne diseases

Drinking water can be the vector of viral, bacterial and parasitic diseases. For those caused by viruses and bacteria water is only a vehicle; contamination can originate just as much from domestic animals as from wild ones: stockmen are conscious of this fact and generally prefer to use their own equipment (buckets, rope, drinking troughs) to water their animals in small lots.

In the transmission of parasitic diseases, water, as regards the wet mud around the drinking troughs, plays an active role since it allows development, at the infectious stage, of parasite eggs dropped in the faeces and urine of parasitised animals that come to drink.

Development continues outside the primary host. For example from egg to infective larvae as in strongyles, or in an intermediate cold blooded host (gastropod) which lives in the water or mud (snail for the fluke).

In the latter case, prophylaxis of diseases should be accompanied by an active attack on the intermediate hosts.

The cost of water

While the water from rivers and pools only costs the labour of getting it to the animals, it is not the same with water originating from artificial pools, wells and boreholes

Among evaluation formulae, the one used by the French Bureau of Geological and Mineral Research for drawing maps of the average costs of exploiting underground water is one to remember:

$$Cu = \frac{I/n + VC}{V} = FCu + VCu \tag{1}$$

where:

Cu	= unit cost of 1 m^3 of underground water produced
I	= total capital cost of infrastructure and equipment
n	= number of years over which the investment is written off
VC	= variable costs
V	= annual volume of underground water extracted (m^3)
FCu	= unit fixed cost
VCu	= unit variable cost

These two parameters being broken down respectively as follows:

$$FCu = \frac{[\,(Cb/nb) + (Cp/np) + (Cm/nm)\,]}{V} \tag{2}$$

$$VCu = a \times TMH \times Co \times Cc \tag{3}$$

where:

Cb = cost of borehole (a function of the depth and yield)

Cp = cost of pumping equipment (a function of yield and the manometric height of delivery)

Cm = cost of motor (internal combustion or solar) (a function of pumping required to deliver the normal operating yield)

nb

np number of years over which the bore, pumping equipment and

nm motor are written off respectively

TMH = total manometric height of delivery

Co = hourly consumption by unit of power, of motor fuel equivalent for the motors (diesel, oil, grease)

Cc = cost per litre of motor fuel equivalent

a = coefficient of proportionality depending upon units chosen

$$Cu \quad = \frac{[(Cb/nb) + (Cp/np) + (Cm/nm)]}{V} + [a + TMH \times Co \times Cc] \quad (4)$$

length = m
yield = cubic metres per hour
power = hp
money = unit of currency concerned

Equally, there are other inputs which do not only concern equipment:

- aquisition of land;
- costs of labour for guarding and maintenance;
- bank charges, depreciation, interest charges for borrowing the money if the works have been carried out on borrowed money;
- incidence of state and local taxes.

An account of construction methods and equipment as a function of the characteristics of the source, in order to obtain water most economically, is beyond the scope of this book (refer to the study by the Bureau of Geological and Mineral Research *Explanatory notes and planning maps for the exploitation of underground water supplies of Sahelian Africa*, 1975).

Conclusions

Drafting a water equipment policy suitable for pastoral use is inseparable from a policy for the exploitation of grazing areas, since pasture without water cannot be exploited by domesticated animals and a well without pasture nearby is pointless.

Planning the exploitation of water resources

In the initial plans for developing tropical livestock production, rural hydraulic equipment had a high priority; Figure 4.12 of the distribution of boreholes in Senegal is tangible proof of this fact.

The sinking of wells allowed, particularly, an expansion of the grazing area, however many people demanded that a harmonious relationship be established between exploited hydraulic resources, livestock density and fodder resources.

In other respects, it was considered that hydraulic resources were almost inexhaustable.

The drought of the years 1960 to 1970 did much, particularly among those least aware of these problems, to spread the idea of harmonious development associated with conservation of resources.

It is not possible to discuss all the methods which have been worked out for planning of hydraulic resources, but the approach of the Inter-African Committee for the study of Water Resources (CIEH) merits particular attention as it can serve as an example.

The hydraulic systems of West and Central Africa have been the object of a number of applied and fundamental research projects. The state water departments have very detailed archives mainly composed of report forms (Figure 4.13) carrying precise information relating to positions of water, wells, boreholes and such as geographical position, depth, qualities of the source, nature and state of repair of the equipment and their associated structures and fundamental status. In the 1950s, hydrological maps were available which used information provided by these records.

The works of CIEH and Bureau of Geological and Mineral Research involved collating all available information, as much on deep and shallow aquifers as on geology, pedology and climate, then combining them and in 1975 publishing 1/1 500 000 maps, in many sheets, which give the following for the regions under consideration (Sahelian zone):

- the productivity of the aquifers;
- the quality of the underground water for irrigation;
- the average cost of harnessing and exploitation of the underground water (see Figures 4.14, 4.15, 4.16).

In 1976 the same organisations published, to the same scale, a planning map of the underground water resources of Soudano-Sahelian Africa.

Each group of maps is accompanied by explanatory notes and each map has an explanatory legend with several boxes detailing the characteristics of zones of greatest interest.

Figure 4.12   (opposite)   Pastoral hydraulic equipment in Senegal

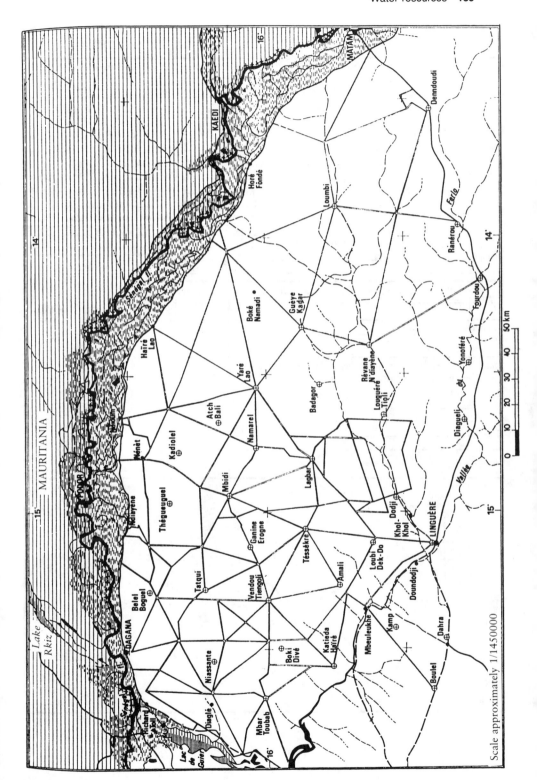

Scale approximately 1/1450000

INVENTORY OF WATER RESOURCES	PROVISONAL S 15 No.	S 8813	NAME _FALA FALA_

Unused Unusable _____ Drinkable-brackish-saline-clear- _____ cloudy-polluted by _____ Approximate yield _____ Shown by _____ Dry from _____ to _____ Irrigation _____ hectares Industry _____ Drinking _____ Number inhabitants animals of villages _____ Other water points on the source Requirements _____	Without lining of wood, masonry _____ forks _____ pulleys _____ Lifting by: bucket elevator _____ _____ Piston/rotary pump Engine: _____ h.p. _____ drinking trough _____ _____ reservoir _____ Cover-paving anti-fouling _____ Executed by _____ in _____ No. of shafts _____ State of wells _____ State of the curb _____ Repairs _____	Well-Source-Bore-Pool-River _____ Longitude _4°06'25"_ Latitude _15°52'10"_ Height of the ground _____ Depth of the hole _____ State _____ _NIGER_ Area _____ District _TCHIN TABARADEN_ Photo No. _425 NO-31-XXII_ Map: _1/ 200000_ Number _NO-31-XXIII_ of _TAKANAMAT_ Edition _____

Sketch of the shaft

Temperature air |water	Wind	Humidy	pH	Cl			Geological sampling by

Name and qualifications
of observer
Date and time of visit: _____

Supplementary observations, reference points and survey
method, surrounding pastures, access etc.
_____
_____
_____
_____
_____
_____

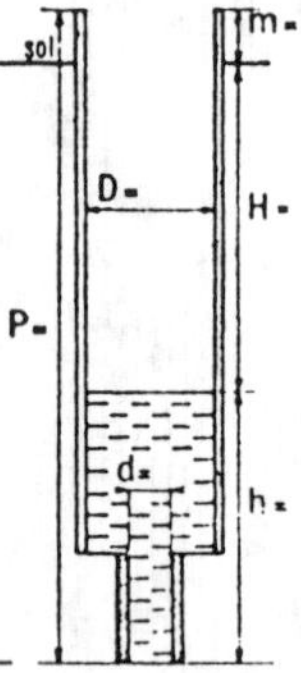

No. of samples _____

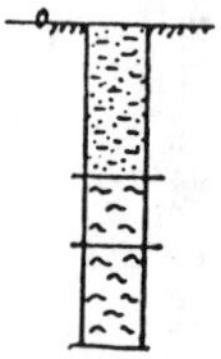

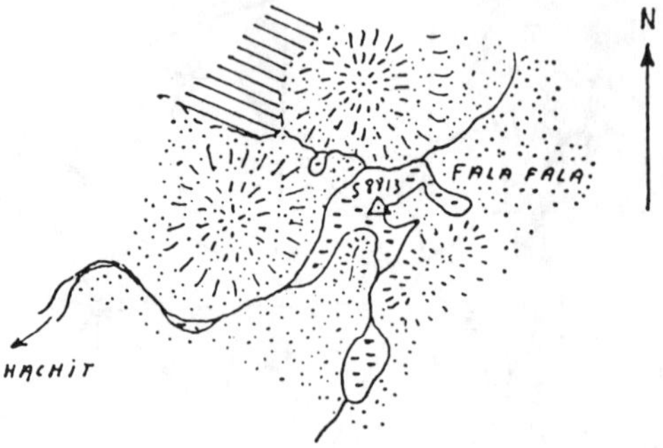

Sketch
Scale 1/ _800_

Extract _Photo_
Scale 1/ _50.000_

Figure 4.13   Report form for water point

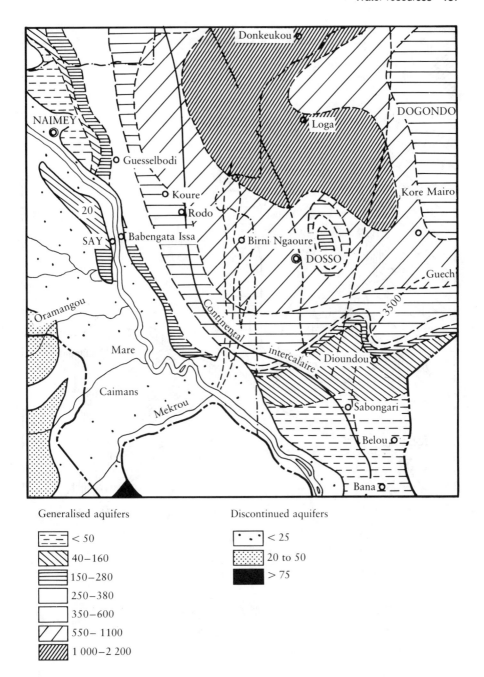

Figure 4.14   Productivity of sources. Initial productivity yields of exploitation works

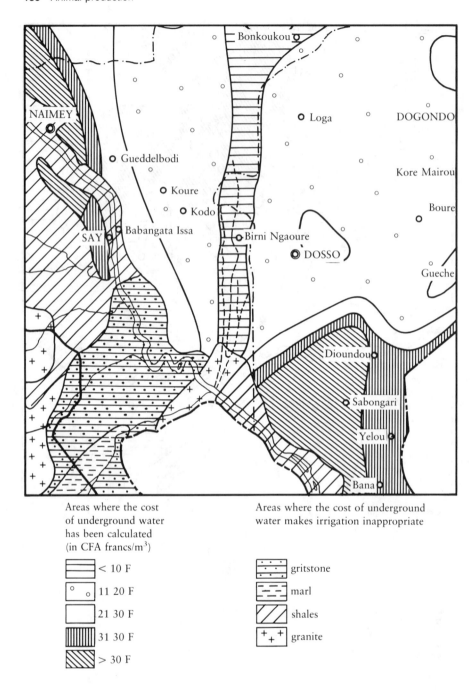

Areas where the cost
of underground water
has been calculated
(in CFA francs/m³)

☰	< 10 F
○ ○	11 20 F
□	21 30 F
▥	31 30 F
▨	> 30 F

Areas where the cost of underground
water makes irrigation inappropriate

⣿	gritstone
☰	marl
▨	shales
+ + +	granite

Figure 4.15   Average cost of collection and exploitation of underground water

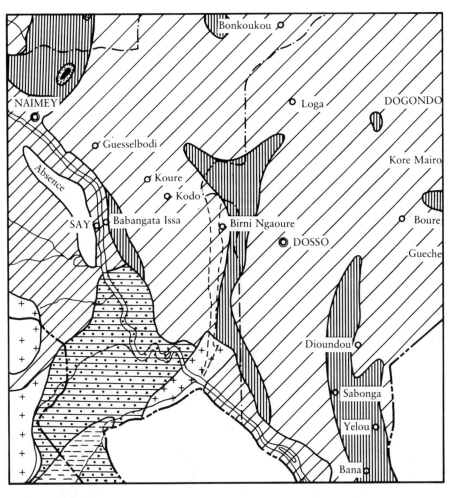

Principal classes
of water found

Excellent

Good

Acceptable

(After BRGM (1975))

Areas devoid of substantial
phreatic sources

Gritstone

Marl

Shales

Granite

Figure 4.16 Suitability of waters for irrigation

The resource planning map gives information:

- on the lithology of the aquifers;
- the depth below the ground of the water table;
- the quality of the water;
- the usable resources.

Starting with the data shown on the maps, it is possible to estimate the natural renewable resources for an area (potential). Expressed in cubic metres per year and per square kilometre, they express that part of the precipitations which reach and feed the aquifers in an average year.

Several hypotheses have been formulated to calculate the exploitable volume in the free water bearing layers. It is assumed that this is the volume liberated by a lowering of the water table through the saturated layers of the source, with a limit of 100 m below the ground.

In captive sources, the exploitable volume is that liberated by a lowering of the water table up to 100 m below the ground. The level of 100 m had been kept for reasons of economy.

For the zones which are the object of the CIEH and Bureau studies and which are spread across eight Soudano-Sahelian countries, the natural renewable resources in the 3 890 000 km^2 mapped represent 60 km^3 per year and exploitable reserves of 770–1625 km^3 (Table 4.5).

Table 4.5 Water resources and reserves in West Africa

Countries (west to east)	Surface areas of countries (km^2)	Areas covered	
		Renewable natural resources (mean potential) (km^3)	Exploitable reserves (km^3)
Gambia	10 000	1.0	9– 19
Senegal	195 000	9.3	89– 187
Mauritania	471 000	0.3	54– 116
Mali	807 000	13.1	82– 186
Burkina Faso	272 000	6.2	1– 3
Niger	989 000	4.6	262– 547
Cameroun	96 000	5.4	11– 23
Chad	1 050 000	20.6	263– 544
Totals	3 890 000	60.0	770–1 625

The maps allow the following questions to be dealt with.

1. Is it possible, in a source whose following characteristics figure on the map:

   - lithological features,
   - renewable resources,
   - exploitable reserves,
   - depth of water below the ground,
   - mineralisation per litre,

to draw a certain volume each day with a lowering of the basic level and, if so, what will be the surface area required to replenish each extraction?

2. In an already exploited area in which the surface area for replenishment of an extraction is less than the preceding optimum, what will the extraction duration be for a given yield to be compatable with responsible exploitation?

3. In an area not already exploited, what will the possible exploitation duration of renewable resources be and what will be the duration of exploitable reserves for a given yield?

4. What is the maximum exploitable yield for a given surface area and for a given yield?

The necessary yields are determined in pastoral water supply by the animals using the pastures in the area of the water supply; in village water supply by the size of the human population who must be supplied; and finally in agricultural water supply by the areas of land and the crops which will be grown. The provision of water is not just an end in itself, it is a major element in development, but it is not the only one.

In the next chapter, it will be seen how one can combine the information supplied by the water resource maps with that provided by forage resource maps.

Definitions

Artesian natural pushing up of water to the surface by the pressure of water at a distance and at a greater height.

Artesian source water bearing layer which feeds a source, well, borehole etc. from which the water is pushed out.

Captive source water bearing layer enclosed by two impermeable layers.

Degree of hardness content of lime and magnesium salts in water measured with the aid of a solution of N/50 EDTA (ethyldiaminetetra-acetate) in the presence of eriochrome black and a buffer solution of pH 10. One degree of hardness is equivalent to 10 or 14 mg/litre of lime or magnesium salts (0.1 ml = 1 degree of hardness).

Dynamic level water level resulting in a well or borehole due to pumping.

Dynamic (level) level of water lowered by pumping.

Effective rainfall annual total of monthly surpluses of rainfall over and above evapotranspiration (Turc's formula).

Flow water which runs on the surface of the ground, normally not infiltrating into it, forming rivers and streams.

Free water source water bearing layer whose ceiling (water table) is only separated from the surface of the ground by permeable layers.

Ground water (phreatic) layer   the first water bearing level struck in digging down into the ground; the well layer.

Hard   water rich in magnesium salts and lime.

Horizon   layer of earth which is characterised by the nature of the rock from which it is formed.

Improved bores   boreholes where a quantity of gravel is gradually placed in the ground between the perforated pipe and the sand of the aquifer.

Laterite   earth made up essentially of iron oxide and aluminium oxide originating, in a tropical climate, from changes occurring in the soil below.

Lateritic (pan)   hardened formation in which the soil particles are cemented by laterite. In Peul, *bowal* describes a semi-arid plateau with an ironstone crust.

Lifting   raising underground water to the surface.

Lowering (of level)   depth which the static level of the source finds itself lowered by as a result of pumping. (The difference between piezometric surface and the dynamic level.)

Natron   natural salt mainly composed of hydrated carbonate of soda.

Natronised   containing carbonate of soda.

Outcrop   appearance on the surface of a horizon or more generally, of a rock type due to erosion or earth movement.

Permeability   property of a rock to allow water to pass through it. **Interstitial permeability** is due to the spaces between constituents of the impermeable rock (between grains of sand, gravel etc.). **Fissure permeability** is due to continuous cracks existing between rock strata; it allows water to pass across impermeable rock layers (limestone, shales, basalts, granite etc.).

Piezometric surface or **static level**   topographical surface of the underground water source or the ceiling of the saturated aquifer which is measured in relation to a reference level (sea level).

Porosity   percentage volume of a rock which is not taken up by elements of the rock (air space; water space).

Quartz sand   loose rock originating from break-up of granite and gneiss.

Reg.   rigorously levelled ground (clay/sand or gravel in desert or sub-desert regions as Fako).

Sealing   suppression of permeability usually by sedimentation of fine clays.

Seismology   method of geophysical study, based on the propagation of waves caused by artificial shocks to the ground.

Spring   area where a water bearing layer appears on the surface of the ground.

Subsidence   progressive falling of ground level and continuing deposition of sediments.

Subartesian source   source which feeds a well or borehole and whose ceiling is such that an equilibrium level is reached where water is not pushed out of the workings.

Texture   relative proportions of particles in a soil or material (sand, clay, silt etc.).

5

Animal production and forage resources

Basic theories

This chapter deals with several problems which, in practice, are the concern of both the stockmen and those whose responsibility is designing and bringing development projects to fruition.

Thus the following subjects will be considered:

1. general principles of feeding;
2. the calculation of chemical composition of foods;
3. systems of expressing the energy and protein values used universally and the bases of rationing;
4. the feeding behaviour of animals and the basic mechanisms of active consumption of foods in herbivores;
5. usable forage resources in the tropics.

A note on measurement of energy and units

The British metabolisable energy system is not covered in this chapter. Where kilocalories are used, they can be converted to kilojoules by the relationship 1 kilocalorie = 4.1868 kilojoules.

Physiological fundamentals of feeding

Contents of a ration

In the internal environment of living organisms, quantitative and qualitative relationships exist between the different constituents of cells and the body fluids. Their stability will be all the more easily maintained by the regulatory mechanisms, within the limits compatable with normal life, if the composition of the ration is chosen more carefully and if energy giving and body building foods and vitamins and minerals necessary to its activity are fed to the animal in neither too large nor too small quantities.

The ration of a domestic animal will be satisfactory if it meets the following conditions.

1. It provides, in sufficient quantity, nutrients whose conversion supply the energy necessary for the functioning of the animal.
2. It contains enough water for metabolism and heat regulation.
3. It contains protein materials in sufficient quantity and adequate quality to assure growth and maintenance of the animal.
4. It contains a sufficient quantity and correct balance of minerals.
5. It contains vitamins.
6. It has bulk in correct proportion to sufficient nutritive value.
7. It is not toxic.

When animals are reared in confinement (poultry, pigs, cattle in paddocks), the most common cause of malnutrition is overstocking. This is caused by an error in estimating the numbers of stock that it is possible to raise in relation to the quantity and quality of available food resources. An additional problem is often the unavailability of certain food stocks, which results in errors in the composition of rations.

When the animals are maintained entirely on natural ranges, which is the case in the majority of tropical rearing situations, the respect for the nutrition rules listed above is rather difficult to maintain, and a number of syndromes have been described whose nutritional origins have been confirmed. One is therefore lead to a consideration of the biosphere formed by the soil, the plant and the animal: the animal can only satisfy its needs via the intermediary of the plant, it only receives the products which the plant synthesises from CO_2 and atmospheric oxygen, and minerals and water taken from the soil.

The presentation of domestic animal food requirements in terms of energy, body building nutrients, vitamins and minerals is now well known, as is the average composition of foods available in tropical regions.

Calculation of the feeding value of forage and livestock feeds

The feeding value of a product would be easy to determine if there was a constant relationship between its chemical composition and that of the production it enabled and if, for a food of given chemical composition, the net energy supplied was the same in all animals and for all productions; this is not so (Chapter 3, page 75).

While it is possible to determine very elaborate rations in the laboratory, for the practitioner, a coherent system, even if imperfect, is better than rations made blindly; and, in development operations where it is suitable to plan the production and the use of food resources, it will become rapidly indispensable.

All systems start with the hypothesis that, if the quantitative needs of body building and vitamins and minerals are covered, the source of net energy matters little. From this concept has been developed the idea of referring to a standard for a known food and its widespread usage.

There is, as yet, no universal system of measurement except perhaps for that which concerns the chemical composition of foods where nomenclature, like analytical methods, is tending towards a coherent standardisation.

The systems of evaluation used in practice for feed value of forage and primary agricultural feedstuffs are:

- the system of starch equivalents (SE);
- the total digestible nutrients (TDN) system;
- the system of forage units (FU);
- the Institut National de la Recherche Agronomique (National Institute of Agronomy Research) (INRA) France, system of lactation forage units (LFU) and meat forage units (MFU).

Chemical analysis of livestock feeds

Feed analysis forms for forage and their nutrients indicate the following constituents.

1. *Dry matter* (DM) obtained by dessication at 102° C to constant weight.
2. *Ash* obtained by combustion in a closed oven at 550° C until only white ash remains; this contains the mineral fraction apart from carbon. It enables calculation of organic matter content: OM = DM − ash.
3. *Crude protein* (CP) titrated by sulphuric acid treatment according to Kjeldahl's method, then titration with ammonia which gives the nitrogen content, this content being multiplied by the coefficient 6.25.
4. *Crude fibre* (Weende cellulose) corresponds analytically to the organic residue, then a deduction is made of the ash obtained after two successive hydrolyses carried out for 30 min, one being made in a sulphuric acid medium and the other in a soda solution. This residue contains the biggest part of the true cellulose, a significant fraction of the lignin, part of the hemicellulose and several glucosidic constituents.
5. *Ether extract* (fats), often designated under the term fats, is obtained by extraction with sulphuric ether*, it not only includes the fats and oils, but also includes essential oils, pigments, sterols and the liposoluble vitamins.
6. *Nitrogen-free extract* (NFE) includes all the constituents which have not been proportioned in the course of the preceding derminations; its value is obtained by the difference:

NFE = DM − (ash + crude protein + crude fibre + ether extract).

* Ether of petroleum is often used in hot countries instead of sulphuric ether where it is too volatile.

This entity is not chemically precise; it includes sugars and their polymers, fructose, pectin, starch, cellulose and lignin, organic acids, resins, tanins, waxes, pigments and hydrosoluble vitamins.

The above clearly defined constituents appear in all animal feed analysis tables. However other fundamentals, which are not systematically treated, are used. The following points are noteworthy:

1. The determination of the composition of ash is sometimes necessary, particularly to detect phosphorus and calcium deficiencies.
2. Total silica (insoluble chlorohydrous fraction of the ash) is often determined in tropical forage, because it reduces digestibility.
3. The other minerals are more rarely treated in routine analyses (magnesium, potassium, sodium, chlorine).
4. The mineral trace elements, which require very well equipped laboratories, are only rarely evaluated in forage of tropical origin and this is regrettable.
5. Determination of proteins and their different amino acid contents should be known for single-stomached animals reared in confinement and this is particularly so for poultry.
6. The soluble nitrogen compounds content is increasingly sought, in the light of its importance in the nitrogen processes in ruminants.
7. Testing for toxic substances is necessary because their presence can render available food resources unusable and can impose detoxification treatments or particular techniques for their use (alkaloids in the by-products of coffee and cocoa, gossypol in cotton seed cake, cyanogenic glucosides in cassava and the young shoots of sorghum, fungal contamination of certain grains and cattle cake), etc.

Feed composition and digestibility

Several terms and definitions are worth remembering:

1. *Maintenance requirements* are covered by the quantity of food (maintenance ration) which should be given to the animal each day to maintain constant weight, good health with nil production.
2. *Production requirements* are covered by the quantity of food (production ration), over and above the maintenance ration, to produce meat, milk, wool, work, eggs etc. without drawing on body reserves.
3. *Growth requirements* are covered by the quantity of food (growth ration), over and above the maintenance ration, necessary to allow building of the skeleton, muscles, organs and build up body reserves, the result being expressed in liveweight gain per day.
4. *Consumption index* (CI): energy value of the ration necessary for the production of unit liveweight gain or unit milk production.

5. *Transformation index* (TI): energy value of the ration, over and above maintenance, necessary for the production of unit liveweight gain or unit milk production etc.

The relationships between heat production and digestibility have been dealt with in Chapter 3; the part of the food which is absorbed after digestion is the *digestible* fraction of that food; the digestibility of a food or of its constituents indicates the degree of utilisation of the food; it is expressed quantitatively by the *coefficient of digestible utilisation* (CDU).

These concepts only appear to be simple; their mathematical expression is subject to discussion.

Apparent digestibility is more simple; this compares the quantities of nutrients consumed and those contained in the excreta:

$$\text{Apparent CDU} = \frac{\text{nutrients consumed} - \text{nutrients in faeces}}{\text{nutrients consumed}} \times 100$$

This coefficient, which gives an overall balance, integrates data which only have a distant relationship to the nature of the consumed feed, close to the non-digested parts of the food, waste materials from the functions of the digestive tract (digestive juices, mucus, discarded cells etc.) and micro-organisms, which the body harbours, are included.

The real coefficient of digestive utilisation:

$$\text{Real CDU} = \frac{\text{nutrients consumed} - (\text{faecal nutrients} - \text{nutrients originating in the gut})}{\text{consumed nutrients}} \times 100$$

is very difficult to measure, particularly in herbivores and especially in ruminants in whom the micro-organisms of the digestive tract participate in digestion by fermentation of soluble carbohydrate, whose methane is a product of degradation, and by fixation of nitrogen within their own constitution and which are carried away with them in the faeces.

For digestion of amino acids, peptides and proteins, one assumes that metabolic nitrogen eliminated in the faeces will be 5–7.5 g/kg of faecal dry matter.

In practice one uses apparent digestibility for the calculations.

All researchers who have studied nutrition problems have attempted to determine, in as exact a way as possible, the overall digestibility of forages and that of their components; their results have been integrated in reference tables by different authors; the ones most used are those of Kellner, Morrison, Woodman, Leroy, Schneider and Butterworth. More recently, Jarrige and the researchers at Institut National de la Recherche Agronomique (INRA) have proposed new ones.

When these tables are used, it must be remembered that they indicate mean experimental data and they refer to a species of animal, of a particular weight and for precise production. Coefficients of digestibility for pigs cannot be used for cattle. Figures for milking cattle do not apply to fattening cattle.

The three principle factors which make up the value of a forage or animal feed are:

- their energy value,
- their nitrogen value,
- their bulk.

For each of these parameters, there are many systems of evaluation which can, with more or less viability, be used to resolve feeding problems in tropical zones.

Expression of the energy value of foods

One has the choice between:

- Kellner's starch equivalent system;
- the total digestible nutrient (TDN) system;
- the forage unit (FU) system adapted by Leroy;
- the INRA system of France.
(See note on energy measurement at the start of this chapter).

For each one, the energy value is estimated taking a widely used feed as a unit of reference, e.g. starch, barley or the energy value deduced from the chemical composition of that feed.

The starch equivalent system

Kellner used starch as his reference product and the coefficients were determined by the quantity of fat deposition obtained by substituting 1 kg of the food or a constituent for 1 kg of starch.

The starch equivalent (SE) is the number of kilograms of starch which would be necessary, in cattle, to give the same gain in fat as would 100 kg of the food under consideration

$$\frac{1 \times 100}{SE}$$

- 1 kg of digestible nitrogen-free extract or digestible cellulose corresponds to 1 starch equivalent unit (SE);
- 1 kg of digestible protein to 0.94 SE;
- 1 kg of digestible lipid to 1.91–2.41 SE, according to their origin (coarse forage 1.94 SE, oil seeds and their derivatives 2.41 SE).

For milk production the coefficients are as follows:

- digestible protein   1.41 kg SE
- digestible oils   2.41 kg SE
- digestible nitrogen-free extract   1.00 kg SE

Kellner formulated tables which give productivity coefficients for each constituent and for each possibility. Table 5.1 shows the method of calculation of the starch value of maize beginning with its composition.

More recently *Dutch* tables give the net energy value in starch units as a function of its content in the dry matter, in crude fibre and in ash, for the different feed classes.

Table 5.1 Calculation of starch equivalent

		Percentage content of the feed			
Product	Constituents	Crude fraction	Digestible fraction	Equivalence coefficient	Starch equivalent
Maize	protein	9.3	4.6	× 0.94	4.32
	fats	3.3	2.5	× 2.12	5.30
	nitrogen free extract	68.0	57.8	× 1.00	57.80
	cellulose	2.5	1.7	× 1.00	1.70
	water	16.9			69.12

one kilogram of maize has a starch equivalent of 0.69

TDN system (total digestible nutrients)

This system abandons the idea of net energy and refers only to digestible elements of the ration.

The value of a feed (expressed as a percentage) is the sum of the digestible constituents which it contains.

Abbreviations are as follows:

digestible crude protein	DCP
digestible crude fibre	DCF
digestible nitrogen-free extract	DNFE
digestible fats	DF
digestible organic matter	DOM

$$TDN = DCP + DCF + DNFE + 2.25\ DF$$
$$= DOM + 1.25\ DF$$

Lipid content is multiplied by 2.25 in the calculations to take account of their higher calorific value (Table 5.2).

TDNs are expressed both in g/kg of the feed or in g/kg of dry matter.

Table 5.2 An example of the calculation of TDN (barley)

Constituent	Percentage of crude material	Coefficient of digestibility	Digestible organic matter	Percentage TDN
Protein	8.9	0.70	6.2	6.2
Cellulose	5.6	0.34	1.9	1.9
Fats	2.5	0.92	2.3	5.75
Nitrogen-free extract	67.6	0.92	62.2	62.2
Organic matter	84.6	0.86	72.6	

$$\text{TDN} = 6.2 + 1.9 + (2.3 \times 2.5) + 62.2 = 76.05$$
$$\text{TDN} = 84.6 \times 0.86 + (2.3 \times 1.5) \quad = 72.6 + 3.45 = 76.05$$

Despite this correction, TDNs are not equivalent to either digestible energy or to metabolisable energy:

- soluble carbohydrates and nitrogen-containing compounds are considered to be isodynamic since, in the bomb calorimeter, they yield 4.15 and 5.7 kcal/g respectively, which takes account of the loss of energy due to organic nitrogen removed in the urine.

On the other hand, energy losses in the form of methane are not deducted since they are no longer taken account of in the level of metabolisable energy.

Roughages, for which gaseous losses are significant, are thus over-valued as opposed to concentrates which are under-valued.

Tables for TDN requirements in different species of animal and in different production situations have been published and those of the Animal Nutrition Committee of the United States National Research Council are used as the reference for all the anglophone countries.

Regression equations have been established which allow TDN calculation down into five classifications), of the composition of its crude chemical constituents (cellulose, ether extract, nitrogen-free extract, proteins) (Table 5.3).

Forage unit system

Scandinavian authors, considering milk production, propose to refer to barley as a *forage unit* (FU); the nutritive value of a feed corresponds to the quantity of barley which would give the same net energy value as the feed.

Forage equivalent (FE) is the quantity of feed which would give the same net energy as a kilogram of barley (Table 5.4).

Leroy developed this method which is largely used in the francophone countries.

Net energy (NE) is equal to the difference between the *metabolisable energy* (ME) and *extra-heat* (Q).

Table 5.3 Regression equations for the calculation of total digestible nutrients (TDN)

Animal species	Food class	Equations
Cattle	1	% TDN = 92.464 − 3.338 (CF) − 6.945 (EE) − 0.762 (NFE) + 1.115 (Pr) + 0.031 (CF)^2 − 0.133 (EE)^2 + 0.036 (CF) (NFE) + 0.207 (EE) (NFE) + 0.100 (EE) (Pr) − 0.022 (EE)^2 (Pr).
	2	% TDN = − 54.572 + 6.769 (CF) − 51.083 (EE) + 1.851 (NFE) − 0.334 (Pr) − 0.049 (CF)^2 + 3.384 (EE)^2 − 0.086 (CF) (NFE) + 0.687 (EE) (NFE) + 0.942 (EE) (Pr) − 0.112 (EE)^2 (Pr)
	3	% TDN = 72.943 + 4.675 (CF) − 1.280 (EE) + 1.611 (NFE) + 0.497 (Pr) − 0.044 (CF)^2 − 0.760 (EE)^2 − 0.039 (CF) (NFE) + 0.087 (EE) (NFE) − 0.152 (EE) (Pr) + 0.074 (EE)^2 (Pr).
	4	% TDN = − 202.686 − 1.357 (CF) + 2.638 (EE) + 3.003 (NFE) + 2.347 (Pr) + 0.046 (CF)^2 + 0.647 (EE)^2 + 0.041 (CF) (NFE) − 0.081 (EE) (NFE) + 0.553 (EE) (Pr) − 0.046 (EE)^2 (Pr).
	5	% TDN = − 133.726 − 0.254 (CF) + 19.593 (EE) + 2.784 (NFE) + 2.315 (Pr) + 0.028 (CF)^2 − 0.341 (EE)^2 − 0.008 (CF) (NFE) − 0.215 (EE) (NFE) − 0.193 (EE) (Pr) + 0.004 (EE)^2 (Pr).
Sheep	1	% TDN = 37.937 − 1.018 (CF) − 4.886 (EE) + 0.173 (NFE) + 1.042 (Pr) + 0.015 (CF)^2 − 0.058 (EE)^2 + 0.008 (VF) (NFE) + 0.119 (EE) (NFE) + 0.038 (EE) (Pr) + 0.003 (EE)^2 (Pr).
	2	% TDN = − 26.685 + 1.334 (CF) + 6.598 (EE) + 1.423 (NFE) + 0.967 (Pr) − 0.002 (CF)^2 − 0.670 (EE)^2 − 0.024 (CF) (NFE) − 0.055 (EE) (NFE) − 0.146 (EE) (Pr) + 0.039 (EE)^2 (Pr).
	3	% TDN = − 17.950 − 1.285 (CF) + 15.704 (EE) + 1.009 (NFE) + 2.371 (Pr) + 0.017 (CF)^2 − 1.023 (EE)^2 + 0.012 (CF) (NFE) − 0.096 (EE) (NFE) − 0.550 (EE) (Pr) + 0.051 (EE)^2 (Pr).
	4	% TDN = 22.822 − 1.440 (CF) − 2.875 (EE) + 0.655 (NFE) + 0.863 (Pr) + 0.020 (CF)^2 − 0.078 (EE)^2 + 0.018 (CF) (NFE) + 0.045 (EE) (NFE) − 0.085 (EE) (Pr) + 0.020 (EE)^2 (Pr).
	5	% TDN = 54.820 + 1.951 (CF) + 0.601 (EE) + 1.602 (NFE) + 1.324 (Pr) − 0.027 (CF)^2 + 0.032 (EE)^2 − 0.021 (CF) (NFE) + 0.018 (EE) (NFE) + 0.035 (EE) (Pr) − 0.0008 (EE)^2 (Pr).

In the equations: CF = cellulose; EE = ether extract; NFE = nitrogen-free extract; Pr = protein.
Class 1: dry forage and harvested roughage, including hay, straw, stubble, husks and all products containing more than 18 per cent cellulose.
Class 2: green forage and grazing
Class 3: silage
Class 4: energy feeds including: cereals and their industrial by-products (bran, extracted seeds, middlings), legume and oil seeds, fruits and diverse seeds, and all products containing less than 20 per cent protein and 18 per cent cellulose
Class 5: animal and vegetable protein feeds: proprietary concentrates, meat meal, fish meal, etc.

Table 5.4 Examples of forage values

Forage	Number of forage units (FU) per kg	Forage equivalent (1/FU)
Barley	1	1
Sorghum	0.91	1.10
Groundnut cake	1.11	0.91
Hay (*Stylosanthes*)	0.45	2.20

For post-weaning ruminants:

$$ME = [DCP + (2.25 \times DF) + DCC + DNFE) \times 3.65 = TDN \times 3.65$$
$$NE = ME - Q$$

ME, NE expressed in kcal/kg DM
TDN expressed in g/kg DM
DCP: represents the digestible crude protein (g/kg DM)
DF: digestible fats (g/kg DM)
DCC: digestible crude cellulose (g/kg DM)
DNFE: digestible nitrogen-free extract (g/kg DM)

The correction factor Q has been evaluated from the results of experiment. It varies from 0.85 to 1.03 according to the nature of the feed.

Expression in FUs for ruminants is calculated by taking the net energy of 1 kg of barley as the reference unit: 1833 cal.

However the term FU remains in use and the methods of calculation have developed; in 1959 the French Association of Zootechnics recommended the calculation of the *forage value* of forages from their crude fibre content and from their ash content (an indication of the organic matter). To do this, the tables formulated by the French National Agronomic Institute are used and which are an adaptation of the forage units in the *Dutch* tables which use, as has been seen above, the basics of the starch equivalent system.

Table 5.5 shows the forage unit values of grasses for several cellulose and ash contents.

Table 5.5 Simplified table for the calculation of FUs for green grasses (FU/100 kg DM)

Crude fibre	Ash 5.0	6.0	8.0	10.0	12.0	14.0	16.0	18.0	20.0	22.0	24.0	25.0
15.0	107.7	106.4	103.7	101.1	95.8	95.8	93.1	89.1	86.5	83.8	81.1	79.8
17.5	103.7	102.4	99.8	97.1	93.1	90.4	87.8	85.1	82.5	78.5	75.8	74.5
20.0	98.4	97.1	94.4	91.8	89.1	86.5	82.5	79.8	77.1	73.2	70.5	69.2
22.5	94.4	93.1	89.1	86.5	83.3	79.8	77.1	74.5	71.8	67.8	65.2	63.8
25.0	87.8	86.5	83.8	81.1	77.1	74.5	71.8	67.8	65.2	61.2	58.5	57.2
27.5	82.5	81.1	77.1	74.5	71.8	67.8	65.2	61.2	58.5	54.5	50.5	49.2
30.0	75.8	74.5	71.8	67.8	63.8	61.2	57.2	54.5	50.5	46.6	43.9	41.2
32.5	69.2	67.8	63.8	61.2	57.2	53.2	50.5	46.6	42.6	38.6	34.6	33.3
35.0	61.2	59.9	55.9	53.2	49.2	45.2	41.2	37.2	34.6	29.3	26.6	25.3
37.5	54.5	51.2	47.9	45.2	41.2	37.2	33.3	29.3	25.3	20.0	16.0	14.6
40.0	45.2	43.9	39.9	35.9	31.9	27.9	23.9	20.0	16.0	10.7	6.7	4.0

INRA (France) systems of energy value measurement

Although the system which INRA proposes for the calculation of energy, nitrogen value and ration quantities has not been used very much yet in the tropical zones, it is convenient, meanwhile, to show the principles, for it will make the development of animal production more effective and, while the subject is in its gestation, it poses identical problems to those experienced in the temperate zones.

In the INRA system formulated for ruminants, the terms *forage unit* and the *principle of the expression of net energy* are kept, but the unit values are adapted to the production situations: growing animals, females in lactation or fattening animals, which express in figures the differences which exist between the energy yields from production: of tissues over and above growth, of milk production or of fat laid down.

Two systems have been formulated:

1. that of *lactation forage units* (LFU) for females in lactation and animals on maintenance or moderate growth;
2. that of *meat forage units* (MFU) for fattening animals and those with a high growth rate (more than 800 g/day).

Two factors are introduced in the calculation of net energy:

1. The concentration of metabolisable energy in the ration:

$$q = \frac{\text{metabolisable energy}}{\text{combustible energy}} = \frac{ME}{CE}$$

2. The output expressed as a percentage of the metabolisable energy for the production under consideration:

$$k = \frac{\text{net energy}}{\text{metabolisable energy}} = \frac{NE}{ME}$$

The net energy is then obtained by the following calculation:

$$NE = CE \times dE \times \frac{ME}{DE} \times k$$

in which CE is the combustible energy measured in a bomb calorimeter, dE the digestibility of the energy and DE the apparent digestible energy.

The estimation of lactation forage units or meat forage units is obtained by making the relationship between the calculated net energy and the reference value of the barley.

The determination of digestibilities relies on a considerable number of observations and experiences which have been made by INRA and the specialised institutes, in the laboratory and in the process of stock rearing. The composition of Leroy's reference barley has been adapted to actual conditions of production (Table 5.6).

The net energy value of this reference feed is:

- 1883 kcal for one kilogram of crude barley in the Leroy system;
- 1730 kcal for the lactation system;
- 1855 kcal for meat production in the new units.

Table 5.6 Composition of barley (1970–75) in relation to Leroy's reference barley (INRA, 1978)

Constituents	(A) Reference barley (Leroy)	(B) Barley 1970–75	(A)–(B) per cent	Coefficients of digestibility per cent
Composition (g/kg crude)				
dry matter	872	859	− 1.5	
protein	89	100.5	+ 12.9	0.75
fats	25	18.2	− 27.2	0.78
crude fibre	56	46.1	− 17.7	0.42
nitrogen-free extract	676	671.7	− 0.006	0.90
minerals	26	22.7	− 12.7	
organic matter	846	836.3	− 1.15	0.86
Composition (g/kg DM)				
protein	102.1	116.9	+ 14.5	
fats	28.7	21.2	− 26.1	
crude fibre	64.2	53.6	− 15.8	
nitrogen-free extract	775.2	781.7	+ 0.008	
minerals	29.8	26.4	− 11.4	

Comparisons and connection between the different energy systems

Comparison between the LFU and MFU methods cannot be made between units because they take account of production.

Thus in expressing the relative values of LFU and MFU by the Leroy system, 100 Leroy FU of maize grain corresponds to 99 LFU and 100 MFU while 100 Leroy FU of medium meadow hay corresponds to 132 LFU and 111 MFU.

Tropical forage, being generally of a distinctly inferior quality to that of hay from temperate zones, are underestimated when Leroy's FU system is used and so the animals do not suffer an error by default.

Table 5.7 Connection between the units of measurement of net energy

Value of reference units	Starch unit	Forage unit	Net energy for fattening (therms) Ruminants	Pigs	Total digestible nutrients (TDN) Bulk feed hay	Concentrates cake
1 starch unit	1.0	1.43	2.36	3.49	1.43	1.08
1 forage unit	0.7	1.00	1.65	2.44	1.00	0.67
1 therm (ruminants)	0.42	0.61	1.00	–	0.61	0.46
1 therm (pigs)	0.29	0.41	–	1.00	–	0.31
1 kg TDN bulk feed	0.7	1.00	1.65	–	1.00	–
1 kg TDN concentrated feed	0.92	1.31	2.18	3.23	–	1.00

(after Brian and Fontaine)

Expression of the nitrogen value of feeds

There are two systems for the evaluation and expression of nitrogen value of foods:

1. the digestible crude protein system (DCP);
2. the system of proteins digestible in the small intestine (PDI).

Digestible crude protein system (DCP)

The DCP system which is used all over the world can be applied to all species of animals.

However, when diets for simple-stomached animals are formulated protein requirement is normally defined in terms of crude protein (CP) and of essential amino acids.

The DCP value of a diet is obtained by multiplying the quantity of crude protein (CP) ingested, by the coefficient of apparent digestibility of the nirtogenous material in that diet (AD).

$$DCP = CP \times AD$$

A number of equations have been derived to enable the DCP protein to be calculated and the following two should be remembered:

- for grasses .... DCP = CP − 4.0
- for legumes .... DCP = CP − 4.5

where DCP and CP are expressed as percentage of the dry matter.

The system recommended by INRA for assessing protein digestibility in the intestine

This method, recommended by INRA in 1978, takes account of the conversion of part of the total nitrogenous material (TNM) into ammonia and amino acids in the course of protein synthesis by micro-organisms in the rumen. These proteins, which are themselves digested in the abomasum and intestine, are called 'microbial proteins digestible in the intestine' (MPDI).

Nitrogenous material not digested in the rumen is digested in the abomasum and the remainder in the intestine; it is classified under the title *food proteins digestible in the intestine* (FPDI).

The ruminant assimilates all the *proteins that are digestible in the intestine* (PDI)

$$PDI = MPDI + FPDI$$

However, it is the intrinsic qualities of the total nitrogenous matter, in particular its solubility that control the degree of breakdown and its effective synthesis by micro-organisms in the rumen.

In addition, the available energy is equally a limiting factor to this process, which means that for each food there is a need to estimate two values of PDI of which one is linked to the available energy (PDIME) and the other to the degradability of the proteins (PDIMN).

Each category of PDI adds up to the digestible protein orginating in the feed (PDIF) and allows the definition of two groups of PDI:

$$PDIE = PDIF + PDIME$$
$$PDIN = PDIF + PDIMN$$

The use of this system allows the most deficient group of PDI in the diet to be identified and for a supplement to be provided in the diet, either of one containing fermentable nitrogen or digestible organic matter. The PDIE and PDIN cannot be summated and the smaller value should be used in any calculation.

Other factors that should be introduced into calculations are: factors to correct for solubility (derived as a result of *in vitro* measurement and chemical analysis), *factor d_r which is the actual digestibility of food proteins*, and finally the digestibility of the organic matter:

PDIF = 0.63 × (total nitrogenous matter) (1 − 5) × d_r
PDIME = 75.6 g/kg (digestible organic matter)
PDIMN = (total nitrogenous matter) (0.196 + 0.364) S)

Figure 5.1 shows the estimation of protein digestibility in the intestine of a mixture of 1 kg of maize grain and 1 kg of rape-seed cake, calculated in two

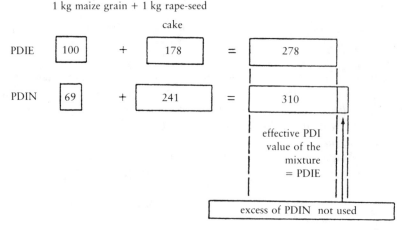

Figure 5.1 Calculation of the PDI value for a mixture of 1 kg of maize grain and 1 kg of rape-seed cake

ways: in the first, the digestible protein associated with the available energy is estimated (PDIE): 100 + 178 = 278; in the second, the digestible protein is estimated from the hypothetical content of protein (PDIN): 69 + 241 = 310.

The effective value of protein digestible in the intestine (PDI) is equal to 278 and there is an excess of PDIN (310 − 278) that is not used.

Expression of quantities of dry matter intake

'Traditional system'

This system is, in fact, a collection of recommendations which indicate the average quantity of material consumed for a species of animal, according to weight and production.

These standards introduce a practical definition used for the establishment of rations, the coefficient of bulk, which is the quantity of dry matter, expressed in kilograms, necessary to provide one forage unit (FU).

This coefficient is also defined by species and by type of production. For example, for cattle and sheep (Table 5.8).

Table 5.8 Coefficient of bulk recommended for different production in cattle and sheep

Species and type of production	Bulk coefficient
Cattle:	
cattle at maintenance	2.1
working cattle (heavy work)	1.5
working cattle (light work)	2.0
fattening cattle	1.4
milking cows giving less than 10 kg of milk	2.0
milking cows giving 10–15 kg of milk	1.8
milking cows giving 15–20 kg of milk	1.6
milking cows giving more than 20 kg of milk	1.4
young stock between weaning and 9 months	1.4
young stock over 9 months	1.6
Sheep:	
ewes in milk	1.6
lambs of 5–6 months	1.4
fattening adults	1.6
adults at maintenance	1.8

System of bulk units (BU) (units proposed by INRA)

The new INRA system of evaluation of feeds is complemented by a system for the evaluation of maximum quantities of a given feed which can be taken in by an animal either on its own or in a mix.

This entity, the *bulk unit*, can be estimated if the quantity of food capable of being taken in by the animal is sufficient to supply the energy and nutrients necessary to cover its needs.

1. The bulk unit (BU) is a unit of substitution; by definition, 1 kg of reference herbage dry matter has a bulk value of unity, in the same way as the reference barley has an energy value of one forage unit.
2. The quantities of forage incorporated in a mixed ration can be calculated directly, taking account of the phenomenon of substitution due to the concentrate feed content.
3. There is a bulk unit for sheep (SBU) and one for cattle (CBU).

In separating out the net energy value of a food, expressed in forage units via its bulk value (BV), one obtains a synthetic parameter, its energy density, which expresses its ability to meet the energy needs of the animal.

Sheep bulk unit (SBU)

The reference herbage contains 15 per cent crude protein, 25 per cent crude fibre, the digestibility of the organic matter is 0.77, which corresponds to 0.95 lactation forage units in the case of milk production and 0.90 meat forage units for meat production, per kilogram of dry matter.

The intake of this forage is 75 g/kg of metabolic weight ($W^{0.75}$); it has been calculated from some 2500 measurements made on castrated rams with ages ranging from 1 to 3 years, weighing from 45 to 75 kg (standard sheep).

By definition, 1 kg of dry matter of this reference herbage has a bulk value equal to unity for sheep. The bulk value of a forage for sheep (or SBU value) is calculated comparing ingestibility of the forage with that of the reference herbage:

$$\text{SBU value} = \frac{75}{\substack{\text{quantity of forage intake for a standard sheep} \\ \text{in dry matter per kilogram } W^{0.75}}}$$

The ingestibility being the capacity of the feed to be taken in a more or less large quantity, varies among other things with the stage of maturity of the forage.

The SBU value varies inversely with ingestibility. It goes from 0.75 to 0.80 for green legumes at the beginning of the first cycle of growth to 2.3 for straw. Tables give the values for different forages.

Cattle bulk unit (CBU)

The principle is the same as for SBU. Starting with observations made on sheep and cattle, the value corresponding to 75 in sheep has been found to be equal to 122.6 for cattle:

$$\text{CBU} = \frac{122.6}{\text{ingestibility of the forage in cattle}}$$

The system which is made up of the whole group of lactation forage units (LFU), meat forage units (MFU), proteins digestible in the intestine (PDI) and bulk units (SBU–CBU) is based on observations made in temperate regions on animals in high production.

Two measurements are fundamental to the establishment of this new system; that of the coefficient of digestibility of the organic matter and that of intake. For nitrogen, the analyses are more delicate.

In the tropics, a number of phenomena have been observed and are continuing to reveal themselves, as much by digestibility experiments on confined animals as by technical study of growth, fattening, or of milk production.

For 20 years, digestibility analyses and feeding experiments have been carried out in African laboratories working in conjunction with IEMVT (Institut d'Elevage et de Médecine vétérinaire de Pays tropicaux). There are national animal production laboratories in Dakar, Senegal, Chad and Madagascar as well as zootechnical research stations in Ivory Coast and Cameroun.

A considerable amount of data and information has been gathered on the nature and quality of forage and by-products available in the tropics. The laboratory of the main IEMVT establishment has started the task of adapting the INRA system for tropical forage and animals. This work should bring about the publication of food value tables and recommendations for rations which will take account of the analytical approach proposed by INRA.

Feed recommendations

Ration tables

For each system described above, ration tables have been published which indicate, by animal species and by type of production, the quantities of energy, nitrogenous matter and minerals that the animals should be fed each day and this is shown as a function of their weight.

Starting with chemical composition tables and digestibility tables, it is possible to calculate the feed value of forages and primary materials available and from this to formulate balanced rations.

Food requirements of cattle

In estimating requirements, those of energy, digestible nitrogenous matter and minerals should be taken as a priority.

In the following tables, growth rates are expressed in g/day. The system used is that of forage units (FU).

Energy requirements for maintenance and growth

These are shown in Table 5.9

Table 5.9 Energy requirements

Live weight (kg)	Intake (kg)	Maintenance (FU)	Maintenance + 100 g/day (FU)	Maintenance + 250 g/day (FU)	Maintenance + 500 g/day (FU)
25	1.0	0.50	0.65	0.80	1.10
50	1.8	0.80	0.95	1.15	1.55
100	3.0	1.20	1.40	1.65	2.10
250	6.25	2.30	2.55	2.90	3.50
300	7.7	2.60	2.85	3.30	3.95

For animals at pasture, it is advisable to add the energy requirements for travelling. 0.48 cal/km per kg of liveweight, or 0.026 FU/km per 100 kg of liveweight, which equals 0.5 FU for an animal of 250 kg walking 8 km day.

Nitrogen requirements for maintenance and growth

These are shown in Table 5.10.

Table 5.10 Nitrogen requirements in g DCP/day

Live weight (kg)	Intake of dry matter (kg)	Maintenance (DCP/FU)	Maintenance + 100 g/ (DCP g/day)	Maintenance + 250 g/ (DCP g/day)	Maintenance + 500 g/ (DCP g/day)
25	15	180	120	145	200
50	30	150	145	170	230
100	60	135	190	225	285
250	150	115	295	335	400
300	180	110	315	360	435

The nitrogen requirements for maintenance are calculated on the basis of 0.6 g of DCP per kg of liveweight.

Mineral requirements

Calcium and phosphorus requirements are shown in Table 5.11 and the units for each are as follows: column 1 is in grams per day; column 2 is in grams per kg of dry matter; column 3 is in grams per forage unit.

Table 5.11 Mineral requirements

Live weight (kg)	Maintenance Calcium 1	Calcium 2	Phosphorus 1	Phosphorus 2	Maintenance + 250 g growth/day Calcium 1	Calcium 2	Calcium 3	Phosphorus 1	Phosphorus 2	Phosphorus 3
25	1.5	1.5	1.0	1.0	6.0	5.0	7.5	4.0	4.0	4.0
50	3.0	1.6	2.0	1.0	8.0	3.9	6.9	6.0	3.3	5.2
100	5.0	1.6	3.0	1.0	11.0	3.7	6.7	8.0	2.7	4.0
250	12.5	1.9	7.5	1.3	18.0	2.9	6.1	13.3	2.1	4.5
300	15.0	2.0	9.0	1.3	20.0	2.8	6.0	15.0	2.0	4.4

Sodium and chlorine requirements are:

- maintenance: 5 g/100 kg liveweight or 2 g/kg of dry matter;
- growth   : a further 2 g/kg of liveweight gain.

Magnesium requirements are 2 g/kg of dry matter.

Magnesium requirements are for male animals or for females which are neither pregnant nor milking, the production requirements being found in the standard feed tables.

Requirements for milking cows

Requirements for milking cows are shown in Table 5.12. It must be remembered that production of 1 kg of milk containing 4 per cent fats requires:

- 0.38 forage units (i.e. practically 0.4 forage units)
- 60 g DCP
- 3 g of calcium
- 1.6 g of phosphorus
- 2 g of sodium chloride
- 1 g of magnesium
- 280 g of dry matter

Table 5.12 Requirements for milking cows

Stage of gestation	Energy (FU/100 kg liveweight	DCP	Calcium g/day	Phosphorus g/day	Calcium in g/kg DM*		Phosphorus in g/kg DM*	
5–6 month	+ 0.1		+ 5 g	+ 3 g	2:3	2:8	1:3	1:7
7 month	+ 0.15	100 g/FU supplementary	+ 10 g	+ 5 g	2:5	3:1	1:5	1:8
8 month	+ 0.20		+ 20 g	+ 10 g	3:1	3:9	1:8	2:2
9 month	+ 0.30		+ 15 g	+ 10 g	2:9	3:5	1:8	2:2

* In a complete ration, variable according to liveweight (between 200 and 500 kg)

Requirements during pregnancy

The requirements during pregnancy amount to those necessary for maintenance, growth and milk production. They increase during the course of the pregnancy.

Requirements during fattening

The energy requirements vary with the stage of fattening according to the kilogram weight gain. The following are necessary:

- 3 forage units at the beginning of fattening
- 4–4.5 forage units at the end of fattening
- 80–120 g of DCP in the total ration
- 15 g of calcium
- 9 g of phosphorus
- 2 g of sodium chloride

Requirements for work

For light work it is necessary to multiply the maintenance energy needs by 1.5 and for heavy work by 2.5

It is necessary to supply a total of 0.7–0.8 g of DCP per kilogram of liveweight.

Vitamin requirements

Vitamin A

For maintenance and growth, 20 000–22 000 international units (IU) per 100 kg liveweight per day, or 20–23 mg of carotene per kilogram of dry matter.

For pregnancy, 13 000 IU or 33 mg of carotene during the last 3 months.

Vitamin D

For maintenance and growth, 250–400 IU per 100 kg liveweight per day.

For pregnancy and lactation, 800–1000 IU per 100 kg liveweight per day.

Vitamin E

Daily requirements vary with age:

- 40–60 IU per 100 kg liveweight from 0 to 3 months;
- 10–30 IU after weaning;
- 80–100 IU for cows in pregnancy;
- 80–100 IU for cows in lactation;
- 100–120 IU for bulls.

Trace element requirements

The trace elements to be taken into consideration are iron, copper, cobalt, manganese, zinc, sulphur, iodine and selenium.

The minimum quantities to supply are expressed in mg/kg of dry matter or in p.p.m. of DM (parts per million of dry matter) (Table 5.13).

Table 5.13 Trace element requirements (p.p.m. of DM)

Element	Cattle in maintenance	Growth	Cows in lactation
Iron	40	50	80–150
Copper	10	10	10
Cobalt	0.1	0.1–1.0	0.1
Manganese	40	50	50
Zinc	50	100	100
Sulphur	0.20–0.28	0.2	0.3
Iodine	0.1	0.1	0.8
Selenium	0.1	0.1	0.2

These simplified tables of feed recommendations enable an understanding of the complexities of calculating rations. The difficulties are increases in the tropics with seasonal variations in the quality and quantity of resources available to the stockman.

General remarks on the different systems of evaluation of requirements

In practice, one can say that all the systems are good, providing they are used properly. From the start of any development project, it is necessary to choose a system and adhere to it. Table 5.7 shows the relationship between the different units defined above.

This is not the place to make a judgement on the respective merits of the different systems. Nevertheless, one must bear in mind that the different systems take in fairly large variations of energy value. The whole process of energy evaluation must be complete for the evaluation of nitrogen, minerals and vitamins which are interpdependent, irrespective of the chosen system.

The whole approach to rationing can be shown diagrammatically as in Figure 5.2.

To be exact, the ration controls production.

In tropical development projects, one is often confronted by problems of shortages, when all the knowledge of potential performance by well-fed

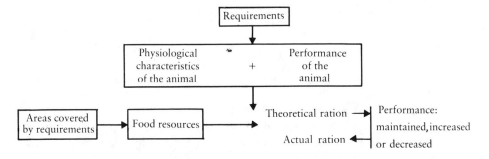

Figure 5.2   The principle of rationing

indigenous animals is still not enough. In order to use the above scheme to best effect, potential performance should not be underestimated.

Feeding behaviour

Plant species eaten

Feeding behaviour is a collection of activities linked to the ingestion of food (searching, choosing, absorption).

In herbivores, digestion of forage is due to the mechanical action of chewing by the teeth, the chemical action of different digestive juices, this action being similar in all animals. However in herbivores, digestion is particularly due to the action of the gastro-intestinal flora which ensure breakdown of the cellulose fraction of the forage as well as the synthesis of amino acids and vitamins, these capabilities being particularly well-developed in animals with several stomachs.

In single-stomached animals (horse, donkey) it is mainly in the colon that the action of the cellulose flora is greatest, whereas in animals with several stomachs, this action takes place in the rumen.

Table 5.14 Woody species eaten by cattle in the Sahel

Woody species eaten in decreasing order of importance	Parts consumed		
	Fresh leaves	Dry leaves	Fruits
Combretum aculeatum	x		
Piliostigma reticulatum	x		x
Pterocarpus lucens	x	x	
Grewia bicolor	x	x	
Dalbergia melanoxylon	x		
Combretum glutinosum	x	x	
Feretia apodanthera	x	x	
Maerua crassifolia	x		
Guiera senegalensis	x	x	x
Anogeissus leiocarpa	x	x	
Dichrostachys cinerea	x		

Tables 5.14–5.17 show the following points about feeding behaviour.

1. Goats, sheep and camels frequent thorny trees and bushes as much as non-thorny ones.
2. Cattle only eat non-thorny species.
3. The parts eaten are very varied which allows animals to space out their use of the plant over time. Some species which are multiple flowering (Acacia) have a substantial advantage as do those which retain their leaves during the critical period of the year (Bauhinia, Balanites, Faidherbia albida).

Table 5.15 Woody species eaten by sheep in the Sahel

Woody species eaten in decreasing order of importance	Parts consumed				
	Fresh leaves	Dry leaves	Flowers	Fruits	Branches
Balanites aegyptiaca	x	x		x	
Combretum aculeatum	x	x			x
Acacia seyal	x	x	x	x	
Ziziphus mauritiana	x			x	
Anogeissus leiocarpa	x	x			
Bauhinia rufescens	x			x	
Pilostigma reticulatum	x			x	
Acacia nilotica	x		x	x	
Feretia apodanthera	x	x			
Pterocarpus lucens	x	x			
Grewia bicolor	x	x			
Acacia tortilis ssp. raddiana	x		x	x	
Dichrostachys cinerea	x				
Guiera senegalensis				x	
Maerua crassifolia	x				

Table 5.16 Woody species eaten by goats in the Sahel

Woody species eaten in decreasing order of importance	Parts consumed				
	Fresh leaves	Dry leaves	Flowers	Fruits	Branches
Balanites aegyptiaca	x	x		x	x
Combretum aculeatum	x	x			x
Guiera senegalensis	x	x		x	
Acacia tortilis ssp. raddiana	x		x	x	
Acacia senegal	x		x	x	
Acacia seyal	x	x	x	x	
Acacia nilotica	x		x	x	
Ziziphus mauritiana	x	x		x	
Bauhinia rufescens	x	x			
Faidherbia albida	x				
Anogeissus leiocarpa	x	x			
Piliostigma reticulatum	x			x	
Pterocarpus lucens	x	x		x	
Grewia bicolor	x	x		x	
Dalbergia melanoxylon	x				
Feretia apodanthera	x	x			
Maerua crassifolia	x				
Dichrostachys cinerea	x				
Combretum micranthum	x	x		x	
Combretum glutinosum	x	x			

Table 5.17 Woody species eaten by camels in the Sahel

Woody species eaten in decreasing order of importance	Parts consumed	
	Fresh leaves	Fruits
Balanites aegyptiaca	x	x
Ziziphus mauritiana	x	
Acacia seyal	x	x
Acacia laeta	x	x
Acacia nilotica	x	x
Acacia tortilis ssp. *raddiana*	x	x
Faidherbia albida	x	x
Maerua crassifolia	x	
Feretia apodanthera	x	

The feeding behaviour of animals varies according to species; single-stomached animals eat their food slowly, chewing the food finely before swallowing it; conversely, animals with several stomachs swallow forage quickly after chewing it into coarse pieces, then in the course of rumination they regurgitate the food back into the mouth where it is finely ground down by a slow powerful action of the jaws.

If one observes the behaviour of herbivores at pasture, one can see very great differences and this is a good thing because it allows many species to live on the same land in harmony.

The animals select the plants which they eat and on the same plant, according to stage of growth, they eat the parts that are appetising to them. Thus cattle eat the young shoots of *Imperata cylindrica* but avoid them when they are fully developed; in dry areas, cattle only eat *Stylosanthes gracilis* with difficulty when it begins to dry out at the base, because of the glandular hairs which cover the leaves.

Sheep eat large graminaceous plants only in exceptional circumstances but willingly pick up dry leaves, fragments of plants, the pods of forage trees and grains which have fallen on the ground.

Goats are often considered to be a 'disaster' in the onset of desertification in parts of Africa, whereas it is the goatherders, who carry out considerable pruning of forage tree species in order to feed their animals, who should be incriminated.

In Kenya and Australia, it has been noticed that when goats have been brought to graze on areas exploited by cattle, they eat shrub species and have prevented excessive growth and choking of the pasture by these species (Tables 5.18 and 5.19).

Camels willingly eat the leaves of thorny trees which are beyond the reach of other herbivores.

One should take account of these food preferences in order to evaluate optimum stocking rates per hectare.

Table 5.18 The importance of the shrub layer in the ration of sheep and goats running together on natural grazing (expressed as a percentage of total consumed)

Species	November	February	June
Goats	67	78	87
Sheep	21	10	19

Table 5.19 Allocation of feeding time spent on different types of vegetation by different animal species (expressed as a percentage of total time)

Type of vegetation	Cattle	Sheep	Angora goats
Grass pasture	76.0	79.0	38.1
Browsing shrubs	8.5	11.0	53.1
Other	15.5	10.0	8.8

Distribution of feeding activities throughout the course of the day

In a study on the influence of biotic factors on the evolution of the woody layer in the Sahel, the behaviour of three herds living in the same area in April and May was observed.

One of the herds exploited bushy land while the other two used a grass steppe. Drinking was undertaken at a well 5 km from the encampment which was situated in the middle of the grazing area.

Table 5.20 gives the allocation of time spent on different activities according to type of land.

Table 5.20 Times at pasture (savanna – tree savanna)

Activity	Bushy pasture	Pasture without trees
Grazing	5 h 30 min	6 h 30 min
Moving	3 h 40 min	8 h 30 min
Ruminating	4 h 30 min	3 h 20 min
Resting	10 h 15 min	5 h 20 min
Drinking	5 min	10 min

In bushy land, browsing only takes place during the day, while for the second herd it is more significant at night than in the daytime.

In the case of the land without trees, the time spent moving is very high and the time resting and ruminating is insufficient. A number of the animals of the herd which use this land are in a poor state, losses by general debility are noticeable and they show signs of vitamin A deficiency (blindness).

At the same time, all the animals of the herd consuming the leaves of trees, with preference for those of *Balanites aegyptica*, *Maerua crassifolia* and *Cadaba glandulosa*, remain in good health (Table 5.21). Food originating from trees (leaves and fruits) can compensate for the shortage of protein matter in straw.

Table 5.21 Composition of some forage from trees

Species and forage	green matter		dry matter		DCP
	FU/kg	DCP g/kg	FU/kg	DCP g/kg	FU
Balanites aegyptiaca					
green leaves and young shoots	0.43	22.4	0.90	48	53
green leaves and young shoots	0.41	38.8	0.90	86	95
green leaves	0.40	30.0	0.90	68	76
young shoots	0.76	51.3	0.80	54	67
Maerua crassifolia					
green leaves and young shoots	0.41	90.1	0.80	174	215
green leaves	0.44	83.6	0.90	171	190
Cadaba glandulosa					
green leaves	0.31	60.5	0.65	126	194

In another series of observations, it was noticed that daily drinking was less favourable in pasture without bushes than drinking every day due to the travelling imposed on the animals.

Natural mechanism for voluntary eating in herbivores

Regulation of voluntary eating of forage in ruminating herbivores is controlled by two mechanisms; the purely physical one takes place at the filling up of the primary gastric reservoirs (rumen and omasum) while the second depends upon the metabolic value of the food eaten.

The first mechanism comes into action when the animals consume forage which has high bulk coefficient per forage unit consumed; the second acts when the ration contains concentrated feed which lowers the bulk coefficient – the impulse to consume food, which involves the relative emptiness of the pre-stomach digestive tracts, is inhibited.

The latter regulatory mechanism is very comparable to that known in single-stomached animals; it comes into play when the animal is subject to heat stress of long duration (see Chapter 3 Animal production and climate).

The speed of movement in the pre-stomach digestive tracts, which condition their emptiness and so the hunger of the animal, depends on the structure of the food and the intensity of cellulolysis within these tracts.

Cellulolysis, which ensures chemical breakdown of the fibrous elements of the forage, is effected by the micro-organisms which live in the digestive tracts and this flora is very sensitive to variations in composition of the ration. Soluble carbohydrates added to the ration are rapidly metabolised compared with the less easily affected fibrous structures; cellulolysis is a slow process.

Proteins, from nitrogenous material, are a factor favourable to cellulolysis and the feed value of straw is improved by the addition of 8–10 per cent crude protein. Oat straw takes 83 h to be digested when it is fed 'straight cut', 67 h if it is ground into flour and only 51 h if it is mixed with urea. The flora in the rumen requires a number of minerals, in particular sulphur is necessary for the synthesis of sulphur amino acids. Cobalt is equally indispensable because it is an actual growth factor of the rumen flora and a major element in the synthesis of vitamin B_{12} of the micro-organisms.

All the factors which accelerate cellulolysis accelerate the process of digestion and by the movement of food, the stomach and intestines empty more rapidly and so the intake of food is increased. It has been established that when the digestibility of the dry matter increases by 1 per cent, the maximum intake level of natural meadow grass increases by 1.76 g dry matter/kg liveweight$^{0.75}$; that of legumes increases by 85 g DM/kg liveweight$^{0.75}$; and that of grasses increases by 1.6 g DM/kg liveweight$^{0.75}$.

At equal digestibility, legumes are consumed more than grasses because the

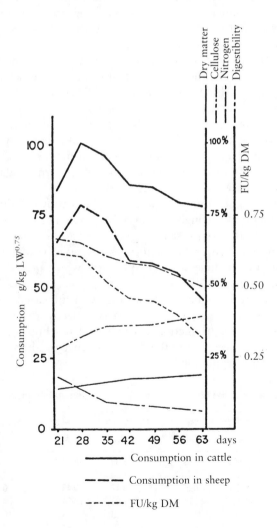

Figure 5.3 Variation of *Panicum maximum* intake as a function of stage of growth

former contain less membranous elements and more soluble constituents and are digested more rapidly.

Maximum digestibility varies with the type of ration and the schemes proposed for temperate zones permit understanding of the difficulties which tropical stockmen encounter on natural pastures; in fact it is only during one month at most that the intake of forages is maximum when they contain 18–23 per cent of dry matter.

Comparison of curves in Figure 5.3 shows the depressive role in cattle and sheep of the reduction of nitrogenous matter content on intake, digestibility and nutritive value of one unit of dry matter as well as increase of total dry matter and cellulose.

Thus, when the forage has its least value, intake falls and in this way when standing forage is no longer composed of anything other than straw of low digestibility, the animals hardly consume more than 1.4–1.6 kg DM/100 g liveweight (60.3 g/kg of metabolic liveweight).

On turning to grass at the beginning of the rainy season, when the animals are hungry for tender grass, the water content of the forage, which represents 90 per cent by weight, is difficult to absorb and fills the stomach and intestines. As the food value of the grass per unit weight is low (insufficient energy, excessive nitrogen and potassium, deficient in sodium and magnesium), physical regulation, which would tend to limit intake, is partly inhibited by metabolic regulation. Here one has an explanation for the weight loss which follows turning to grass; the appetite only becomes normal again when the dry matter content of the forage reaches 18 per cent.

At the end of the dry season, reduction of intake is above all due to physical factors, passage of food through the digestive tracts is slow because of the difficulty of reducing the coarse straw to fine particles. As their feed value is low, the addition of unfavourable factors lead to considerable weight losses of 6–10 per cent in the course of the 3–4 months which precede the onset of the rainy season, (Table 5.22).

When the animal receives balanced rations, with increased digestibility, it regulates intake as a function of its energy needs determined by its physiological state and its productivity, with a tendency however to lay down fat reserves (the cause either being the direct influence of abdominal fats or a hypothetical lipostatic regulation).

Table 5.22 Variation of the composition of forage on a natural Soudanian pasture

Constituent	End of the dry season		Middle of the rainy season		Start of the dry season	
	March	April	August	Sept.	Nov.	Dec.
Moisture	9.50	8.2	75.00	74.00	51.00	48.00
Protein	1.27	0.70	1.58	1.47	1.70	1.80
Fats	0.68	0.55	0.42	0.45	0.71	0.69
Nitrogen-free extract	48.60	50.26	11.83	13.24	24.00	25.60
Cellulose	31.90	31.00	8.23	9.64	16.50	18.50
Minerals	7.30	9.20	2.29	2.54	4.60	5.40

Intensive pasture trials carried out in tropical Africa have noted that an animal, usually maintained on natural pasture, took 8–15 days to become accustomed to a ration composed of concentrates. Its daily consumption developed according to the rate, measured by weight gain/feed value, of putting on flesh and the transformation index went on increasing, proof of energy storage in the form of fat.

Drinking water

Cattle

It is accepted that ruminants consume 2–4 kg of water per kilogram of dry matter eaten, thus a tropical cattle unit of 250 kg liveweight consuming

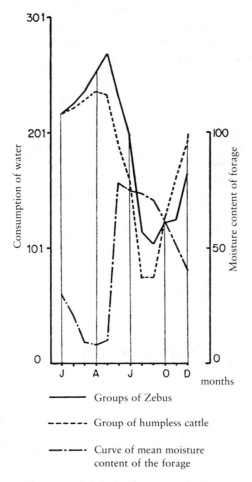

Figure 5.4 Mean monthly curves of daily water consumption

$2.5 \times 250/100 = 6.25$ kg of dry matter should have 25 litres of water each day and this would be supplied in the form of drinking water or contained in the food (see also page 88).

Zebus weighing from 247 to 297 kg maintained on natural Soudanian pasture and having free access to drinking water once a day, have drunk, according to the time of year, an average of 10.42 litres of water per animal per day in September (height of the rainy season) to 27.33 litres in April (height of the dry season). Cattle weighing 234–250 kg maintained in the same conditions consumed 7.42–23.28 litres (Figure 5.4) (see Chapter 3 Animal production and climate).

Sheep and goats

For sheep, it is estimated that drinking requirements are 2–3 litres of water per kilogram of dry food with an additional 50 per cent for females in the final stages of pregnancy or those feeding lambs i.e. between 2.5 and 5 litres/day, according to physiological condition and the environmental situation.

Goats drink as much as sheep but can withstand deficiency periods better.

Camels

Drinking water requirements are influenced in the same way as other ruminants, particularly by the water content of the forage and the climatic conditions. In a warm, dry climate the camel must have 20–30 litres of water but it has the ability to go without drinking for 5–7 days. When eating forage containing a high percentage of water, it can survive without drinking for 15 days.

Forage resources

Natural pastures

In the tropics there are all types of agricultural systems. There are to be found systems of animal production from the most archaic, which only exploit natural plant and water resources in a subsistance economy, to the most sophisticated which benefit, in a market economy, from modern animal production methods used in the temperate zones.

Whatever the animal production technique used, the production system can be defined according to the origin of the forage resources which the domestic animals convert, assuming that drinking water supply has already been taken care of:

1. natural pasture;
2. artificial pasture;
3. cultivated forage;
4. agricultural by-products;
5. industrial by-products.

The more animal production techniques are perfected, the more 'natural pasture' is reduced. In temperate zones only in the hill farming system is

Plate 5.1   Land with acacia shrub cover near Tombouctou

Plate 5.2   Savanna with *Acacia tortilis* tree cover (East Africa)

natural vegetation grazed rather than cut, while in the tropics the majority of herds usually exploit natural vegetation. The term 'natural pasture' is a convenient label, but it covers many different types of vegetation.

Description of tropical natural pastures

The classification of natural pastures relies on the relative importance of the grass and tree cover which are found there.

The artificial classification which follows is adequate for the understanding of the problems which the stockman faces when he exploits pastoral land.

Plate 5.3   Savanna with *Acacia radiana* tree cover (West Africa)

Plate 5.4   Plain with *Panicum turgidum* vegetation cover (Northern Niger)

Grassland types

Steppe and savanna are two terms which define grassland type and the presence and significance of woody species found in them allow completion of their definition.

Steppe

The term 'steppe', applied to tropical vegetation, concerns a characteristic type distinguished by a herbaceous cover where annual plants predominate, while hardy plants are rare and thin on the ground. Hardy Gramineae, when they are present, have narrow rolled or folded leaves and these are often placed on the stem close to the ground (basal). Herbaceous cover is not usually more than 80 cm high.

One can distinguish:

1. *Mesophile steppe* is characterised by an abundance of Gramineae, adapted to the dry conditions, with large flattened leaves.
2. In *xerophile steppe* the annual Gramineae are adapted to the dry conditions, the leaves being narrow, rolled on themselves or folded.
3. *Contracted steppe* does not cover all the land; it is made up of patches of herbaceous cover localised in those areas most suited to vegetation by the quality of the soil or the water available: water courses, places of rainwater collection and spread . . . this is the predesert type of steppe.

Savanna

The term 'savanna' applies to a type of vegetation characterised by a grass cover of less than 0.80 m high where the species are separated into two layers (strata).

The Gramineae predominate and constitute the higher strata; the leaves are either basal or caulescent (attached to the stem); most form isolated tufts whose stems often form a solid mass when they have reached full growth.

Mixed savanna is a low grass type which resembles a steppe, but in which tall tufts of hardy grasses, often more than 2 m high with large flat leaves, are found.

Mixed types: grass, tree, shrub

Steppe or savanna are *grass types* when the woody species, i.e. tree or shrub, are missing or cover less than 2 per cent of the ground, which represents a density per hectare of 50 individuals of 2 m diameter overhead growth, 12 individuals of 4 m diameter overhead growth or 3 individuals of 8 m diameter overhead growth.

Table 5.23 Classification of tropical pastures

Type		Climatic limits			Human activities		
Zones	Sector	Annual rainfall (mm)	Active period (months)	Soils	Agriculture	Livestock production	Forestry
Desert	Sahara			crude mineral	oasis	nomadic/wells	nil
		100	0				
Sahel	Sahelo-Saharan			crude mineral	oasis	nomadic/wells transhumance /pools	nil
		200	0				
	Sahelian			brown brown-red hydromorphic	between dunes (millet) irrigated rice	transhumance pools – wells	firewood construction (trad)
		400	1				
	Sahelo-Soudanian			brown brown-red hydromorphic vertisols	shifting/sand (millet, groundnuts) irrigated rice	transhumance pools – wells	firewood construction (trad)
		600	3				
	Soudano-Sahelian			tropical ferruginous	shifting (millet, groundnuts) irrigated rice	transhumance pools – wells	firewood construction (trad)
		800	3– 4				
Soudan	Soudanian			tropical ferruginous	shifting (sorghum cotton) irrigated rice	sedentary + transhumance (Zebus)	firewood construction (trad)
		1000–1200	5				
	Soudano-Guinean			ferrallitic	shifting (yam, maize, sorghum, cotton) irrigated rice rain-fed rice	sedentary (villages) (humpless cattle)	firewood construction (trad) carpentry
		1300–1500	7				
Guinean	Forest edge			ferrallitic	shifting (yam, cassava, cotton) rain-fed rice	sedentary (villages)	firewood construction (trad) timber milling
		1600	10				
	Forest			ferrallitic	shifting/cut and burn, cassava, banana, cocoa, coffee, rain-fed rice	sedentary (villages)	firewood construction (trad) timber milling
Altitude	Plateau (800–1500 m)	1400–1600	7–10	ferrallitic	shifting (cassava, sorghum, maize)	transhumance (Zebus) + sedentary	firewood construction (trad)
	Mountain (1500 m and above)	1600–3000	10–12	andosols	shifting maize, potato	transhumance (Zebus)	firewood construction (trad)

Table 5.23 (Continued)

Vegetation			Dominant flora		Production DM	
General name	Edaphic variants		Woody	Herbaceous	Yield (kg/ha/year)	Productivity (kg/ha/day)
	Substrate (ground)	Grassland type				
contracted steppe	silt	contracted steppe	Acacia ehrenbergiana	Panicum turgidum		
	sand sheets	contracted steppe	Acacia tortilis	Stipagrostis pungens		
contracted steppe	silt	contracted steppe	Acacia ehrenbergiana	Panicum turgidum	500	
	sand sheets	contracted steppe	Acacia tortilis	Panicum turgidum	400	
xerophile steppe	rolling dunes	shrub steppe	Acacia senegal	Aristida sieberana	1 000	
	levelled dunes	shrub steppe	Acacia tortilis	Aristida mutabilis	1 500	
	colluvial slopes	shrub steppe	Balanites aegyptiaca	Schoenefeldia gracilis	2 000	
	skeletal	shrub steppe	Commiphora africana	Aristida adscensionis	500	
	prone to flooding	wet land	nil	Echinochloa stagnina	6 000	3 (exempt)
mesophile steppe	rolling dunes	shrub steppe	Combetum glutinosum	Cenchrus biflorus	1 500	
	levelled dunes	shrub steppe	Sclerocarya birrea	Eragrostis tremula	1 200	
	colluvial slopes	shrub steppe	Acacia seyal	Schoenefeldia gracilis	3 000	
	skeletal	shrub steppe	Pterocarpus lucens	Loudetia togoensis	800	
	prone to flooding	wet land	nil	Echinochloa stagnina	15 000	10 (exempt)
mesophile steppe	peneplain	woodland steppe	Combetum glutinosum	Diheleropogon hagerupii	1 500	
	colluvial slopes	mixed savanna	Piliostigma reticulatum	Andropogon gayanus	2 000	2 (DS)
	skeletal	shrub steppe	Combetum micranthum	Loudetia togoensis	800	
woodland savanna	peneplain	woodland savanna	Anogeissus leiocarpa	Diheteropogon hagerupii	2 000	
	colluvial slopes	orchard savanna	Butyrospermgum paradoxum	Andropogon gayanus	2 500	30 (RS)
	skeletal	tree steppe	Combretum nigricans	Andropogon pseudapricus	800	
rain forest	peneplain	thin forest	Pterocarpus erinaceus	Diheteropogon amplectens	3 000	
	colluvial slopes	thin forest	Daniellia oliveri	Andropogon gayanus	3 000	11 (RS)
	flood valleys	grass savanna	nil	Hyparrhenia rufa	8 000	15 (DS)
	subskeletal	tree savanna	Isoberlinia doka	Andropogon ascinodis	2 000	
	skeletal	shrub savanna	Combetum glutinosum	Louditia simplex	1 500	
dense dry forest	deep alluvial clay	shrub savanna	Crossopleryx febrifuga	Hyparrhenia diplandra	13 000	12 (RS)
forest corridors	sand	tree savanna	Lophira lanceolata	Hyparrhenia smithiana	3 000 2 500	5 (DS)
tree savanna	subskeletal	shrub savanna	Hymenocardia acida	Loudetia arundinacea		
dense humid forest	sand	shrub savanna	Annona senegalensis	Brachiaria brachylopha		
		anthropic savanna	Trema guineensis	Imperata cylindrica	3 500	20 (RS)
woodland savanna	deep	woodland savanna	Daniellia oliveri	Hyparrhenia rufa	4 000	12 (RS)
	skeletal	shrub savanna	Burkea africana	Loudetia simplex	500	
grass savanna dense forest	deep	grass savanna	nil	Sporobolus africanus		

(DS) = dry season   (RS) = rainy season

Steppe or savanna is *tree type* when there is a thin tree and shrub cover, i.e. they cover a surface area of between 2 and 20 per cent which corresponds to a density per hectare of 500 individuals of 2 m diameter, 125 individuals of 4 m diameter or 30 individuals of 8 m diameter.

Tree savanna is classed as orchard savanna when the trees which it contains are free-standing but of good stature, because they have been saved during clearing for the purpose of harvesting products from them. Often they are fruit trees: mangos, avocados, shea-nuts, etc., or feed providers from their leaves or fruits (*Faidherbia*, baobabs, etc.)

Steppe or savanna is *shrub type* when the shrubs, with valueless trunks and less than 5 m high, form a ground cover of between 20 and 40 per cent.

Shrub steppe or savanna is *thicket type* when the shrubs are gathered in

Plate 5.5   Sahelian woodland steppe with *Acacia radiana* (Mauritania)

Plate 5.6   Cattle browsing

Plate 5.7   Sahelian mixed steppe with *Aristida siberiana*

closed formation such that man or large mammals have difficulty in moving through them, the branches of the woody plants are intertwined at all levels and the grass formations at the lower levels are themselves closely matted.

Steppe or savanna is *woodland type* when the trees, with good trunks and generally of a height more than 5 m, form a ground cover of between 20 and 40 per cent.

Tree types

Thin forest type is a vegetation type in which the tree cover remains open, a grass cover dominated by thin Gramineae subsists under tree canopies which do not touch each other and this grass cover is often dicontinuous.

In *dense forest type* the tree canopies touch each other, the apparent tree cover is more than 90 per cent and there is no longer a grass cover.

Evaluation of grazings

Methods

Whatever the botanical formations might be, the stockman takes into consideration the number of animals which can be maintained on the grazing land for a whole year.

Such an estimation is easy enough when the vegetation cover is homogeneous and grass growth continuous but unfortunately this is not often the case in the tropics.

Two approaches are possible: in the first, the animals are used as indicators of the qualities of the pasture: in the second, one evaluates the qualities and quantities of the usable forage and one estimates their potential for animal production.

The first technique is simpler and consists of grazing the area by estimating from the number of animals which stay there permanently or for periods; weighings of the animals at repeated intervals enable ongoing assessment of the growth and state of health of the animals.

Productivity is then expressed in kilogram of meat per hectare, the maximum stocking rate corresponding to that point at which the weight of the animals remains stationary, i.e. when they only find their maintenance ration from the pasture.

The second method of measurement is more elaborate but less limiting and consists of measuring the productivity of the vegetation beginning with a sample of forage from the area in question, then evaluating the number of animals which can be stocked there.

Areas of several square metres are closed off from grazing, the grass is completely harvested at the end of the period of growth, a botanical inventory is made and the harvested grass (fresh weight) is weighed after dessication in an oven (dry matter). Finally, determination of the different chemical constituents is made in the laboratory.

This method gives information on the *potential production*, but is insufficient for an objective assessment of the real situation, because the animals selectively eat certain plant species and, on the same species, these are not the same parts of the plant throughout the year.

It is necessary to complete the information above by observation of the behaviour of the animals on the pasture; direct observation allowing identification of pallatable or non-pallatable species and indirect observation of the pasture being the identification and estimation of the parts not eaten.

If the area in question is set in pastureland, the information gained in the enclosure is completed by observations and samples taken in the open locations to which the animals have free access. Thus, by comparison, one knows the evolution of forage quantity and quality consumed in the course of the year, the quantities lost by treading underfoot and, above all, the nature and significance of the parts not eaten.

A simplified technique consists of selecting on site the pallatable and non-pallatable species from the samples grown in the enclosures and in the open areas, and weighing them separately.

Determination of the food value of the samples grown is made starting with botanical surveys, weighings and chemical analyses of the samples.

So that the estimations might be as near to reality as possible, it is necessary to secure the following information:

- location of the area;
- nature of the soil;
- time of sampling;
- plants and their parts eaten;
- number of analyses carried out in order to obtain the mean;
- total dry matter (DM);
- total crude protein as a percentage of dry matter;
- total cellulose as a percentage of dry matter;
- total minerals as a percentage of dry matter;
- forage value of 1 kg of forage in forage units (FU);
- the ratio of DCP/FU;
- the equivalent of 1 kg of dry matter of the food, expressed in FU and DCP.*

The most important data for pasture evaluations are:

- quantity of dry matter produced per unit area;
- energy value of the forage;
- the quantity of digestible crude protein per kilogram of dry matter consumed;
- the mineral content (both macro and trace elements) of consumable forage.

Expression of results

Units

In order to make comparisons easier, a concept of stocking rate per hectare

* Standards used:
  maintenance = DCP requirements 0.5 g/day per kg liveweight
  movement   = 0.022 FU per km travelled per 100 kg liveweight
  movement   = 0.022 FU per km travelled per 100 kg liveweight,
              1.42 g DCP per km travelled per 100 kg liveweight

has been introduced (per day, per month, per year), which corresponds to the amount of animals, expressed in 'head' or in liveweight, which can be carried on the pasture without damaging it.

This value is easy to determine when one uses animals to measure the productivity of the pasture. It is less easy when one does not possess information on the nutritional value of the forage.

In order to integrate all the recorded information, one relates the possible stocking rate to a theoretical unit for which one has defined, *a priori*, the weight and for which the requirements have been calculated as a function of this weight and of the chosen production (meat, milk).

The pasture's usable production of the requirements of the reference animal are brought together, the possible stocking rate is worked out, and the period during which this level of stocking is applicable is estimated.

Livestock unit (LU)

In temperate zones the livestock unit is the reference point; it is a cow of 550 kg liveweight, on the land for 12 months, producing 3000 litres of milk with an approximate consumption of 3000 forage units per year, taking in 455 g of DCP per day.

Tropical cattle unit (TCU)

For the tropics, where cattle are between 200 and 350 kg, researchers from the Animal Science Research Centre in Bamako-Sotuba (Mali) have proposed the tropical cattle unit (TCU) – this being an animal of 250 kg whose requirements have been defined taking into account the tropical conditions of exploiting pasture.

Standards for the evaluation of stocking rate per hectare

Maintenance ration

The consumption of dry matter has been estimated at 2.5 per cent of liveweight, or 6.5 kg, which corresponds to the consumption of a medium quality forage.

The definition of energy needs is more tenuous because, in the conditions which prevail in temperate zones, the animals are housed and, if they are at pasture, they do not have to make long journeys in order to graze and drink. It is not the same in the tropics where, from experience, it is estimated that a beast at pasture in the Sahel walks 7.5 km each day in the rainy season and double this in the dry season; in the Soudanian and Guinean zones the figure is 7.5 km throughout the year.

Taking account of its weight, 250 kg, it is calculated that the Tropical Cattle Unit (TCU) must receive a daily ration containing:

- 2.3 forage units (FU) to cover maintenance;

- 0.5 forage units for short journeying (7.5–8.0 km/day);
- 0.9 forage units for long journeying (15 km/day);

To summarise, a TCU must receive, each day, for its maintenance on natural pasture, 6.250 kg of dry matter having a forage value of:

- 2.8 FU with 156 g of DCP in the case of small distances travelled;
- 3.2 FU with 1 g of DCP in the case of large distances travelled, the ratio DCP/quantity of fodder unit (Nb FU) being 56 and 57 respectively.

Ration for meat production

The requirements of the TCU as defined above correspond to minimum input, the weight of the animal remaining constant. This concept has been used in preference to a unit of production as in the temperate zones because, from experience, it is known that over the course of a year on a natural pasture, the weight of the animals varies – rising and falling.

It is possible to estimate the requirements of a TCU producing meat or milk starting with the standards shown, if one maximises the requirements to cover travelling.

For a TCU gaining 100 g/day, it is necessary to increase the requirements above by 0.25 FU, i.e. a total of 3.05 FU for small distances travelled.

If the TCU produces 1 kg of milk at 4 per cent fats, it should receive a further 0.38 FU or better still 0.4 FU, i.e. a total of 3.2 FU for small distances travelled.

Equivalent ration

If knowledge of the TCU requirements permits calculation of stocking rate per hectare, it is also important to know the relationship which exists between the nutritive value of the food eaten (energy and DCP) and the unit weight of dry matter. This new entity is termed the equivalent ration of a kilogram of dry matter; it is connected to the INRA energy density.

In the case of standards adopted in the definition of TCU, the maintenance requirements will be assured if the ration contains the following per kilogram of dry matter:

$$\frac{2.3}{6.25} \ \# \ 0.37 \ \text{FU}; \ \frac{12.5}{6.25} \ \# \ 20 \ \text{g of DCP}$$

and the requirements for maintenance and travelling will be assured it if contains:

$$\frac{2.7}{6.25} \ \# \ 0.432 \ \text{FU}; \ \frac{151}{6.5} \ \# \ 24.2 \ \text{g of DCP (small journeys)}$$

$$\frac{3.1}{6.25} \# 0.496 \text{ FU}; \quad \frac{177}{6.25} \# 28.3 \text{ g of DCP (long journeys)}$$

If 1 kg of forage dry matter gives an energy value higher than 0.432 FU and contains more than 24.2 g of DCP, the TCU which eats it will have the possibility of gaining weight; conversely, if 1 kg of dry matter has an energy value less than 0.432 FU and/or contains less than 24.2 g of DCP, the animal will not be able to consume more than 6.25 kg, its condition will deteriorate and it will lose weight.

Thus it will be possible to determine the following for a pasture whose qualities are known:

1. the maximum stocking rate;
2. the production possibilities;
3. the best forecasts possible (meat, milk).

Standards for other domesticated species

In the calculations relating to other species of tropical domesticated animals, one uses the following standards expressed in TCUs:

1. sheep	maintenance for adults	0.20
	young and growing	0.15
2. goats	maintenance for adults	0.2
	milking goats	0.3–0.4
3. camels	maintenance for adults	1.20–2.0
4. horses	maintenance for adults	1.00–1.20
5. donkeys	maintenance for adults	0.2–0.4

Soils – climate – forage – animal

Values for stocking rates per hectare

An average evaluation figure cannot be given for the whole tropical area but for the areas with a Sahelian or Soudanian climate, there is a saying which has a certain value: it is necessary for an ox to have as many hectares of pasture as there are months in the dry season.

In the desert zones, the flora consists of a small number of different species. One can assign the possible stocking rate to the species which grow in a given year. Values for the Western Sahara are shown in Table 5.24.

The tropical agricultural plant species have been classified as a function of rainfall, of the nature of the soils and of the composition of the flora, and indicating the human activities which arise from them. This is shown in Table. 5.23.

When one envisages vast areas, which is the case in establishing a

Table 5.24 Relationship between camel stocking rate and Saharan vegetation

Vegetation of the Western Sahara	Dry weight (kg/ha)	Maximum camel stocking rate (day/ha)	Area necessary for camels (day/m²)
Stipagrostis pungens:			
dry (Mauritania, Spring 1964)	2200	330	30
dry (Iguidi, May 1961)	684	130	70
Flowers (Mauritania, April 64)	154	30	220
Flowers (Iguidi, April 1961)	58	12	830
Stipagrostis acutiflora (ibid)	42	8	1250
Panicum turgidum: (Mauritania, Spring 1964)	800	100	90
Nucularia perrini (ibid)	470	70	140

development plan, it is interesting to be able to relate the capacity of the pastures to the rainfall.

From recent research it has been shown that mean grass production was 4 kg DM/ha per millimetre rainfall and it is accepted that the part of the biomass exploited by ruminants represents one-third of it. Thus each millimetre of rainfall corresponds to 1.33 kg of consumable dry matter per hectare, or 133 kg for 100 mm.

Assuming that a TCU has to consume 2280 kg DM/year for its maintenance, the theoretical number of hectares necessary per TCU, as a function of rainfall, are given in Table 5.25.

It is only when the rainfall index reaches a value approaching 1700 mm that 1 TCU can be kept on 1 ha all year round, it being understood that the forage value of the ration which the animal can consume is at least equal to 0.432 FU.

These figures apply in the same way in the situation where irrigation makes up the deficit of water supply from rainfall.

Table 5.25 Rainfall and the capacity of pasture

Rainfall (mm)	Total DM/ha (kg)	Usable DM/ha (kg)	Number of ha/TCU for maintenance
200	798	266	8.6
400	1596	532	4.3
600	2394	798	2.8
800	3200	1066	2.1
1000	4000	1333	1.7
1200	4797	1599	1.4
1400	5598	1866	1.2
1600	6396	2132	1.07
1700	6783	2261	1.0
1800	7197	2399	0.95

Survey and cartography of pastoral areas

Historically, prospecting had originally been for drinking water, then for the qualitative inventory of species and finally to determine the pallatability of the forage. These works, mainly conducted by botanists such as Chevalier, led to the composition of catalogues of flora of which the most well known are those of Hutchinson and Dalziel, and Pere Berhaut. The bibliographical publication of Curasson: *Pasture and foods in the tropics and sub-tropics* records the whole of this period.

The introduction of plant sociological methods of the Montpelier School by Braun-Blanquet and Emberger and of the Toulouse School by Gaussen and Trochain, permitted the making of maps.

The 1/10 000 000 map of the grass cover of Africa, published by FAO is a practical example of these works which started with the sole objective of gaining scientific knowledge.

The systematic use of the interpretation of aerial photographs, associated with plant sociological information on the ground, served to establish maps of very large scale which are very useful in the field of agricultural development and the listing of natural vegetation resources.

Thus maps of natural pastures were drawn up by Mosnier, Boudet, Peyre de Fabregues and their collaborators with equipment from Institut d'Élevage et de Médecine Veterinaire des Pays Tropicaux (Institute of Animal Production and Veterinary Medicine in the Tropics) (IEMVT) France; from 1952 to 1980, some 2.5 million km^2 have been mapped in tropical Africa, Madagascar, the Middle East and in South America.

Using very similar methods, the anglophone researchers Blair, A. Rains, N.H. Dawson, R. Perry and D.J. Pratt are mapping vast areas of East and West Africa and Australia.

The advent of ground observation satellites has given a new instrument of research to ecologists: remote sensing.

The first, called Erts 1 (Earth Resources Technology Satellite) was launched in July 1972, and later renamed Landsat 1. The second (Landsat 2) entered service in January 1975 and Landsat 3 joined them in March 1978.

These satellites, which travel on a circular subpolar orbit at 900 km above the Earth, carry sensors whose life is limited.

They permit, among other things, the study of the dynamics of vegetation over the period of the observations. They pass vertically over the same area every 18 days and are theoretically capable of recording the data on this time scale.

The images, drawn from the information transmitted by apparatus carried on the satellites, allow generalisation of the observations of plant communities and soil types made on the ground in the same way as data obtained from the interpretation of aerial photographs and drawn to a scale of 1/20 000 and 1/50 000.

From July 1972 to September 1981, the sensors on the satellites Landsat 1, 2 and 3 have thus 'photographed' the continents of our planet offering to the users information in the form of images or numerical data.

Table 5.28 shows the number of 'shots' recorded by the Eros Data Centre at Sioux Falls up to September 1981, each shot being made up of a collection of data corresponding to a surface area of the Earth of 185 km × 185 km.

Pastoral maps

The objective of the map is to describe, in a systematic fashion, the pastoral possibilities by carrying information on a topographical base, of the plant sociological and nutritional data recorded on the ground and of the generalisations obtained by photo-interpretation.

The cartographic document should give the following information:

1. nature and area of the ground;
2. the possibilities for use of the pastoral area in the different seasons of the year;
3. possible stocking rate per hectare;
4. use of the agricultural area by the human population.

Table 5.26 shows, with scales the potential value of such maps, their interpretation and planning future uses of the land, by professional personnel.

Scales

It is common to distinguish between: planning maps, survey maps and detailed maps; their scale is a function of the research objectives.

Planning maps, drawn to 1/1 000 000 or 1/500 000, cover large areas and give an idea of the general problems which are posed in very large territories.

Survey maps, drawn to 1/200 000 or 1/250 000, are established by interpretation of aerial photographs which, up to the last few years, were taken on a 1/50 000 scale at an altitude of about 4750 m. The progress made in the manufacture of photographic emulsions and in the construction of aircraft (Mystere or Falcon type) have permitted high altitude photography on a 1/100 000 scale with very fine definition. These maps are used for the preparation of regional plans.

For more precise development plans, the use of detailed maps on a 1/100 000 or 1/50 000 scale and even a 1/25 000 or 1/10 000 scale can be shown to be necessary (ranch management, creation of new towns etc.) and one should start from aerial photographic cover at 1/25 000 or 1/5000. On these scales, the mosaics made by each photographic frame are used directly to create *photomaps*.

Table 5.26 Maps of pastoral areas produced by IEMVT

Scale	Area covered	Format	Origin	Objectives	Intended users	Qualified personnel producing the map
General scales 1/2 000 000 1/1 000 000 1/ 500 000	2 660 000 km² 665 000 km² 166 250 km²	95 × 70	Formulated by the author. Eventually: put in the form of a record of the author by a map maker.	1) Research on the potential of pasture lands of the State or large natural region.	Economists	Qualified cartographers
1/2 000 000 1/1 000 000 1/ 500 000	1 300 000 km² 325 000 km² 81 250 km²	65 × 50	Basic documents of the author. Satellite imagery. Scales: 1/ 500 000 1/1 000 000	2) Statistics on vegetation changes 3) Studies of widespread phenomena (e.g. drought 1973)	Decision makers Planners	1 Remote sensing research worker 1 Cartographic engineer
Medium scales 1/250 000 (American) 1/200 000	13 750 km² 12 100 km²	55 × 55	a) Photo-interpretation from aerial coverage at 1/50 000 or 1/60 000) b) Satellite imagery from a research point of view according to the importance of the area studied	1) Statistics for region, county and district 2) Determination of suitable areas for ranching (zoning) 3) Inventory of cultivated areas 4) Planning measures	Staff responsible for regional administration Livestock departments	1 Qualified photo-interpreter 1 Remote sensing research worker 1 Map maker 1 Cartographic engineer
Large scale a) 1/100 000 b) 1/ 50 000 c) 1/ 25 000 d) 1/ 20 000	3 025 km² 756 km² 189 km² 121 km²	55 × 55	a) Photo-interpretation from photographs at 1/50 000 b) Idem c) Photo-interpretation from photographs at 1/25 000 d) Photo-interpretation from photographs at 1/20 000	a) Studies of ranch lands for the possibilities of extension b) Well defined studies of ranches c and d) Ranch studies completed by data with a view to further exploitation (determination and allocation of parcels of land) e) Planning measures	Staff responsible for production units Livestock technicians Persons allocating land	1 Qualified photo-interpreter 1 Map maker 1 Cartographic engineer
Large scale in detail 1/15 000 1/10 000	of the order of 150–75 km²	Limited to 95 × 70 55 × 55	Photo-interpretation from photographs at: 1/15 000 1/10 000	Plans of experimental units (farms, parcels of land, soils)	Staff responsible for experiments Engineers of works	1 Qualified photo-interpreter 1 Cartographer 1 Cartographic engineer

Interpretation of maps

On every map there is a legend of colours and hatching, each of them corresponding to a type of pasture.

Attached to every map, there is an explanatory note in which the detailed information is given on the composition of the different botanic groups, on their forage value, production potential and use and, finally, considerations on the evolution of the pasture as a result of the possible political or commercial exploitation of the land.

Making of a pastoral map

Aerial sensing

Available stereoscopic aerial photographs taken on the vertical axis are used. Most of the time, this amounts to black and white photographs taken on 'special aero' panchromatic film sensitive to radiation in the 'visible' spectrum whose wavelengths are between 400 and 750 nm (0.4–0.75 μm).

The scale of photograph most frequently available is 1/50 000. These frames are often old (10–20 years) and it is sometimes necessary to make new shots.

When studies require maximum information aeroplanes are equipped with two cameras loaded with films of different sensitivities and which film the ground at the same time.

The combinations depend on the information to be recorded:

- panchromatic black and white film;
- black and white film sensitive near to infra-red;
- classic colour film;
- 'dummy colour' film sensitive to infra-red.

The last category is well adapted to detailed study of the vegetation because it records the real characteristics of the vegetation and soil in a sensitive manner: nature of the leaves, stage of vegetation growth, humidity, etc.

Photo-interpretation

Photo-interpretation allows illustration, on the frames, of the vegetative characteristics observed on the ground in conjunction with their representation on the original 'shots'.

Thus the photo-interpreter recognises a vegetation type from *criteria* which are defined by the intensity of the shading or colour, the texture and the structure of the image. Stereoscopic vision allows localisation of a pasture type in relation to the topography of the terrain.

The vegetation types being signified, they are transferred on to an existing topographical base (geographical map) or on to a map which has itself been made by photorestitution from the frames which have been used for the photo-interpretation. The latter case is more favourable because the previous planimetric bases have the inconvenience of often being several years old and of not giving viable information on communication networks and human populations.

Plates 5.8a and 5.8b assist understanding of the principles of the method.

Plate 5.8a corresponds to the steroscopic 'shot' as it is given to the photo-interpreter who analyses the series with stereoscopic viewers in order to create a picture (5.8b) in which the vegetation types (Table 5.27) are individualised.

The original of the pasture map is then drawn by transfer of all the interpretations on to a topographical base.

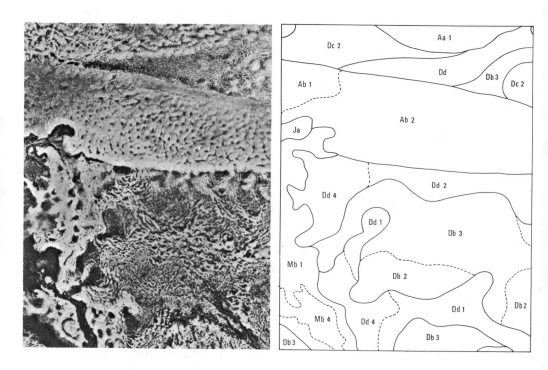

Plate 5.8 a and b   Aerial photography (IGN France) and its interpretation. The figures indicate the state of the vegetation and correspond to different classes of productivity.
1 – Vegetation in a good state
2 – Beginning of a good state
3 – Significant degradation
4 – Very advanced degradation
For the complete legend see Table 5.27

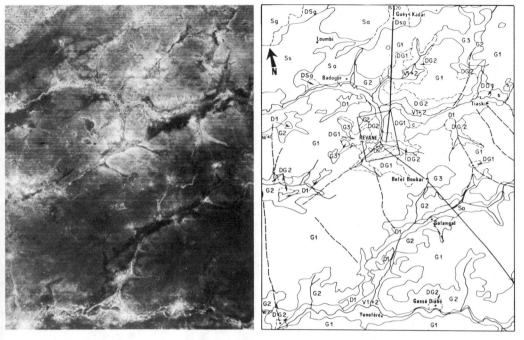

Plates 5.9 a and b   Landsat satellite image and its interpretation.
Formations identified on the satellite image
Sa: Light shrub steppe on sand-clay sheet
Ss: Light shrub steppe on slightly rolling dunes
Sg: Light shrub steppe on sand-gravel sheet
G1: Shrub savanna on gravel plateau
G2: Sparse shrub savanna on slopes
G3: Thin forest in endoroic depressions on pan substrate } D = degraded features
D1: Thin shrub steppe on continental dune
V1: Forest: corridors and wind breaks
      water eroded
C { crops
    fallow

Colours and hatching

Colours

The range of colours whose use is recommended by UNESCO (principally on the general scale) corresponds to Gaussen's ecological scale which goes from blue, for the hydromorphic types (heavy rainfall, high humidity), to red for the xerophylic types (extremely dry, high temperature).

Yellow indicates average ecoclimatic conditions.

The combination of colours provides a scale which goes from violet, for equatorial forest, to orange-red for desert steppes.

Table 5.27 Vegetation and productivity of pastoral areas, from aerial photography

| Designation | | Vegetation | | | | Mean annual productivity t of dm/ha | Grazing value | |
Symbol	Geomorphology	Type *	Woody strata (dominant species)	Herbaceous strata (dominant species)	State **		Mean annual stocking rate ha/TCU***	Period of optimum utilisation
Aa	Fixed dunes and flattened dunes	Xerophile grass steppe - Herbaceous strata almost continuous - Woody strata very thin	Guiera senegalensis Commiphora africana	Aristida mutabilis Schoenefeldia gracilis	1 2 3	2.2 1.3 0.5–1.0	3.0 5.0 7–14	Good pasture in all seasons Excellent in the rainy season
Ab	Fixed dunes	Xerophile grass steppe - Herbaceous strata almost continuous - Woody strata very thin	Combretum glutinosum	Cenchrus biflorus	1 2 3 4	2.4 1.5 0.5–1.0 insignificant	2.8 4.5 7–14	Good pasture in all seasons Excellent in the rainy season
Db	Sahelian slopes and flat-lands with gravelly skeletal soils	Xerophile shrub steppe with thickets - Mixed herbaceous strata thin and discontinuous - Woody strata dense contracted	Pterocarpus lucens Combretum micranthum	Aristida adscensionis Schoenefeldia gracilis	2 3 4	0.9–1.2 0.3–0.8 < 0.3	6–8 > 9 > 25	Mediocre pasture Usable particularly in the rainy season (aerial forage)
Dc	Sahelian slopes with gravelly skeletal soils ± sand on the surface	Xerophile shrub steppe with thickets - Mixed herbaceous strata thin and discontinuous - Woody strata dense contracted	Pterocarpus lucens Combretum glutinosum Combretum micranthum	Schoenefeldia gracilis Chloris prieurii	1 2 3 4	> 1.5 1–1.5 0.3–0.9 < 0.3	< 7 5–7 > 8 > 25	Grazing in all seasons especially at the beginning of the dry season (aerial forage)

Table 5.27 (continued)

| Designation | | Vegetation | | | State ** | Mean annual productivity t of dm/ha | Grazing value | |
Symbol	Geomorphology	Type *	Woody strata (dominant species)	Herbaceous strata (dominant species)			Mean annual stocking rate ha/TCU***	Period of optimum utilisation
Dd	Sahelian depressions with skeletal soils ± gravel	Shrub strata in thickets - Dense herbaceous strata in irregular bands - Woody strata quite dense	Pterocarpus lucens Grewia bicolor Acacia seyal	Aristida adscensionis Panicum laetum	1 2	1.8–2.5 1.0–1.7	3–4 5–7	Grazing in the rainy season and at the beginning of the dry season
Mb	Sahelian clay pools	Tree savanna - Herbaceous strata thin and very discontinuous - Woody strata variable from dense to very thin	Acacia nilotica Mitragyna inermis Acacia seyal	Vetiveria nigritana	–			Mediocre posture Good re-growth in the dry season
Ja Jb Jc	Fallow and crops	–	variable	variable				

* The type described corresponds better to a given state

** The state of vegetation is expressed according to the following classification:

1. good cover of herbaceous and woody strata

2. beginning of decline: herbaceous cover clears, woody strata remains stable

3. serious decline: herbaceous cover very sparse, death of some trees

4. very advanced decline: herbaceous cover severely reduced or non-existent, numerous dead trees.

*** Topical cattle unit (adult animal of 250 kg)

Hatching

Using only three or four basic colours makes map drawing rather onerous, so one can limit oneself to one or two colours: black only, black and blue, black and red, etc. and attribute to each vegetation type a specific type of hatching whose design, symbols and density depend on the intended purpose of the map. This is how maps for development projects (creation of ranches, integrated development areas, paths of transhumance, etc.) are drawn.

Cartographic expression of forage production

In the maps drawn by the IEMVT researchers, the possible stocking rate in Tropical Cattle Units (TCU) per hectare is shown by reference to an index comprising five classifications evaluated on the basis of potential dry matter production for the whole year (Table 5.28).

To estimate the possible stocking rate, one begins with the assumption that an animal can consume a layer of the biomass existing on the pasture at the time the estimation is made.

Such an exploitation would be under good management.

Table 5.28 Classification of pasture type according to dry matter yield and stocking rate per hectare

Pasture type	Number of hectares per TCU	Days of grazing per TCU per year	Potential dry matter production (kg/ha)
1	10 and more	36 and less	675 and less
2	5.1–10	36– 75	675–1400
3	3.1– 5	75–125	1400–2300
4	1.1– 3	125–365	2300–6850
5	3 and less	365 and more	6850 and more

Satellite imagery

Collection of information

In the Landsat series of satellites, the information is recorded by two types of sensors. The first records the data with the aid of a scanning radiometer (*multispectral scanner*) and the second is equipped with television cameras (*return beam vidicom*).

Multispectral scanner (MSS)

This radiometer provides almost all the observations of the Earth transmitted by the Landsat satellites. The radiometer (Figure 5.5) is a piece of optical measurement apparatus in which the oscillating mirror scans the ground piece by piece (57 m × 79 m), along a line perpendicular to the orbit of the satellite and then line by line made one in front of the other. Thus each image, which

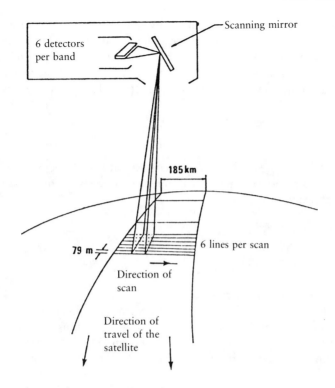

Figure 5.5 Multispectral scanner (MSS)

covers an area of 185 km × 185 km (about 34 000 km²), is obtained in about 20 sec.

The light from the sun is transmitted by the mirror to an optical system which breaks down the beams of light into four beams of different wave lengths (channels 4, 5, 6 and 7) (Table 5.29). Each beam is analysed by a bank of six detectors which transform the light energy into electrical energy. On Landsat 3, a fifth beam uses channel 8. The basic section of ground (*Pixel*) is 57 m × 79 m, as shown below.

Table 5.29 Characteristics of the MSS sensors (Landsat 1, 2, 3)

Channel	Wavelength (nm)		Corresponding colours	Dimensions of the basic coverage
4	500	600	green yellow	
5	600	700	orange red	
6	700	800	beginning of near infra-red	57 m × 79 m
7	800	1 100	near infra-red	
8	10 400	12 600	thermal infra-red Landsat 3 only	

The information is either transmitted by radio directly to the ground, if the satellite is within radio range of a receiving station (2400 km), or stored in the satellite's memory until the transfer can be made when the satellite passes close enough to a station. In the latter case, the capacity of the memory being limited, the frequency of acquisition of the information becomes more uncertain.

Video cameras (Return Beam Vidicom: RBV)

On Landsat 1 and 2, the RBV system consists of three independent cameras operating simultaneously each in a different spectral band over the whole of the Landsat scope of vision:

- channel 1 = 475–575 nm;
- channel 2 = 580–680 nm;
- channel 3 = 690–830 nm;

These cameras were hardly functioning.

On Landsat 3, the RBV system, which became functional again in January 1982, differs significantly from the previous ones. It comprises two cameras (Figure 5.6) which operate in the visible spectrum (510–750 nm). Each image covers 99 km × 99 km with a resolution on the ground of about 40 m.

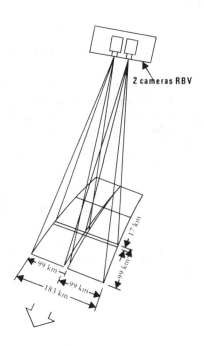

Figure 5.6 RBV cameras

Treatment of information

In the land-based receiver stations, the information is stored on magnetic tapes which are used in two different ways.

In one, the information is made up into a picture by transfer of the signals, relating to each basic area of ground, to film and an image is obtained for each channel, hatched in black and white, and to the scale of 1/3 369 000 which can be enlarged to 1/1 000 000, 1/500 000 or 1 250 000 (Plate 5.9a)

Photographic treatment

Starting with photographic negatives, it is possible to create images in colour at 1/1 000 000 or 1/500 000 by allocating a conventional colour to three of the four channels:

- channel 4 : yellow;
- channel 5 : magenta;
- channel 7 : cyan.

Superimposing the three negatives on top of each other gives an acceptable colour composition very close, as regards the characteristics of photographs obtained with infra-red colour emulsions, but dependent on the quality, to original photographs.

Information treatment

In the other treatment, the signals recorded on the magnetic tapes are transferred to computer compatible tapes (CCT).

Whereas reproductions by photographic processes involve loss of quality at each stage of the process, computerised copies are effected without any loss of information.

From the computer tapes it is possible to create:

1. very high quality images enlarged to 1/100 000 with improvement of contrast and geometric corrections which have now been possible for a number of years;
2. classifications using either simple statistical analytical methods (non-supervised classification) or analytical methods using objective observations made on the ground (supervised classification). These classifications lead to an automatic mapping of research topics with very little delay.

Interpretation of satellite imagery

Because of their nature and their low resolution of the ground, satellite images offer a synoptic view of vast areas and are perfectly adapted to regional studies. However, the absence of a view of relief of the land requires that one relies completely on the variations of shade and structure and a good knowledge of the terrain, linked to experience of photo-interpretation methods, in order to analyse the satellite images (Plate 5.9b).

On the subject of vegetation mapping, the automatic methods from the Landsat data remain, for the moment, in the experimental phase and their use is limited to the separation of large specific entities of widely differing natures (forest/grass savanna, denuded areas or those with dense vegetation, flooded areas (etc. . . .).

Table 5.30 Number of Landsat 'shots' recorded by Eros Data Centre from July 1972 to September 1981 (fiscal years*)

	1973	1974	1975	1976	1977	1978	1979	1980	1981	Total
MSS LANDSAT 1	46 354	11 754	55 284	14 109	12 286	4 954	51	0	0	
LANDSAT 2	–	–	10 962	53 704	25 282	44 715	12 886	8 325	20 457	
LANDSAT 3	–	–	–	–	–	12 350	22 452	18 042	13 237	
Total	46 354	11 764	66 246	67 813	37 568	62 029	35 389	26 357	33 694	387 214
RSV LANDSAT 2	–	–	575	479	949	24	24	11	46	
LANDSAT 3	–	–	–	–	–	3 221	4 234	16 684	15 112	
Total	–	–	575	479	949	3 285	4 258	16 695	15 158	41 399

* 1973–1975: July to June
1976   : July 1975 to June 1976
since 1977 : October to September.
From Landsat data users notes, no. 21 January 1982

The next generation of land resource satellites with improved performance will offer their users 'finer' resolution. So, Landsat 4 (USA) launched in 1982 carries a seven band radiometer with a ground resolution of 30 m, while the French satellite SPOT (Systeme pour l'observation de la terre)(= system for land observations) has two resolution levels, one of 10 m for the 500–900 nm panchromatic mode and the other of 20 m for the multispectral mode:

$$S \times 1 = 500-590 \text{ nm}$$
$$S \times 2 = 610-690 \text{ nm}$$
$$S \times 3 = 790-900 \text{ nm}$$

In addition, it is possible with SPOT to take stereoscopic views. The characteristics of the new sensors allow evaluation and mapping of pastoral resources with a precision which so far had been confined to certain aerial photographic coverage.

Conclusion

The combined use of the three observation methods allows one to obtain more or less detailed maps. Their scales should be chosen according to the objectives sought: local or regional development, continuous surveillance of the agro-sylvo-pastoral situation; i.e. all the operations which contribute to a more balanced management of renewable resources in the tropics.

Meanwhile one must not underestimate the cost of producing maps and this should dictate the choice of their presentation (low altitude aerial photographs, high altitude aerial photographs, satellite imagery).

Organisation of pastoral areas

General

The extensive exploitation of pastoral areas has been possible as long as livestock density, in close correlation with the human population, allowed each group to use its pastoral area on its own and, if transhumance was imposed by climatic conditions, the group returned each year to its own lands with the same resources to exploit.

The population explosion, brought about by medical progress and the improvement of political conditions, has involved an increase in the area of land used by farmers, as much for their own sustenance as for industrial markets such as cotton and groundnuts, with the result that there is a reduction in the amount of land available for graziers.

On their part, the graziers have increased their cattle, sheep and goat numbers and the intensification of exploitation of the natural biomass has reached such a critical level in a number of countries that the problem is all too obvious when the dry years hit the Sahel. What one sees in the arid or semi-humid zones is a reduction in the quality and quantity of available forage, due largely to overgrazing and the indiscriminate use of fires. Without trying to determine precisely whether 'the advance of the desert' is a reality, recent work by IEMVT researchers in Niger, Mali and Burkina Faso has given evidence of an often irreversible degradation of the grass cover, a reduction in the density of forage trees and bush species and, finally and the most serious, the disappearance of the best forage species from the zones to which the transhumance herds move during the dry season (Table 5.31).

In East Africa, the same causes have produced the same effects, intensified in certain countries by the politics of forced settlement and by agricultural development projects set up on the pasturelands without sufficient consideration of the needs of the graziers.

There is now a consensus of opinion on the causes of the degradation of the pastoral areas. Their production capacity is limited and the stocking rate must be adapted to this capacity. Management of the pasturelands must be improved.

The application of technical measures is not as simple as their formulation because one is confronted by social and political problems.

While rotation is easy when one considers land in which the grazing is enclosed and which is the property of one or a few stockmen, as is the case in the ranches of East Africa, Brazil, Colombia and Argentina, it is not the same

Table 5.31 Vegetation regression in a zone with a Sahelo-Soudanian climate
(Assale-Serbewel, Chad)

Original flora Predominant species	Intensive overgrazing Dominant species	Total erosion Dominant species
Woody		
Sclerocarya birrea	*Acacia senegal*	*Acacia seyal*
Anogeissus leiocarpa	*Balanites aegyptiaca*	*Balanites aegyptiaca*
Commiphora africana	*Ziziphus mauritiana*	*Ziziphus mauritiana*
Perennial grasses		
Hyperthelia dissoluta	*Boscia senegalensis*	
Annual grasses		
Aristida mutabolis	*Aristida mutabilis*	*Panicum laetum*
Schoenefeldia gracilis	*Chloris pilosa*	*Chloris pilosa*
Aristida funiculata	*Schoenefeldia gracilis*	

(After A. Gaston, D. Dulieu (1977) *Assale-Serbewel Project. Second agronomic study of pastures for the control of vegetation evolution.* IEMVT, Maison-Alfort, p. 59.)

when the pasturelands are freely exploited by human groups whose sole aim is profit maximisation from the grazing which they neither own nor have the responsibility. 'Good husbandry' is not a common concept to these people. The governments of the pastoral zones have not taken enough notice of these problems to date.

Of the technical solutions adapted to the ecological conditions which exist, there are few which have been applied other than in books: very often proposed solutions have been ignored by those to whom the message has been directed.

If one examines the directives of the foresters' code, it can be seen that they are imperative; and their non-compliance involves financial penalty or indeed severe and immediate punishment. The areas concerned are clearly defined and the property of the state: exploitation is controllable and the infringements as easily verified.

The facts are quite different in the field of animal husbandry. In the pastoral area it is exceptional for there to be appropriation of land even when 'ranch' type systems have been set up. The activities of the relevant authorities have not produced tangible results and they are now looking to define new socio-economic groupings in which the pastoral groups will exercise control adapted to local conditions, whereby the public authorities and technical services only intervene in an advisory capacity.

Social and political factors take priority over technical ones. More so than the herds, it is the herdsmen themselves who are the problem and the directives of a pastoral code will only have a chance of success if the human population has a hand in their creation and unanimously, continuously and manifestly observe them and do this of their own volition, assuming responsibility for their own communal management.

It is not necessary to hide the fact that the directives of a pastoral code will differ according to the political options as regards their choice of type of society, but pastoral reality will dictate actions whose aims will be identical.

Between the option of the centralised authoritative state, where the graziers and the members of the pastoral society are only the executors of the planned process defined by the administrators, and the liberal option of 'laisser faire', there is a place for solutions which encourage the graziers to organise themselves into collectives, for whom the choice of technical solutions will be sensible and responsible. The public authorities need to reserve a right of control and above all ensure education of the graziers on the job, the ultimate objective being to see the groups of graziers and their associates assume the organisational tasks of control and correct exploitation of their animal and forage resources.

Procedure for establishing a pastoral code

First, the public authorities should collect all the relevant information on ecology, demography and traditional rights, after having researched both into the written material and on the ground among the people affected. Traditional rights have become an amalgam of customary law and administrative law. The independence of states has certainly been accompanied by a setback in the racial cause for public and private legal rights, which have not always been honoured in practice.

The groups of people affected should, by necessity, participate in this collection of information and be largely informed of its objectives.

The contents of a pastoral code will necessarily vary from one area to another, but basically it must create the means of bringing together the interests of the people concerned so that they adhere to the rules, which ought to lead to an increase in their revenues.

It is necessary then that there are groups of people who are prepared to work together to control their communal resources. The term *pastoral communities* suggests this concept. One cannot, from the start, give an order as to the size or importance of these communities; it must remain at the level of the people and the members should aquaint themselves with and be able to assume, the responsibilities which they are accepting.

Thus the code relies on the existence of pastoral or agropastoral communities (the latter being where agriculture is associated with livestock rearing), which are constituted by voluntary grouping of villages and administrative areas which involve their whole populations. They are founded on the basis of traditional goodwill for the use of land and the exchange of services.

They tend to constitute community territories for which they hold responsibility and have for their objective: an intensification of livestock production, an improved integration with agriculture where both enterprises exist and, above all, conservation and if possible improvement of the production potential of the agricultural and grazing areas.

Contents of the pastoral code

The pastoral code will deal with:

1. the intrinsic nature of the pastoral communities;
2. the organisation of their territories;
3. the relationships between neighbouring communities and between communities and the public authorities;
4. technical measures relevant to the management of the grazing land and the herds.

The intrinsic nature of the communities will vary according to the region, but their oganisation will aim to instill the notion of common interest into the members of the community and to ensure their representation in neighbouring communities and in the public authority.

In this part of the code, directives relevant to the devolution of the rights of community members will necessarily figure and, in particular, the conditions of acceptance of new members. Another thing to be considered will be the children of members of the community wishing to create their own herds.

There will be interest in the fact that access clauses for migrants may be recognised by all the communities of a region even if they may be obliged to write a new pastoral agreement a generation later.

The organisation of new lands will certainly be the most delicate to agree upon because it is necessary to take into consideration what is possible in the new situations. The territory exploited by each community should be precisely defined in such a way that the members of the community, who hold the responsibility for the control of the land resources and shallow and deep water resources, aquire a new way of thinking with regard to future planning. On the other hand however, one cannot ignore the fact that some lands, such as the salty lands, natron wells, areas of commerce and transhumance and watering places, are traditionally exploited by graziers belonging to many of the 'new communities' and from whence comes recognition of 'inter-community territories' whose control is assumed by the interested communities according to the fixed rules of their agreement.

What should be considered separately are those areas or territories, for example nature reserves, which are not suited to redistribution or which are the subject of specific projects, for example irrigation schemes, water projects for industrial purposes and areas where mineral extraction is being carried out. The use of these *government lands* will be regulated solely by government authorities but with safeguard clauses for the communities who will exploit them after their devolution from the government and might be associated with their development and also may be able to profit from the new possibilities which the projects introduce.

The technical measures related to the management of the pasturelands will first of all ensure control of the herds by marking each animal. This operation is such that it will necessitate the most sensitive psychological preparation because there is general agreement on the relativity of the numbers from the census. The use of the animal in social relationships brings about situations where the keeper of the animal is not always the owner, even though he might milk it or use it for work.

In each community, an annual stocking plan will be established and grazing reserves will be set up so as to ensure regeneration of the pasture vegetation.

The possible activities in the field of pasture management are numerous and can be used in its care. These may include the use of fire, the creation of watering places, the reconnaissance of tracks, plans for medication, disease prevention and sanitation or the fight against parasites and the creation of quarantine areas etc.

Those things which might be absolutely correct for the management, for the organisation and for the pastoral communities never come without cost. Since the proposed activities ought to have an economic benefit, it is useful, from the start of the application of the pastoral code, for the communities to have access to a budget which they will manage themselves and which will be financed as follows:

1. by contributions from members of the community;
2. by grants provided from government budgets or from aid organisations;
3. by loans from national or international credit organisations.

If one shows the community management techniques for their territory, then one must also teach them correct financial management.

This side of things is certainly the one which will be the least well administered by the financial infrastructure because the controls often cost more than the economic benefits they are supposed to bring.

'Pastoral revolution' is possible if a political will motivates the government personnel, if a number of technicians have been trained and if, whatever they might have learned in theory, they know their subject and above all have the confidence of the stockmen.

Technical methods for the improvement of pasture management

The appropriate technical solutions to improve pasture management have the following objectives.

1. To adapt the stocking rate per hectare to the production possibilities of the natural pasture biomass.
2. To avoid overgrazing during the periods to which the vegetation is sensitive.
3. To avoid the destruction of tree and shrub species as much by excessive exploitation by the stockmen as by wood-cutting and bush-clearing for agriculture (Plate 5.11).

Some explanations would now be in order.

1. *Pasture rotation*: This is successive use of parcels of land which have been closed off to obtain regrowth of vegetation.
2. *Destruction of plants rejected by the grazing animals*: To avoid plants, which are unpalatable to livestock, over-running the grazing; their removal is mainly carried out by hand or by burning.
3. *Judicious associations of animal species*: This involves putting different animals on the pasture, whose feeding habits are not the same, in order to gain maximum exploitation of the biomass (cattle, sheep/cattle, goats).

Plate 5.10   Contracted steppe with *Aristida pungens*

Plate 5.11   Bush clearing with heavy machinery (Brazil)

Plate 5.12 Sub-soiling and root cutting with heavy machinery (Brazil)

The solutions differ according to rainfall. In the humid zones, improvement of management aims to use the forage at a young stage when their protein content and feeding value is highest and thus to regularise production over successive years.

In the humid zones, the limiting factor is available nitrogen content of the soil. The taking of young forage is followed by regrowth which takes out more nitrogen from the soil because the favourable water balance allows almost continuous recovery of the pasture. If there is no compensation for the nitrogen losses, there will be a decrease in productivity and it is because of this that grassland management has an interest in taking account of the nitrogen balance. If a savanna produces a maximum biomass, BM, containing n grams of crude protein per kilogram of plant material, and if one wishes to use the material at a stage where it contains four times more nitrogen, one cannot hope to take more than BM/4 without seriously affecting the savanna. Sowing nitrogen fixing legumes can be a solution.

In the dry zones, the same limitation exists but it is not so obvious and this is only in the overgrazed areas during the rainy season where the degraded quality of the grass cover is evident. Here the grass has become like standing straw or maybe completely consumed without being able to grow again in the next rainy season. Everything rests on the maintenance of a tree and shrub layer which is indispensible to the survival of the animal and whose destruction leads to the desertification which is now so widespread.

In conclusion, one can say that the improved management of pastureland has a limit which is imposed by the characteristics of the soil and climate. To require a basic increase in production per hectare of land supposes that one will compensate for the resource demands which accompany it and this must be understood to mean feeding the land, work etc.

Artificial pastures

Clearing

Under this label one frequently hears of pasture produced after sowing with perennial species on ground which has been prepared by clearing, sub-soiling or ploughed after the spreading of manure.

Up to now, even in the countries such as Brazil, Australia and the Caribbean, where livestock rearing is organised on the basis of maximum financial return, the areas treated in this way are negligible.

Of other types of artificial pasture to be taken into consideration are those which are established in the areas that have been cleared or where the shrub and tree flora has been heavily thinned. Complete clearing, as is practical in certain areas of Brazil, renders mechanical methods easier but when the animals are grazing, they suffer very badly from the sun. It is convenient to house them in shelters with roofs made of either straw, which has good insulating properties, or of aluminium sheets, which have the highest coefficient of reflection.

Clearing techniques are dependent on manpower resources. More elaborate techniques use heavy bulldozer equipment mounted on 100–200 h.p. caterpillar tractors weighing as much as 20 tonnes, which work in pairs and pull a heavy chain between them to rip out the bush. According to the density of the vegetation, the chain is pulled through the vegetation once or, more often, twice in opposite directions.

The task is completed by a subsoiler or a rooter (with a 2–4 m wide blade which cuts the roots to a depth of 40 cm to 1 m (Plate 5.12).

After the work on the soil, the trees are left in place or piled on the edges of the area being cleared. These are left to rot or are burned at a suitable time.

Clearing of land can be carried out by hand and with light tractors in areas where the density of the vegetation is not too heavy, in particular in zones with a tropical climate where the rainfall is between 500 and 1200 mm.

The latter methods allow selective clearing and the forage trees and bushes can be conserved. The equipment can be limited to knives, axes and forest winches.

The wood, which is stacked for burning, can be given to the people living in the vicinity of the clearing operations who will use it for firewood or often for building material.

Forage crops

Under this heading, it is necessary to include those crops for which the aim is to provide food for the animal and when harvested are given to the livestock fresh or after storage in a dry state or in the form of silage.

Plate 5.13 Soil enrichment by sowing *Stylosanthes* in a pasture of *Heteropogon contortus* (Madagascar)

Plate 5.14 Plantation of cactus interne (South Morocco)

Forage crops are generally part of the crop rotation and replace the fallow phase, but this is not obligatory.

The techniques for preparation of the soil do not differ initially from those described for establishing an artificial pasture, however the subsoiling must be complete and the levelling of the ground far better.

Plate 5.15   Harvesting straw with sickles

Species suitable for cultivation in the tropics

Names of forage plants

Whereas publications dealing with the botany of forage plants use the Latin name of the genus, of the species and often of the variety, it is not the same in those dealing with extension and development.

Also, it is exceptional for authors to point out the origin of the plants and their cultivars and this often leads to duplications.

Tables 5.32 and 5.33 give a list of the principal forage plants used in the tropics along with their Latin name, the name used most in the vernacular, in French, English, Spanish and for each species the area of origin.

The researchers from the Offices des Recherches Scientifiques et Techniques Outre-Mer (= Offices of Overseas Scientific and Technical Research), France (ORSTOM), using a collection of some 300 cultivars, have selected those which yield 170 tonnes of fresh material per hectare (or 38 tonnes of dry matter per hectare) under irrigation and 30 tonnes per hectare without irrigation.

Panicum maximum can only be propagated by cuttings but they have now obtained a polyploid variety which reproduces by seed and the yields under irrigation have reached 267 tonnes per hectare of fresh material.

Table 5.32 Names used for the principal tropical forage crops – Gramineae

Latin names	Local names	French names	English names	Spanish and Portuguese names	Origin
Andropogon gayanus Kunth	Ouaga (Bambara) Khat (Ouolof) Gamba (Hausa) Raniéré (Peul)	Andropogon	Gamba grass		Tropical Africa
Andropogon pseudapricus Stapf	N'Dianga (Ouolof) Jan barko (Hausa) Sénekô (Peul)				Africa
Brachiaria mutica (Forsk.) Stapf syn.: Panicum barbinode auct. non Trin.	Dugup (Ouolof) Shémé (Hausa) Talul, Talud (Peul)	Herbe de Para Herbe de Maurice	Para grass Mauritius grass Water grass		Zaïre preforest sector
Brachiaria ruziziensis Germ. et Evrard			Prostrate signal grass		Zaïre
Cenchrus ciliaris L. syn.: Pennisetum ciliare (L.) Link.	Ahitokotoko (Madagascar) Ahitranga (")		Buffel grass African Foxtail Grass Bloubuffelgrass Blue buffalo grass		Dry tropical parts of East Africa
Chloris gayana Kunth syn.: C. anyssinica A. Rich.		Herbe de Rhodes	Rhodes grass	Hierba de Rhodes (S) " (P) Capim Rhodes Grama Rhodes	East Africa Zaïre South Africa
Cynodon dactylon (L.) Pers.	Tsirkya'r zomo (Hausa) Lallamé kéina (Peul) Arampandrotra (Madagascar) Fandrotsan (Madagascar)	Chiendent Pied de poule	Bermuda grass Starr grass – Wire grass Dhub grass – Kweek	Bremura Grama (Cuba) Capim de burro (Portuguese) Braxil	Africa
Cynodon plectostachyus (K. Schum.) Pilger			Giant star grass	Pasto estella	from Ethiopia to Tanzania

Table 5.32 (continued)

Latin names	Local names	French names	English names	Spanish and Portuguese names	Origin
Digitaria pentzii Stent syn.: *D. decumbens* Stent *Digitaria 'umfolozi'*			Pangola (Pongola) grass	Pangola	South Africa Transvaal South Africa Natal
Echinochloa stagnina (Retz.) P. Beaeuv.	Garnarawal (Peul) Burgu (Hausa) Burgu abbahi (Peul) Singarivary (Madagascar)	Bourgou	Burgu		Africa
Hyparrhenia rufa (Nees) Stapf syn.: *Andropogon rufus* (Nees) Kunth	Yayali (Ouolof) Tayalé (Bambara) Tiélé (Peul) Sy (Madagascar)	Fausse avoine	Jaragua grass	Jaragua (Portuguese) (Brazil, Cuba. Mauritius)	Africa
Melinis minutiflora Pal.	Ahitsolika (Madagascar) Sandrahirika ")	Herbe à miel	Molasses grass	Capim gordura (Portuguese) Zacate gordura (Cuba)	Africa (guinean zone)
Panicum maximum Jacq. syn.: *P. jumentorum* Pers.; *P. giganteum* Mez	Fataque (Réunion, Maurice) Verotsanga. Fataka (Madagascar)	Herbe de Guinée	Guinea grass Buffalo grass Green panic	Capim sempre verde Coloniao (Portuguese) Brazil Herbia de Guinea	Tropical Africa
Paspalum scrobiculatum L.	Garganda (Ouolof) Mousso Komona (Bambara) Kananéghô (Bambara)		Ditch millet		
Pennisetum clandestinum Hochst. ex Chiov.		Kikuyu	Kikuyu grass	Capim Quicuio (Brazil) Kukullo (Cuba)	Central Africa (Uplands)
Pennisetum purpureum Schum. incl. cv. *P. merckeri, P. kisozi*		Herbe à éléphants	Elephant grass Mercker grass Napier grass	Hierba elefante o Hierba Napier	Kenya

Table 5.32 (continued)

Latin names	Local names	French names	English names	Spanish and Portuguese names	Origin
Rottboellia exaltata L.f.	Pellen (Ouolof), Sian chan (Bambara), Gasamma (Hausa), Naniérého (Peul), Fataque duvet (Réunion), Kalay (Ouest Madagascar)		Kelly grass		Africa
Setaria sphacelata (Schum.) Stapf et Hubb.	Diembou (Ouolof), Oulouni Kou (Bambara)		Golden Timothy grass, Foxtail grass		Africa
Sorghum sudanense (Piper) Stapf		Sorgho menu	Sudan grass	Sorgho dulce	Tropical Africa
var. *sudanense* var. *dulcis* Stapf		Sorgho sucré	Sweet Sudan grass		U.S.A.
Tripsacum laxum Nash		Herbe du Guatémala	Guatemala grass	Zacate de Guatemala (Cuba), Hierba de Guatemala	Central America, Mexico, Guatemala

Table 5.33 Names used for the principal forage crops – Leguminosae

Latin names	Local names	French names	English names	Spanish (S) and Portuguese (P) names	Origin
Cajanus cajan (L.) Huth syn.: *C. indicus* Spreng.	Dahl	Pois d'Angole, Ambrevade	Pigeon pea, Congo pea, Red gram	Cuandu (P)	Probably tropical Africa
Centrosema pubescens Benth.			Centro, Butterfly pea	Centro (SP), Cunha (P)	Tropical Africa
Clitoria sp.			Conchita grass	Conchita (SP), Pspelvia (P)	

Table 5.33 (continued)

Latin names	Local names	French names	English names	Spanish (S) and Portuguese (P) names	Origin
Desmodium intortum (Mill.) Urb.			Desmodium greenleaf		Central and Southern America
Glycine wightii (Wight et Arn.) Verdc. syn.: *G. javanica* auct.mult.non L.		Glycine de Java	Perennial soybean	Soja perene	East Africa
Glycine max (L.) Merrill syn.: *Dolichos soja* L. *Glycine soja* auct. mult. non Sieb. et Zucc.		Soja	Soybean; soyabean China soybean	Soja (P) Soya (SP)	Unknown in its natural state
Lablab purpureus (L.) Sweet syn.: *Dolichos lablab* L. *Lablab niger* Medic. *L. gulgaris* Savi	Antaka (Madagascar) Ossangue (Zaïre) Lablab (Middle-East)	Dolique d'Egypte Pois d'Egypte Dolichos	Egyptian kidney bean – Lablab bean Hyacinth bean Hyacinth Dolichos	Chimbole verde Dolicho lablab	Africa
Macroptilium lathyroides (L.) Urb. syn.: *Phaseolus lathyroides* L. *P. semierectur* L.			Phasey bean Field Bean	Feijao de rola	Tropical America
Macrotyloma uniflorum (Lam.) Verdc. syn.: *Dolichos biflorus* auct. mult. non L.		Haricot de kulthi	Horse gram		Indies var. uniflorum
Moghania faginea (Guill. et Perr.) O. Ktze syn.: *Flemingia faginea* (Guill. et Perr.) Bak.					West Africa
Pueraria lobata (Willd.) Ohwi syn.: *P. hirsuta* (Thumb.) Schneid. *P. triloba* sensu Makino non (L.) Makino	Kudzu		Tropical kudzu Kudzu		Asia

Table 5.33 (continued)

Latin names	Local names	French names	English names	Spanish (S) and Portuguese (P) names	Origin
Pueraria phaseoloides (Roxb.) Benth. syn.: P. javanica (Benth.) Benth.	Kudzu	Kudzu		Puero	Asia
Stizolobium atterimum Piper et Tracey syn.: Mucuna atterima		Haricot velouté	Velvet bean	Oja de venado (SP)	Brazil
Stylosanthes guianensis (Aubl.)Sw. syn.: Stylosanthes gracilis Kunth		Luzerne du Brésil Stylo Luzerne tropicale	Stylo	Vassourinha (P) Alfalfa do Nordeste (P)	Central and South America
Stylosanthes humilis Kunth syn.: S. sundaica Taubert (Mal.) S. mucronata sensu White, non Wild.			Townsville luceren Townsville stylo		Central America in a semi-natural form near the port of Townsville
Trifolium alexandrinum L.	Birsîm (arabic) Fahli Muscavi	Trèfle d'Alexandrie Bersim	Berseem clover Egyptian clover		probably in Palestine
Vigna unguiculata (L.) Walp. syn.: V. sinensis (L.) Hassk.; Dolichos biflorus (L.) non sensu auct. mult.	Niébé (West Africa) Loubia (arabic) Voamba (Malgasy)		Cowpea	Feijao de Corda	
Sub-family Mimosaceae Leucaena leucocophala (Lam.) de Wit syn.: Leucaena glauca Benth. non Mimosa glauca L.	Ipil-ipil	Tamarin bâtard	Leadtree White popinac Wild tamarind Horse tamarind		Tropical America

Table 5.34 Agronomic information – Gramineae

Species	Per/An	Soils Quality	pH	Mode of planting	Number of seeds per 100 g	Germination rate per cent	Mode of seeding or planting	Seeds (kg) or cuttings per hectare	Irrigated	Rain-fed	Trampling	Grazing	Drought	Humidity	Additional notes
Andropogon gayanus	Per	Deep / Water balanced		Se		30	Vol Li 50	17–20	+	+	+	+	+	+	
Andropogon pseudapricus	An	Sandy		Se		60–70				+	+	+	+	+	
Brachiaria mutica	Per	Sandy/clay organic / Water logged for several months a year		Cu Poq											
Brachiara ruziziensis	Per			Sto Cu		15–40		25–30			+	+	–	+	
Cenchrus ciliaris	Per	Sandy		Sto		85	Li 40	3 – 5		+		+	+	+	
Chloris gayana	Per	Deep organic well drained		Sto		50	Vol Li 50	8 – 9 / 5				+	–	+	Seed Age 1 year
Cynodon dactylon	Per	Deep damp			35 000					+			–	–	
Cynodon plectostachyus	Per	Deep organic		Cu Sto			100 × 100	10 000		+	+	+		–	
Digitaria pentzii	Per	Sandy / Sandy/clay		Cu Sto	–		–	–		+	+	+	+	+	
Digitaria 'umfolozi'	Per	Sandy clay deep organic		Cu	–		–	–			+	+	–	–	
Echinochloa stagnina	Per	Sandy clay clayey water-logged		Cu Sto	–		–	–	+	+	+	+	–	+	Regrows in the dry season on soils with a positive water balance
Hyparrhenia rufa	Per	Clay / Poor				50	Li Vol								
Melinis minutiflora	Per	Well drained		Se	15 000		Vol Li 50	3 – 5					+		

Table 5.34 (continued)

Species		Soils		Mode of planting	Number of seeds per 100 g	Germination rate per cent	Mode of seeding or planting	Seeds (kg) or cuttings per hectare	Type of culture		Resistance				Additional notes
		Quality	pH						Rain-fed	Irrigated	Humidity	Drought	Grazing	Trampling	
Panicum antidotale	Per	Deep		R	20 000	90	Po	+	+	+	+	+	−	−	
Panicum maximum	Per	All the organic types				60–80	50–150 Li 50	5–10	+	+		+	+	+	
Paspalum scrobiculatum	Per	Damp				90	Li				+	+	+	+	
Pennisetum clandestinum	Per	Deep damp well drained		Rh Sto	−	−	50 × 50	40 000			+	+	+	+	
Pennisetum purpureum		Deep organic well drained													
var. *merckeri*	Per	clayey sand		Cu	−	−	100 × 100	10 000	+	+		+			
var. *kisozi*	Per			Cu	−	−	100 × 100	10 000	+	+	+		+	+	
Rottboelia exaltata	Per	Deep damp organic well drained													
Setaria sphacelata	Per	Well drained damp		Se R		30	50 × 50	40 000			+		+	+	Regrows quickly in low lying land can be irrigated
Sorghum sudanense	A	Sandy sandy clay deep well drained													
Sorghum sudanense var. dulcis	A	Sandy sandy clay deep well drained		Se			Li								Subject to waste
Tripsacum laxum	Per	Deep rich damp		Cu			100 × 100	10 000			+				Very exhaustive of soil

Legend Rh: rhizome Sto: stolons Po: plant in lines
R: root division Li: in line with distance Vol: broadcast
Se: seed An: annual
Cu: cutting Per: perennial

Table 5.35 Agronomic information – Leguminosae

Species		Soils Quality	pH	Mode of planting	Number of seeds per 100 g	Germination rate per cent	Mode of seeding or planting	Seeds rate kg/ha	Type of culture Irrigated	Rain-fed	Resistance Humidity	Drought	Grazing	Trampling	Additional notes
Cajanus cajan	Per	poor			1700	80				+	+	+	+	+	Planted on all soils
Centrosema pubescens	Per	well drained		Gr	3500	Average	Li 0.50	3–5		+	+	+	+	+	Can be asociated with *Panicum maximum*
Clitoria sp.															
Desmodium intortum				Se				3							Planted at higher altitudes
Lablab purpureus	A BA			Se	300		Li 0.50	10–20							
Glycina wightii	Per				40										Cultivate with *Pueraria phaseoloides*
Glycina max	A				150							+			Enriches the soil in nitrogen
Macrotyloma uniflorum	A			Se		45	Li 0.30								Used above all for hedgerows
Moghania faginea = Flemingia faginea	Per					40–50					+		+	+	
Macroptilium lathyroides	Per	heavy		Se			Voul. 0.30	15–20	+	+	+	+	–	–	Irrigation in the Sahel 600 m³/day every 10 days
Pueraria phaseoloides					9 000	50									Soak the seeds before sowing – soil very clean

Table 5.35 (continued)

Species	Soils Quality	pH	Mode of planting	Number of seeds per 100 g	Germination rate per cent	Mode of seeding or planting	Seeds (kg) or cuttings per hectare	Type of culture Irrigated	Rain-fed	Resistance Humidity	Drought	Grazing	Trampling	Additional notes
Stizolobium aterrimum = *Mucuna aterima*				200	90					+	+	+	+	Cropping on all pure or mixed soils
Stylosanthes guianensis = *S. gracilis*			Se		65	Li 0.50	A.Per							Cropping on all natural pure and mixed soils, Cameroun Madagascar
Stylosanthes humilis														
Trifolium alexandrinum				2000			A			+				Seed 20–50 kg/ha
Vigna unquiculata var. *V. sinensis*					75					–	+	+		
Vigna unquiculata var. *Dolischos bilorus*					45						+	+	+	Crop possible
Mimosaceae *Leucaena leucocephala* = *L. glauca*				2500		P 0.50	Per							Shrub

Legend Se: seed
Gr: seeds
A: annual
BA: biennual
Per: perennial
Li: in line with distance
Voul: to sow broadcast
P: plant in lines

List of species suitable for cultivation (Tables 5.34 and 5.35)

The literature dealing with forage crops is abundant, but the number of species which have been the subject of extension work is very small and hardly more than thirty.

Furthermore, intensive research works on the biology, genetics and economics of tropical forage plants only cover about twenty species.

The most significant results concerning the economics of tropical animal husbandry are those obtained with *Stylosanthes* and *Panicum maximum*.

Stylosanthes guianensis is a legume of Brazilian origin which Germain imported into Zaire for the Institut National pour l'Etude Agronomique du Congo Belge (= National Institute for Agronomy Studies of the Belgian Congo) (INEAC) research station at Yangambi in the 1940s.

The stock initially transferred to Loudima near Brazzaville was then sent to Adamaoua in Cameroun, then to the Ivory Coast and thence to Mali and Madagascar. The work of Australian researchers on the different varieties of *Stylosanthes* and those begun many years ago by Centro Internacional de Agricultura Tropical (CIAT) in Colombia with cultivars from all over the world, are proof of the interest which this forage aroused and which some people call 'the tropical lucerne'.

Although in the whole domain of the Gramineae, some species, and many of African origin, might have been spread throughout the world (*Melinis minutiflora, Pennisetum purpureum, Digitaria* spp.) the most desirable species, as regards yield per hectare and the improvements which can be made, remains *Panicum maximum*.

In the light of results obtained in Brazil, some authors have recommended the use of cactus inermes (*Opuntia ficus indica* var. *inermis*) in the tropics as a complimentary food, but it is important to note that this species required particular ecological conditions. If the humidity of the air falls below 7 per cent for a period longer than 2 months, the growth stagnates. Furthermore, although they do not have large thorns, the wounding hairs of the sub-stomatic spaces cause haemorrhagic mucous enteritis in animals which consume large quantities of cactus.

Whereas in the temperate zones there are forage species exclusively for artificial meadows which are used for grazing and there are others exclusively for cutting, in the tropics the species are used for cutting as well as for grazing and that is the same for the large Andropogoneae and Paniceae which spread in prostrate tufts when they are subjected to intensive grazing.

Also, the same species are cultivated either in rainfed agriculture, under irrigation or used for the enrichment of the grazing.

Forage production and irrigation

Whichever month is considered, the mean temperature is always favourable to plant growth as was shown in Chapter 2. The low productivity of pastures is due to the low water resources in the soil and the level of evapotranspiration.

Recourse to irrigation for forage crops is tempting because all trials have shown that, using this technique, one can obtain considerable yields of the order of 267 tonnes per hectare of fresh material (i.e. 52 tonnes of dry matter) for *Panicum maximum* over several harvests.

The techniques are well tried and tested but the cost of the water is the limiting factor. They can only be used in farming systems where there is an assured market for the products at prices which give adequate financial returns, such as milk production in close proximity to large centres of population or the production of forage to carry over to the dry season in arid zones.

In the latter case, the cost can be reduced by using only 'free' irrigation waters in the rainy season which will ensure maximum yields during the normal period of plant growth.

In some favoured areas, there can be an interest in envisaging the irrigation of forage crops as a means of increasing the financial returns on large hydro-agricultural projects, these crops being cultivated in the areas where overspill waters can be spread or in areas where land levelling, essential for the irrigation of cotton, rice or sugar cane, would be too onerous.

Characteristics of tropical forage crops

The ecological classification of the species used is based on rainfall:

- arid type;
- sub-humid type;
- humid type;
- forest type.

Tables 5.36 and 5.37 give a summary of the agronomic and nutritional characteristics of grasses and legumes which are used. Their choice has been dictated by their widespread use or by the role they could play if they were better known.

Arid areas

Rain-fed crops

Practically no forage crop is known to be of any value without irrigation in the arid zones.

Table 5.36 Feed qualities – Graminae

Species		Suitable zones UNESCO				Habit	Uses									Yield in tonnes per hectare				Per kg forage		Additional notes
		Arid	Semi-arid	Sub-humid	Humid		Natural pasture	Artificial pasture	Forage crop	Green forage	Hay	Silage	Litter	Cover crop	Green manure	Fresh Rain-fed	Fresh Irrigated	DM Rain-fed	DM Irrigated	FU	DCP	
Andropogon gayanus	Per	+	+	++	+	erect 3/4 m	+	+	+	+	+	+	+			60	200	6–7	44	0.13	13	Excellent for cattle all year
Andropogon pseudapricus	Per			+	+	erect 3/4 m	+	+	+	+		+	+			15–18						Eaten at the beginning of the growth but then less.
Brachiaria mutica	Per		+	+	+	creeping	+	+	+									10–15				Humid zones and water logged meadows
Brachiaria ruziziensis	Per					erect 1 m		+	+	+								20				Six harvests per year
Cenchrus ciliaris	Per	+	+			tufts 1 m				+								3–7				Improvement of steppes
Chloris gayana	Per					Small tufts 1 m				+	+							4–8				One cut temporary meadow
Cynodon dactylon	Per		+	+	+	erect and spreading	+	+		+						5						Selected varieties
Cynodon plectostachyus	Per				+	spreading stoloniferous 1 m running to seed		+										7–15				
Digitaria pentzii	Per			+	+				+									10–20				
Digitaria umfolozi	Per			+	+	spreading stoloniferous 0.70–1 m																

Table 5.36 (continued)

A: annual; Per: perennial; FU: forage unit; DCP: digestible crude protein

Species		Suitable zones UNESCO (Arid / Semi-arid / Sub-humid / Humid)	Habit	Uses (Natural pasture / Artificial pasture / Forage crop / Green forage / Hay / Silage / Litter / Cover crop / Green manure)	Yield Fresh Rain-fed	Yield Fresh Irrigated	Yield DM Rain-fed	Yield DM Irrigated	FU per kg	DCP per kg	Additional notes
Echinochloa stagnina	Per	waterlogged areas									
Hypparhenia rufa	Per	Sub-humid +, Humid +		Natural +, Artificial +, Green forage +, Silage +, Litter +							Artificial pastures, South America
Melinis minutiflora	Per		tufts 1 m	Natural +, Artificial +	45–50		10–12				Odour reduces appeal to cattle and gives taint to butter
Panicum antidotale	Per	Sub-humid +, Humid +	erect spread	Forage crop +, Green forage +	12						Irrigated pasture
Panicum maximum	Per	Sub-humid ++, Humid ++	tufts 3 m	Natural +, Artificial +, Forage crop +, Green forage +, Silage +, Litter +			25	50	0.09	10	
Paspalum scrobiculatum	Per			Natural +	26						
Pennisetum clandestinum	Per		matted dense spread	Artificial +, Green forage +	6 –10						
Penniserum purpureum: var. merckeri	Per	Sub-humid ++, Humid +	large tufts 5 m	Artificial +, Forage crop +, Green forage +, Silage +, Litter +	70			40	0.10	20	Nine cuts
var. kisozi	Per	Sub-humid ++, Humid +	large tufts 5 m	Artificial +, Forage crop +, Green forage +							Drought resistant
Rottboellia exaltata	A	Sub-humid ++, Humid +	erect	Forage crop +, Green forage +, Hay +							Very good for horses and cattle
Setaria sphacelata	Per	Sub-humid +, Humid +	tufts spread 2 m	Natural +, Artificial +, Forage crop +, Green forage +	20						Rapid growth
Sorghum sudanense											
Sorghum sudanense var. dulcis											
Tripsacum laxum	Per			Forage crop +, Green forage +			15	30	0.19	16	

Table 5.37 Feed qualities – Leguminosae

Species		Suitable zones UNESCO Arid	Semi-arid	Sub-humid	Humid	Habit	Uses Natural pasture	Artificial pasture	Forage crop	Green forage	Hay	Silage	Litter	Green manure	Cover crop	Yield t/ha Fresh Rain-fed	Fresh Irrigated	DM Rain-fed	DM Irrigated	Palatability	Per kg forage FU	DCP	Additional notes
Cajanus cajan	Per	+	+	+	+	erect	+	+	+	+	+	+		+	+	20				VG	0.16	26	
Centrosema pubescens	Per	+	+	+	+	erect creeping	+	+	+	+				+	+					G			
Clitoria sp.																							
Desmodium intortum	A								+	+				+	+								
Lablab purpureus	A BA					spread creeping		+	+	+	+			+									Slight toxicity
Glycina wightii	Per					creeping			+	+				+	+								
Glycina maxima	A					spread creeping		+	+	+		+		+	+								
Macrotyloma uniflorum = Dolichos biflorus	A					spread	+	+	+	+	+			+	+			5 t		VG			
Moghania faginea	Per					erect		+							+					M			Mediocre forage hay
Macroptylium lathyroides	Per					erect		+											30 t 7 cuts		0.16	25	
Pueraria phaseoloides	A Per					spread creeping	+	+	+	+	+			+	+			6 t		VG			Necessary to introduce slowly
Stizolobium atterimum = Mucuna atterima																				VG			Beans can be used for feeding pigs
Stylosanthes guianensis = S. gracilis	A Per		+	++	++	erect spread	+	+	+	+	+			−	−			5 – 15		G			
Stylosanthes humilis																							
Trifolium alexandrinum	A					erect		+	+	+		+			+								
Vigna unguiculata syn. V. sinensis																				G			Unappetizing when green
Vigana unguiculata syn. V. dolichos biflorus															+					VG			Improves degraded pasture
Mimosaceae																							
Leucaena leucocephaa = L. glauca	Per					erect	+	+	+	+					+								

A: annual; Per: perennial; FU: forage unit; DCP: digestible crude protein; VG: very good; G: good; M: medium

The use of forage shrubs is only possible with high level political and social organisation for the strict application of a pastoral code fixing the conditions of exploitation.

In favoured sites where water is collected naturally, it is possible to grow the following legumes which need minimal cultivation and which endure temporary waterlogging of the soil:

- *Centrosema pubescens,*
- *Macrotyloma uniflorum,*
- *Lablab purpureus.*

Cenchrus ciliaris, Chloris gayana and other perennial grasses often quoted can only be cultivated for hay and the production per hectare in rain-fed agriculture is low.

Irrigated crops

In the arid zones of the tropics, only irrigation will enable usable production to be obtained economically and this irrigation may be from streams, lakes or permanent water supplies drawn from ground water sources.

Irrigation of swamp land, mostly stocked with *Echinochloa stagnina*, can yield from 17 to 40 tonnes of dry matter per hectare or 7–16 thousand forage units per annum per hectare.

In Chad it has been shown, on the polders, *Pennisetum purpureum* could give 39 tonnes of dry matter per hectare in nine cuts per year with an average of 40 days' growth and this amounts to about 100 kg/hectare per day of dry matter.

The interplanting of rows with *Macroptilium lathyroides* will provide a source of nitrogen.

It would not be proper to make general recommendations of these methods for all the arid zones, but in favoured areas where profitability is assured, they can be used.

Sub-humid areas

Rain-fed crops

The intensity of rainfall allows planting of perennial crops and use of the fallow by one forage break.

The most commonly used stoloniferous perennial grass species are:

- *Cynodon plectostachyus,*
- *Digitaria 'umfolozi',*

which can form windbreaks.

The replacement of the fallow by a several-year forage crop should fulfil certain conditions that the regeneration of the soil would normally require.

The forage plant is sown in between the rows after the stubble of the last crop of sorghum or maize has been ploughed in.

The cow pea (*Vigna unguiculata*), which produces a bean favoured for human consumption, provides a forage of high nutritive value as well as enriching the soil.

Some other grasses and legumes which are used to enrich the fallow are:

- *Andropogon gayanus*
- *Brachiaria ruziziensis*
- *Cenchrus ciliaris* } Gramineae
- *Chloris gayana*
- *Pennisetum purpureum*

- *Lablab purpureus*
- *Macrotyloma uniflorum*
- *Stylosanthes humilis* } Leguminosae
- *Stylosanthes guianensis*

For permanent forage crops:

- *Brachiaria ruziziensis*
- *Panicum maximum* } Gramineae
- *Pennisetum purpureum*

- *Pueraria phaseoloides* } Leguminosae
- *Stylosanthes guianensis*

Humid Guinean areas

The same species used in the Soudanian areas have more chance of success and to these can be added:

- *Digitaria pentzii*
- *Melinis minutiflora* } Gramineae
- *Setaria sphacelata*

- *Centrosema pubescens* } Leguminosae
- *Desmodium intortum*

In the humid zones, the legumes give yields of the order of 6–10 tonnes per hectare of dry matter.

In the forest zone of Brazil, after clearing with bulldozer and fire, *Panicum maximum* is planted at wide spacings. The large perennial grasses advisable with *P. maximum* are:

- *Pennisetum purpureum*
- *Setaria sphacelata.*

Other forage resources

Crops

Herbaceous forage is used almost exclusively by ruminants while the other domesticated animals, pigs, horses and poultry require feed of high energy value and high protein content. Peas, beans and other seeds can provide these requirements on their own.

Furthermore, certain species used by man can also be used by livestock and thus Table 5.38 gives a list of feeds which is by no means exhaustive.

Table 5.38 Characteristics of some crops used for animal feed

Animal feed crops		Human food	Cattle	Pigs	Horses	Poultry	Yield t/ha	
English name	Latin name						Extensive cropping	Intensive cropping
Grains								
Maize	Zea mays	+		+		+	0.5–0.8	1 – 2
Bullrush millet (Small millet)	Pennisetum typhoides	+			+	+	0.3–0.7	1.5–2.0
Rice	Oryza sativa	+				+	0.7–0.8	1.3–3.0
Soyabean	Glycina max	+		+		+	0.3–0.5	1 –1.5
Sorghum (Large millet)	Sorghum bicolor	+		+	+	+	0.3–1.2	2.0–3.0
Fruits								
Banana	Musa sapientum	+	+	+			15–25	22–38
Mango	Mangifera indica	+		+			5–10	15–20
Papaya	Carica papaya			+			0.5– 1	1.5–2.5
Roots and tubers								
Yams	Dioscorea spp.	+		+				
Cassava	Manihot esculenta	+	+	+				
Sweet potato	Ipomoea batatas	+		+			6–10	20–50
Potato	Solanum tuberosum	+		+			5 –11	20–25
Cocoyam	Colocasia esculenta	+		+			8 –15	25–35

In a development project, it is necessary to take account of the Man/animal competition which can occur for the quantities produced or at the level of cost of animal products in expensive primary products.

Forage reserves

Hay and straw (Plates 5.15 to 5.19)

Harvesting of hay should only be considered when it is possible to feed it on site or very close to the harvesting site.

In fact, taking into account the humidity of the atmosphere at the time when harvesting is optimum (grasses at the start of flowering), in reality it is generally straw which is harvested at the beginning of the dry season.

Plate 5.16   Ox-drawn mowing machine (Madagascar)

Plate 5.17   Swath rake (Madagascar)

Mechanisation of grass cutting and baling is only economic when the hay is fed to improved herds at the height of production (milk).

Although implements for working animals are difficult to come by, mowers and hay rakes pulled by bulls are very robust and economical.

Silage

Grass conserved in a closed environment without air undergoes fermentation which makes it more digestible and permits conservation in a year when the moisture content is 70 per cent. Distributed in the dry season, it gives a rich and easily eaten ration.

Plate 5.18   Average density hay baler

Plate 5.19   Hay stack of pressed bales in the guinean zone (Ivory Coast)

All the Gramineae, including sorghum and maize, can be ensiled as they are harvested or better still, after chopping.

The only precaution to take consists of rolling the grass before closing off the silo. In silage pits (Plate 5.22), the covering is made with earth separated from the silage by a plastic cover.

The cracks which appear in the covering of earth should be filled immediately to avoid entry of air into the silo. Exclusion of air is necessary to ensure that anaerobic fermentation by bacteria producing lactic acid and butyric acid takes place. If excess butryic acid (smelling of rancid fat) is present, this renders the silage unpalatable and gives a bad odour to the milk.

Plate 5.20 Soil preparation with disc harrows pulled by Jersey–N'Dama cross bulls

Plate 5.21 Forage harvester

Plate 5.22   Silage pit (in the process of being filled)

Plate 5.23   Silage clamp

In modern systems, in the Guinean zone where maize and sorghum forage crops can be produced with significant yields, the silage can be harvested with tractor-drawn (Plate 5.21) or static choppers.

Chopping improves the quality of silage and reduces the amount of waste.

Agro-industrial by-products

Agro-industrial by-products used in animal feeds come from two sources: the first by-products, direct from the making of legume hay or the straw of Gramineae, are consumed on site or near the production site and the second

Plate 5.24   Tree felling by goat herdsmen forming an umbrella

come from treatment of the harvest. One can see that the by-products from food manufacture and grain milling, (for example the bran of rice and sorghum) and the by-products of industrial processes, have become the object of an important international trade.

Among the latter can be found cattle cake from the extraction of oilseeds, groundnuts, cotton, sesame and copra, molasses from the treatment of sugarcane, brewer's grains and left-overs from the brewing and fruit juice industries, bran and middlings from flour mills, germ and flour from the polishing processes in rice mills and finally meat meal and blood from abattoirs.

Generally, the use of all these by-products poses no problems but hazards are known.

Aspergillus flavus, associated with mouldy groundnuts and cotton seed, is a fungus which produces aflatoxins known to be toxic to animals. Aspergillosis of Man and animals, is caused by the inhalation of *Aspergillus* spores commonly present in damp hay and straw. The fungus grows within the animal's tissues developing chronic infections of the lungs and other body organs, (see also page 238).

Bovine spongiform encephalopathy (BSE) a progressive neurological disease of cattle, was first recognised in 1986 in the UK. Although unconfirmed to date, it is suggested that the causal agent for BSE may be transmitted via meat and bone meal of animal origin used as protein supplement in concentrate feedstuff. Likewise *Salmonella* spp. could be transmitted via poultry waste that is used in animal feed.

The only problems arising are concerned with availability except for those which come from the preparation of human food (the bran of rice, sorghum etc.) and from mills which are operating beyond the level of the village community. Almost all the by-products cited are the object of a significant international trade and governments export them in order to obtain foreign exchange.

For the most part, the flow of exports go from the developing countries, particularly tropical ones, to the developed countries where the improved animal husbandry and commercial conditions value concentrated feeds more, even though the price of the latter is inflated by the cost of transport.

In 1987, the tropical countries exported 676 000 tonnes of groundnut cake, or 95 per cent of world exports (712 000 tonnes).

The corresponding figures for cotton cake are 293 000 tonnes and 34 per cent and for oil palm cake are 998 000 tonnes and 97 per cent.

Considering all the developing countries are not only the tropical ones, the exportations in 1987, for all kinds of oilseed cakes were about 20 576 000 tonnes or 57 per cent of the world trade.

Such figures are quite eloquent; they show that the problem of the use of concentrates in the tropics is more a political one than a technical one – that is to say should they export the concentrate foods or use them in the local livestock industry?

6

Animal production and disease

In studies of the health of herds reared in the tropics, it is rare to find a herd in which all the animals are not subject to some form of viral or bacterial infection or parasitic infestation.

This situation has three main causes – the number of diseases that are endemic in the tropics, livestock rearing methods and periodic shortages of water or feed.

In addition to the diseases of the temperate zones there are also those which have disappeared from the rest of the world because of adequate prophylactic measures (rinderpest, pleuropneumonia) and those which are specifically tropical (trypanosomiasis, certain piroplasmoses).

The conditions in which herds are reared, stock movements over considerable distances and mating between different herds near watering places are all factors favouring disease transmission.

The periods of drought and famine reveal the syndrome of malnutrition and render the animals less resistant to other debilitating conditions of the environment so that, for example, parasitic diseases are more deadly in the tropics than elsewhere.

Principal diseases of livestock, in the tropics are listed in Tables 6.1, 6.2 and 6.3.

Aetiology of diseases

Determining causes

Causes of disease are:

1. either the development within the organism of pathogenic agents: viruses, bacteria, protozoa, fungi, parasites;
2. or the effect of intrinsic factors: malnutrition, poisoning, climatic or intrinsic stress, body malfunction and genetic abnormalities etc.

Table 6.1 Principal diseases of livestock in the tropics

Disease	Affected species	Symptoms	Prognosis	Prophylaxis
Sheep pox	sheep	high fever – eruption of papula – development of pus – scab formation – sometimes dead skin	death due mostly to secondary infections of the order 15–20 per cent	vaccine
Lumpy skin disease	cattle	irregular fever – appearance of nodules of dead skin	serious illness – few deaths	vaccine
Foot-and-mouth disease	cattle, pigs	lesions in the mouth, on the tongue, on edge of the hoof, on teats – salivation	serious economic damage – loss of milk	vaccine
Blue tongue	sheep	serious form: intense fever congestion buccal lesions coughing mild form: similar lesions	serious form: death 2–4 days mild form: gradual recovery	action against vectors: mosquito
Teschen disease	pigs	initial high fever then syndrome of increasing paralysis	very serious for improved breeds, often less for indigenous pigs	vaccine
Cattle plague (rinderpest)	cattle	very high fever – weeping mucous congestion – erosion of buccal mucous membranes – diarrhoea	death in a few days (4–8) – mortality rate very severe in the young over 3 months	vaccine
African horse-sickness	horses	high fever at the plateau – oedema of the lung and subcutaneous tissues	declining to death in several days in non-vaccinated horses	vaccine + action against mosquito
African swine fever	pigs	high fever – prostration – dyspnoea – enteritis – signs of skin haemorrhage	very acute – death often in 90–100 per cent of cases	no vaccine
Hog cholera	pigs	high fever – prostration – large clinical polymorphism (bleeding lesions, ataxia, reproduction problems)	septicaemic forms always fatal – chronic infections with carrier status	vaccine
Rabies	dogs, cattle, wild carnivores, man	widespread progressive paralysis – change of posture paralysis of the larynx	death is the rule in dogs 15 days after appearance of the first symptoms	vaccination of dogs slaughter of stray dogs

Table 6.2 Principal bacterial diseases of livestock in the tropics

Diseases	Causative agent	Species affected	Symptoms	Prognosis	Prophylaxis
Botulism	Clostridium botulinum	cattle, sheep, horses pigs	pica by hypophosphorus toxicity: eventual paralyis, wasting of flesh	rapid death or slow death over 2–7 days – chronic form, decline	distribute phosphate supplement in high risk areas
Brucellosis	Brucella abortus, B. melitensis B. suis	cattle sheep and goats pigs	abortion, non-delivery, still-births, chronic metritis, sterility – serum diagnosis or ring test on the milk	loss of young stock, serious economically, tendency towards chronic herd sickness	slaughter or vaccine according to degree of infection in the herd
Bacterial anthrax	Bacillus anthracis	cattle, sheep, goats, wild ungulates	high fever, widespread congestion, dark red mucus	death is usual	vaccine
Black-quarter	Clostridium chauvaei	cattle, sheep	bursting gaseous tumours in upper parts of the limbs, widespread congestion, purple-blue mucus	death in 95 per cent of cases	vaccine
Bovine pleuropneumonia	Mycoplasma mycoides	cattle	fever, cough, frothing of mucous saliva, wasting of flesh	deaths higher than 50 per cent, long convalescent period, chronic carriers are dangerous	vaccine

Table 6.2 (continued)

Diseases	Causative agent	Species affected	Symptoms	Prognosis	Prophylaxis
Caprine pleuropneumonia	*Mycoplasma agalactiae*	goats, sheep	high fever, widespread signs of oedema, weeping, frothing of mucous saliva	death in 60 to 90 per cent of cases	experimental vaccine
Haemorrhagic septicemia	*Pasteurella multicida*	cattle, sheep, camels, goats, pigs	high fever, widespread signs of oedema, dyspnoea	death inescapable in the septicaemic forms (almost 90 per cent of cases)	vaccine
Dermatophilosis	*Dermatophilus congolensis*	cattle, sheep, goats	skin lesions with hair loss at first on the hind quarters and back	loss of hide, sometimes obliged to slaughter sick animals	no effective vaccine
Tuberculosis	*Mycobacterium tuberculosis*	cattle, pigs	chronic illness, damage in all the organs: lung, intestine, udder, uterus, with corresponding injury of the lymph glands	death exceptional but losses due to rejection in the abattoir by the authorities	slaughter of animals with a positive reaction to the tuberculine test

Table 6.3 Principal protozoan and rickettsial disease of livestock in the tropics

Diseases	Causative agent	Species affected	Symptoms	Prognosis	Prophylaxis
Heartwater	Rickettsia (Cowdria) ruminantium	cattle, sheep, goats	intense fever – paralysis – pericarditis	rapid death	action against bont ticks
Babesiosis piroplasmosis	Babesia spp.	ruminants, pigs, horses, dogs	attack of fever – jaundice – haemoglobin-urinitis (discoloured urine) – sometimes nervousness	death; if attacks mild recurrence, establishment of immunity in recovered animals	action against ticks; chemical prevention
Theileriosis (East coast fever)	Theileria spp.	ruminants	attack of fever – widespread adenitis	mortality 20–80 per cent according to breed; immunity in recovered animals	action against ticks
Anaplasmosis	Anaplasma spp.	ruminants	fever – mild jaundice – lingering anaemia – leading to chronic debility	lingering death, immunity in recovered animals	action against ticks and insects
Trypanosomiasis	Trypanosoma spp.	cattle, horses, pigs, dogs	fever – wasting of flesh – chronic debility	zebus very sensitive, some African humpless breeds are tolerant to trypanosomiasis	use tolerant breeds

Contributory factors

Contributory factors take account of the reactions of the animal, as an individual, *vis-à-vis* the pathogenic agents.

Reactions differ from one individual to another and depend upon the animals' own genetic characteristics, physiological state, medical history and current living conditions.

In order to maintain animals in good health, there are two types of measure to take: either to protect the animals from the action of the pathogenic agents or to render the animals resistant to them. The former are hygienic and sanitary prophylactic measures and the latter medical prophylactic measures, and all measures complement each other.

Elaboration and understanding of the rules of hygiene and prophylaxis require a knowledge of pathogenic agents, of the nature of their processes and also of the optimal conditions for keeping healthy animals, considered separately from the adverse climatic, viral, bacteriological factors or parasitic factors.

Pathogenic agents

The pathogenic agents are classified as viruses, bacteria, protozoa, fungi and parasites. This classification takes greater account of the size of the organisms than of their biological properties.

Viruses

Viruses are the most elementary living form. They are extremely small, having dimensions varying from 20 nm to 300 nm and are only visible with an electron microscope. They cross the finest of filters. They can only be grown on live cultures (cell cultures, fertile eggs, small living animals). Their pathogenic action is due to their multiplication in the organism and to the disorders that they bring to the metabolism of their host by their own metabolism.

Bacteria

Bacteria are single celled living beings, visible by light microscopy, with dimensions from 2 μm to 10 μm. They do not have nuclear membranes, they reproduce by division and their forms are very variable – a property which serves in their classification:

spheres .... *Streptococcus, Staphylococcos*
straight rods .... *Bacillus*
curved rods .... *Vibrio* spp.
spiral flexible rods .... spirochetes

Bacteria can be cultured on synthetic media containing chemical compounds necessary for their metabolism: sugars, amino acids etc. Isolation and identification is effected using *selective media* on which only some species of bacteria will thrive, and *identification media* which show specific reactions (fermentation of different sugars, production of indole etc.).

Pathological problems caused by bacteria occur:

1. in infections caused by multiplication of bacteria within the organism (anthrax, swine erysipelas);
2. in cases of poisoning by toxic substances (toxins) secreted by the bacteria which may be only small in number (tetanus, botulism);
3. in toxic infections caused by the multiplication of bacteria *and* the production of toxins (*Salmonella*).

Fungi

Pathogenic fungi, sometimes classed with parasites, cause external damage when they develop in the coat and on the skin (ringworm). They can, by their presence, cause injury of the organs (pulmonary aspergillosis) and finally they can induce damage of the organs by their toxins (hepatic injuries by the aflatoxins of *Aspergillus flavus*).

Parasites

Parasites occupy a prominent place in tropical pathology, as much because of the number of species involved as for the diversity of illnesses they cause.

Perhaps parasites should be defined as: *all living things which, during all or part of their lives, live at the expense of another being, called the host, causing it some damage but not necessarily destroying it.*

Parasitism is a way of life which concerns very different living species: insects, mites, ticks, helminths, fungi, protozoa.

To classify them as a function of their habitat in the host is a convenient method, but bears no relation to the biological peculiarities that help establish the rules of hygiene and prophylaxis which are used in disease control and prevention.

There are *obligatory parasites* which can only live at the expense of other individuals, *facultative parasites* which can lead a free life or a parasitic one, and there are *accidental parasites* which are introduced into the host almost by error.

Generally, parasites have privileged habitats within their hosts: intestine, liver, muscle etc., and some, known as *specific parasites*, develop only within certain species: horse bot fly in the stomach of a horse, strongyles in sheep, while others, known as *ubiquitous parasites*, live off many species: ticks *Amblyomma variegatum* and *Ixodes ricinus*.

There are parasites which remain permanently with the host: *permanent parasites (Ascaris, Sarcoptes)*; others which only stay for the time necessary for feeding (biting insects), *intermittent parasites* and finally *temporary parasites* which, in the course of their life, must live successively and obligatorily in different hosts so that their life cycle can be completed.

All parasites have a spoiling action of which the consequences on the host and the clinical manifestations of the infestation depend on the locality in the organism, on the mode of life and on the number of parasites:

1. enteritis and general signs of malnutrition in helminth infestation of the digestive tract;
2. jaundice and enteritis in helminth infestation of the liver;
3. acute bronchitis in helminth infestation of cattle by *Dictyocaulus* species;
4. anaemia and development of cachexia when trypanosomes live in the blood;
5. haematuria when eggs laid by *Schistosoma* species cross the small veins of the bladder;
6. rhinitis when the larvae of *Oestrus* species develop in the sinus of sheep.

The reactions of the host can determine the damage and serve as a diagnosis on the living animal or on the carcasses, for example, parasitic cysts of *Trichinella* under the tongue of pigs, larvae of tapeworms in the muscles of cattle (*Taenia saginata* in man), in the muscles of pigs (*Taenia solium*) and of fish (*Botryocephale* spp.).

Intermittent external parasites can be vectors of bacteria or parasites which they carry or inoculate at the infective stage.

Transmission of diseases

General

Knowledge of the methods of transmission of pathologic agents is indispensable when devising effective methods of control.

As there is no spontaneous generation, transmission of pathogenic micro-organisms is from animal to animal, and in zoonoses (diseases common to both man and animals) from animal to man and vice versa.

The effect of micro-organisms varies during the course of the illness and it is useful to distinguish:

1. the *sick*, who manifest the symptoms of the illness;
2. the *convalescents*, who no longer show the pathological symptoms;
3. the *symptomless carriers*, who excrete pathogenic agents without showing clinical signs of the disease:

- infected but in the incubation phase;
- recovered patients who continue to harbour pathogenic agents;
- chronically sick with the disease where the clinical symptoms only show themselves later (tuberculosis);
- healthy animals (healthy carriers) in which the pathogenic agents cause no obvious symptom of infection, but which pass on the agents which they harbour (*Salmonella*);

4. and finally, the *corpses* of dead animals with the infectious disease are sources of contagion, man or animals becoming contaminated by contact with the corpse or by eating its meat (carnivores).

When the pathogenic micro-organism has the capacity to form endospores, corpses are the origin of soil infection (e.g. anthrax).

Pathogenic agents are excreted:

1. by the *digestive route*: they are passed in the faeces and this is the normal route in the diseases where diarrhoea is a major symptom: rinderpest, coccidiosis, Johne's enteritis;
2. by the *respiratory route*: pathogenic agents are expelled when the patient coughs; this is the usual route in the diseases which cause pulmonary damage: bovine pleuropneumonia, tuberculosis;
3. by the *urinary route*: agents of renal infections (coliform bacteria) and viruses in the septicaemic phase of the disease, are expelled with the urine;
4. by the *genital route*: microbes are present in lesions of the urinogenital system and are passed on in the secretions and exudates. The same is true with the afterbirth, the amniotic liquid and even the fetus at the time of parturition. The sperm itself can be contaminated (brucellosis);
5. by the *cutaneous route*: superficial lesions of the skin and mucous membranes are routes of contagion in the poxes (cow-pox, sheep-pox), foot-and-mouth disease, rinderpest, and in the diseases which are specifically skin complaints: ringworm, scabies etc.;
6. by the *oral route*: the saliva is infectious in viral diseases; the spittle of rabid dogs can transmit the disease by simple licking;
7. by the *tears*: viruses in the septicaemic phase can be passed out in the tears (rinderpest, African horse-sickness).

There are cases where contamination of the environment is accidental as when bleeding takes place or when post-mortems of animals result in septicaemic infections (anthrax, pasteurellosis, swine erysipelas).

The natural environment is less favourable to the life of pathogenic micro-organisms; some are destroyed by desiccation and by sunlight, whereas others remain in 'suspended animation' by desiccation or form endospores which protect them from the surrounding environmental conditions. For parasites, the mechanisms adopted to ensure continuation of the species are more complex and call upon intermediate hosts.

Routes of infection

There are many infection routes.

The undamaged *skin*, except for the diseases of the hide and skin, is an obstacle to the penetration of pathogenic micro-organisms, but it is not always an obstacle to parasites which pass actively through the skin (some worms, insect larvae etc.)

If the skin has breaks due to wounds, scratches or even therapeutic actions (bleeding, blood samples), then protection ceases. Thus the bite of a rabid dog is the source of viral infection.

Infection by the *respiratory route* has been demonstrated for tuberculosis, bovine pleuropneumonia, chronic respiratory disease and pullorum of poultry. This is due to the presence of pathogenic micro-organisms in suspension in the air. Pneumonia, due to inhalation of dust from the skins of dead animals which suffered from anthrax, is a recognised hazard among workers at leather markets and tanneries.

Digestive infection is the most frequent. Micro-organisms swallowed with contaminated food infect the organism, either by way of abrasions and lesions in the upper diestive tracts, or by developing in the mucous membranes, or by actively crossing these membranes (helminth larvae).

Genital infection (venereal diseases) are transmitted at the time of mating.

Mechanisms of contagion

Transmission from sick animal to healthy animal is made by contact, but more generally in an indirect way via the surrounding environment: the air, water, cleaning materials, food contaminated with pathogenic agents excreted by sick animals.

One should note the 'diseases of the syringe' due to the use of badly sterilised syringes and needles (abscesses at the point of injection, viral diseases etc.).

Ambient air is contaminated with micro-organisms that can attach themselves to dust particles and/or water droplets which are then inhaled by the healthy animal, as in the case of pneumonia. When animals are confined in very large numbers in one location, the density of micro-organisms increases in these conditions such that certain, normally unimportant, species can, by their number, cause serious problems.

The soil can be the site of a disease reservoir as is the case in illnesses due to soil borne bacteria which form endospores and remain viable in the soil for up to 20 years and more. These spores can be brought up to the surface by earthworms (*Bacillus anthracis* bacterial anthrax, *Clostridium chauvaei* black-quarter, *Clostridium tetani* tetanus).

The soil, and particularly its moisture content, plays an important role in the mechanisms of parasitic diffusion and infestation.

Drinking water can be the vector of viral, bacterial and parasitic diseases. For those caused by viruses and bacteria, the water is in fact only a vehicle, but the contamination can originate, especially in open water, as much from wild animals as from domestic ones. The stockmen are well aware of this fact and they prefer to use their own equipment (buckets, rope, troughs) for watering their herd in small numbers.

In the transmission of parasitic diseases the water, or more so the wet mud around the drinking troughs, has an active role because it allows development, up to the infective stage, of the eggs of parasites expelled in the faeces and urine of parasitised animals which come to drink.

Finally, the animals can be the vectors of the diseases either because they infect the pathogenic agent by means of the blood which the agent takes from the animal (trypanosomiasis by tsetse fly and horse flies, piroplasmosis by ticks), or because they transport infections over very long distances. Birds are vectors of the foot-and-mouth virus, insects transmit togaviruses, and flies are vectors of bacterial anthrax.

Transmission of parasites

The study of the method of transmission of parasites is inseparable from that of their biology because specific mechanisms exist to ensure their survival and diffusion.

The method of reproduction plays an important role here. In the most simple case, the male and female parasites mate to ensure perpetuation of the species (Figure 6.1). The eggs develop in the host or are expelled into the natural environment and reinfest the same species. The infective stage can be the non-embryonic egg, the egg at a more or less advanced stage or even the free embryo.

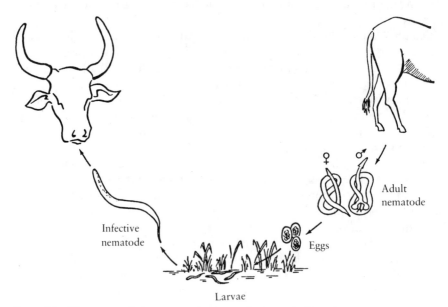

Figure 6.1 Direct transmission: nematode worms, for example *Oxyuris*

Finally, for a number of parasites, the cycle includes successive stages in which the anatomical and physiological structures of the parasite are very different; the eggs hatch to release an embryo or larva which, after one or many metamorphoses, reaches the mature state.

The ultimate host harbours the parasite in its mature state. At the intermediate stages, the embryo or larva can parasitise the same host, but this is the exception and more generally it parasitises a host of a different species from the ultimate host.

Suppression of an intermediate host can be a good method of control (Figure 6.2, Table 6.4).

Multiplication can occur by asexual means; this is called parthenogenesis. This method of reproduction can occur at any stage in the life of the parasite and is found as much in metazoans as in protozoans. When the infecting unit reproduces itself in an intermediate host, action against this host is a good means of avoiding its multiplication of the infecting units.

Main groups of parasites and parasitic diseases

External parasites

By their presence, these parasites cause characteristic cutaneous lesions: pruritus and scab in scabies caused by mites which bore galleries in the skin, pruritus and filth in pediculosis, where the lice live on the surface of the skin, hair loss, with or without scabs in ringworm (*Tinea* sp.) which develops in the coat and epidermis.

Larvae hatched from the eggs deposited on the skin or the hair by insects can perforate the skin and develop in the subcutaneous conjunctive tissues such as *Cordylobia* larvae of the tumbu fly, or burrow deep into the muscles and they can penetrate into the natural cavities (sheep nostril fly, *Oestrus ovis*, in the sinus of sheep).

Other blood-sucking insects and ticks draw blood by puncturing the skin (horse flies, *Simulium* sp., tsetse flies, ticks). If they are numerous, repitition of the punctures can lead to anaemia. It has been estimated that the animals which live in the flood zone of the central delta of the river Niger during the rainy season could lose up to 150–300 g of blood per night, as much by the punctures themselves as by the small haemorrhages which follow.

Blood-sucking insects and ticks either transmit agents of viral, microbial, or parasitic diseases into their hosts either by effecting a mechanical transmission of infection (e.g. flies transmit anthrax after feeding on the corpse of an animal which has died of anthrax and mosquitoes transmit African horse-sickness after feeding on a sick horse) or, as intermediate hosts, they participate in the conservation and multiplication of the diseases (e.g. ticks act as vectors for piroplasmosis, tsetse flies act as vectors of trypanosomiasis) (Figures 6.3 and 6.4).

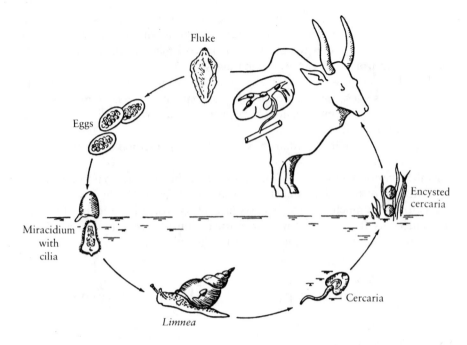

Figure 6.2 Life cycle of the liver fluke showing the intermediate host, snails

Table 6.4 Life cycle of the liver fluke (*Fasciola*)

Phase	Environment	Stage of development	Location	Transmission
1	cattle sheep	mature	liver ducts	fluke lay eggs
2	external environment	eggs	faeces	embryonic eggs
		embryo with cilia (miracidium)	water, mud	free infective phase for the gastropod
3	*Limnea* (snail)	embryo with cilia	pulmonary cavity of the snail	transformation of embryo sporocyte
			hepato-pancreas of the snail	asexual sporocyte reproduction
		free cercaria	hepato-pancreas	leaves by bursting into external environment
4	external environment	cercaria	water and mud	attaches to grass and changes to parasitic cyst
5	grass	encysted metacercaria	on grass	passive wait until eaten by sensitive host
6	cattle sheep	cercaria	migration from digestive tract to liver	young fluke emerges from cyst and cycle starts again

Control: break the cycle by parasite treatment in phase 1; decontaminate the environment in phase 3 by drainage of pastures; apply moluscicides in phase 3 (also introduce ducks).

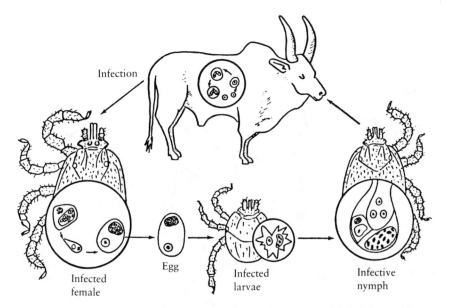

Figure 6.3 Life cycle of *Babesia bigemina* in cattle (piroplasmosis) and *Boophilus*, a tick

Table 6.5 Life cycle of the protozoa *Babesia*

Phase	Host	Stage of development	Location	Additional notes
1	cattle	infective spores merozoites	red blood cells	schizonts develop and reproduce by schizogamy in the red blood cells which they destroy
2	adult female tick *Boophilus*	gametes zygotes vermicule sporoblasts	digestive system haemocoel ovary	
3	*Boophilus* egg	blastocyst		
4	infected larvae of *Boophilus*	sporoblasts vermicule	various tissues haemocoel	
5	infective nymph *Boophilus*	sporogonia sporozoites	salivary glands salivary ducts	
6	cattle	trophozoites	blood	

Control: destroy ticks on the cattle by antiparasitic dipping at phase 1 and between phases 5 and 6.

Internal parasites

Parasitic infestations are due to the development and also very often the multiplication of living organisms which have exclusive or certainly privileged use of well defined parts of the host organisms as their habitat.

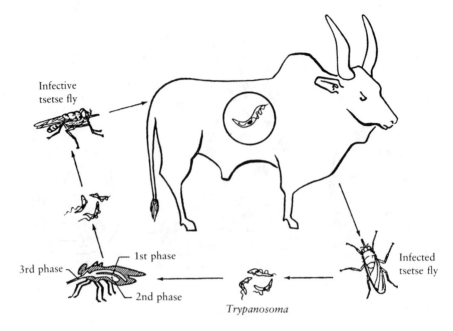

Figure 6.4 Life cycle of *Trypanosoma* of cattle (trypanosomiasis)

Table 6.6 Life cycle of the protozoa *Trypanosoma*

Host	Stage of development	Location	Duration of development
cattle	trypanosomes	blood	
tsetse fly			
1st phase	trypomastigotes	middle intestine	
2nd phase	epimastigotes	proboscis	7–53 days
3rd phase	infective metatrypanosomes	fixed in hypopharynx then labium	
cattle	infective metatrypanosomes	subcutaneous inoculation by tsetse fly	

Parasites of the blood and circulatory system

Haematozoa (blood parasites), of microscopic size, live in the blood and effectively parasitise the blood cells (e.g. *Plasmodium* of malaria) or live freely in the blood plasma and the lymph (*Trypanosoma*). The development of these parasites is very complex. With the exception of dourine, of which the agent *Trypanosoma equiperdum* is transmitted from stallion to mare or vice versa at the time of mating, transmission of haematozoa from sick animal to healthy animal occurs necessarily via an invertebrate intermediate host, and sometimes via a warm blooded intermediate host (Figure 6.5) and Tables 6.4, 6.5, 6.6 and 6.7).

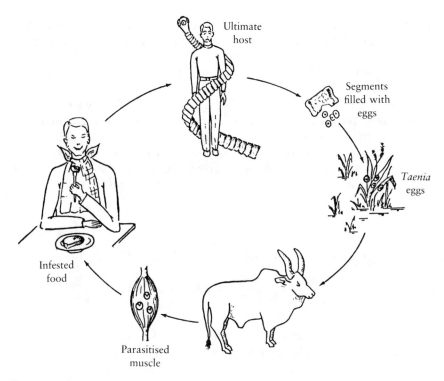

Figure 6.5 Life cycle of *Taenia saginata* (beef tapeworm)

Table 6.7 Life cycle of *Taenia saginata*

Host	Stage of development	Location	Transmission
man	mature phase	intestine	the worm develops – segments filled with eggs expelled with faeces
moist external environment	eggs begin to develop larval stage with six hooks	mud and grass soiled with human excreta	egg transformed, its wall is thickened, it becomes infective to cattle
cattle	development up to cyst stage infective to man or degeneration	cysts in the muscles	larvae issued from the eggs migrate through the body of the animal, cysts formed in tongue, body wall, oesophagus and pterygoidian muscles, cardic psoas = pillars of diaphragm
man	first the larva then the worm	intestine	infestation of man by cysts consumed in the meat

Control: *for humans*: eat pieces of meat which are not too thick and eat well cooked or boiled; freeze meat thoroughly and hang all meat to be eaten raw for several days; *for livestock*: the cycle will be broken if the animal can eat herbage not contaminated with human defaecation. Practise collective hygiene in villages.

Haematozoa cause serious progressive anaemia, with wasting of flesh, which can end in death by general debility and more rarely in a death with an acute phase.

Parasitic helminths also live in the blood:

1. Schistosomes (also known as bilharzia worms), whose larvae penetrate the host via the skin, cause anaemia and haematuria when the eggs, laid by the female in the small vessels of the bladder, move through its wall;
2. Filarial worms which, as well as anaemia, can cause very serious damage in specific organs by establishing themselves in them e.g. blindness in onchocerciasis (river blindness) transmitted by biting insects.

Parasites of the organs and tissues

Parasites of the digestive system and associated glands are:

1. either *helminths*:
   - trematodes: flat worms without segments (fluke) (*Fasciola*),
   - cestodes: segmented flat worms (*Taenia*),
   - nematodes: smooth round worms (*Ascaris, Filaria, Strongyloides* species);
2. or *larval forms*:
3. or *sporozoans*:
   - unicellular parasites, intracellular parasites (coccidiosis).

The symptoms which they bring about depend on their biology. The worms which live in the digestive reservoirs and intestine (*Ascaris, Taenia*) act as predators and their toxins also affect the host. Nematode worms which attach themselves to the intestinal villi cause haemorrhaging and anaemia. Coccidia which destroy the intestinal cells reduce food absorption and occasionally cause haemorrhagic enteritis and then anaemia.

Certain worms encyst in the intestines and cause necrotic abscesses which can involve perforations and peritonitis.

Flukes, which mainly parasitise ruminants, live in a mature state in the liver ducts and infestation is via the digestive route when the animal absorbs infective encysted larvae which are attached, in a free stage, to grasses in the humid zones (Figure 6.2).

If these larvae are very numerous, they can cause acute hepatitis with jaundice in the course of their migration to the liver ducts.

When they develop in the lumen of the ducts and gall bladder, which are their normal habitat, they cause inflammation of the walls which, as a secondary effect, leads to a thickening and cirrhosis of the neighbouring hepatic tissue.

The infested animal shows signs of serious anaemia; emaciation, loss of colour in the tooth gum mucous membrane and oedema between the branches of the lower jawbone.

Coccidia, unicellular organisms which develop in the liver of the rabbit, cause lethal abscesses there. In cattle and poultry, they parasitise the intestinal epithelial cells and cause serious haemorrhagic enteritis.

Method of reproduction of parasites in the digestive tract

Expulsion of parasite eggs with the faeces via the digestive tract assures their dispersion.

Transmission is made either directly to another definitive host by the eggs, which are or are not embryonic (*Ascaris, Oxyuris* Figure 6.1), or by encysted or free infective larvae which originate from the intermediate host (Figure 6.2). The larvae, hatched from the eggs expelled by the major host after a free phase, infect an intermediate host, they multiply there, then after a new phase they reach a stage which is infective to the major host (Figure 6.2).

Parasites of the muscles and body cavities

For these parasites, domestic animals are only intermediate hosts, the major host being another mammal (man, dog, pig).

The infective stage for the major host is a cyst lodged in the muscle or fixed on the peritoneum or the pleura and they originate from eggs taken in with the food (cysts of *Taenia saginata* in the muscles of beef cattle). If the cyst is consumed by a major host with the meat, it develops there (*Taenia saginata* in man) and the eggs expelled with the faeces complete the cycle (Figure 6.5 and Table 6.7).

The animal carriers of the parasitic cysts show practically no symptoms of illness even though, by their number, they cause functional troubles.

Parasites of the respiratory tract

The most numerous are the nematodes which cause serious infective bronchitis, particularly in the young, because of the small diameter of the bronchi and because of the pulmonary damage which follows their inflammation.

Transmission is via the digestive tract, the eggs being swallowed after having been coughed up from the lungs (Figure 6.1). The eggs are expelled with the faeces, other animals become infected by eating the soiled forage, the larvae pass actively from the intestine into the circulatory system and finally achieve their migration to the lungs.

Methods of controlling disease

For an animal to remain in good health it is necessary to either avoid becoming infested or infected or, if this is impossible, it must enable itself effectively to resist the infestation or infection.

In the first case, one applied sanitary measures and in the second one applies medical measures. The choice between the intervention methods is based on the contagiousness of the diseases.

Epidemic diseases reach a very large number of animals in a relatively short space of time and their geographic spread can extend throughout continents. Endemic diseases are those regularly found in restricted areas.

Diseases that are simply infectious and do not have a tendency to spread are due to accidental contamination and so a wound can lead to a localised infection with formation of an abscess or lead to septicaemia and death of the animal without invoking 'contagion'.

However, if in a livestock enterprise the population of a pathologic agent is concentrated, the risks of disease are correspondingly increased. Thus in over-stocked piggeries and poultry houses, if the rules of hygiene are not respected, one can observe the results quite clearly.

The rules of sanitation are a matter of common sense and can be applied by the stockman himself. All new animals introduced into the herd should be subjected to a health inspection and the necessary isolation in a quarantine area so that the symptoms of disease can be observed in the course of their development or the appearance of the symptoms can be watched for if there is a period of incubation.

Contagious diseases ignore frontiers and so administrative controls or even coercive measures, which can only be applied by governmental authorities, are necessary. They form what are conveniently known as 'statutory health regulations'.

The epizootics which were widespread after the First World War encouraged governments to create, by international agreement, the International Office of Epizootic Diseases (OIE) on 25 January 1924 and the headquarters were set up in Paris. They set themselves the objective of helping member states to institute statutory health regulations to be recognised world-wide and to communicate to the governments rapid information on the appearance of epizootic and enzootic diseases.

OIE has established lists of diseases known legally as contagious and which should be notified.

The ethical authority of OIE is reinforced by publication of the International Animal Health Code which indicates the statutory health regulations to be respected as much in the member states' own territories as in cases of commercial exchanges of live animals, meat, animal products and sperm etc.

This authority is sometimes considered excessive but is necessary and will facilitate international exchange and avoid non-tariff clauses which could be an obstacle to commercial exchanges.

Table 6.8 Lists of legally contagious diseases recognised by the International Office of Epizootic Diseases (OIE)

LIST A

Foot-and-mouth disease
Vesicular stomatitis
Swine vesicular disease
Rinderpest
Peste des petits ruminants
Contagious bovine pleuropneumonia
Lumpy skin disease
Rift Valley fever

Bluetongue
Sheep pox and goat pox
African horse sickness
Hog cholera
Teschen disease
Fowl plague
Newcastle disease
Vellogenic virus

LIST B

Multiple species diseases
  Anthrax
  Aujeszky's disease
  Echinococcosis/Hydatidosis
  Heartwater
  Lepospirosis
  Q fever
  Rabies
  Paratuberculosis

Cattle diseases
  Anaplasmosis
  Babesiosis
  Bovine brucellosis (*B. abortus*).
  Bovine genital campylobacteriosis
  Bovine tuberculosis (*Mycobacterium bovis*)
  Cysticercosis (*C. bovis*)
  Dermatophilosis
  Enzootic bovine leucosis
  Haemorrhagic septicaemia
  Infectious bovine rhinotracheitis
  Theileriasis
  Trichomoniasis
  Typanosomiasis
  Bovine malignant catarrh

Sheep and goat diseases
  Brucella ovis infection
  Capine and ovine brucellosis (*B. melitensis*)
  Capine arthritis/encephalitis
  Contageous agalactia
  Contagious caprine pleuropneumonia
  Enzootic abortion of ewes
  Pulmonary adenomatosis
  Nairobi sheep disease
  Salmonellosis (*S. arbortus ovis*)
  Scrapie
  Maedi-Visna

Horse diseases
  Contagious equine metritis
  Dourine
  Epizootic lymphangitis
  Equine encephalomyelitis

Equine infectious anaemia
Equine influenza (Virus type A)
Equine piroplasmosis (Babesiosis)
Equine rhinopneumonitis
Glanders
Horse pox
Infectious arteritis of horses
Japanese encephalitis
Mange
Salmonellosis (*S. abortus equi*)
Surra (*Trypanosoma evans*)
Venezuelan equine encephalomyelitis

Pig diseases
  Atrophic rhinitis
  Cysticercosis (*Cysticerus cellulosae*)
  Porcine brucellosis (*B. suis*)
  Transmissible gastronenteritis of pigs
  Trichinellosis

Poultry diseases
  Avian infectious bronchitis
  Avian infectious laryngotracheitis
  Avian tuberculosis
  Duck hepatitis
  Duck virus enteritis
  Fowl cholera
  Fowl pox
  Fowl typhoid (*S. gallarum*)
  Infectious bursal disease (Gumboro disease)
  Marek's disease
  Mycoplasmosis (*M. gallisepticum*)
  Psittacosis and Ornithosis
  Pullorum disease (*S. pullorum*)

Rodent disease
  Myxomatosis
  Tularaemia

Table 6.8 (continued)

Fish diseases Viral haemorrhagic septicaemia Infectious pancreatic necrosis Myxoblosis (Myxosomiasis) Spring viraemia of carp Infectious haematopoietic necrosis Herpesvirosis of salmonids Yersiniosis Renibacteriosis Pseudomonosis Pike fry rhabdovirosis Herpesvirosis of ictalurids Branchionephritis	**Bee diseases** Acariasis of bees American foul brood European foul brood Nosemosis of bees Varroasis **Diseases of other animal species** Leishmaniasis

LIST C

Multiple species diseases
  Listeriosis
  Toxoplasmosis
  Melioidosis
  Blackleg
  Botulism
  Other clostridial infections
  Other pasteurelloses
  Actinomycosis
  Intestinal *Salmonella* infections
  Coccidiosis
  Distomatosis (liver fluke)
  Filariasis

Cattle diseases
  Mucosal disease/Bovine virus diarrhoea
  Vibrionic dysentery
  Warble infestation

Sheep and goat diseases
  Contagious pustular dermatitis
  Foot-rot
  Contagious ophthalmia
  Enterotoxaemia
  Caseous lymphadentis

Horse diseases
  Equine coital exanthema
  Ulcerative lymphangitis
  Strangles

Pig diseases
  Swine erysipelas

Poultry diseases
  Infectious coryza
  Avian encephalomyelitis
  Avian spirochaetosis
  Avian salmonellosis (excluding Fowl typhoid
    and Pullorum disease)
  Avian leucosis

Dog and cat diseases
  Canine distemper

Fish diseases
  Infectious dropsy of carps
  Furunculosis of salmonids

List A diseases – Definition: Communicable diseases which have the potential for very serious and rapid spread, irrespective of national borders, which are of serios socio-economic or public health consequence and which are of major importance in the international trade of livestock products. Reports are submitted to the OIE as often as necessary to comply with Articles 1.2.0.2 and 1.2.0.3 of the International Zoo-Sanitary Code.

List B diseases – Definition: Communicable diseases which are considered to be of socio–economic and/or public health importance within countries and which are significant in the international trade of livestock products. Reports are normally submitted once a year, although more frequent reporting may in some cases be necessary to comply with Articles 1.2.0.2 and 1.2.0.3.

List C diseases – Definition: Communicable diseases with important economic influence at individual production level.

General rules of hygiene and prophylaxis

So that a livestock enterprise might maximise its output, it is necessary that the animals should be in good health. What will be the point of genetic improvement if the animals are at the mercy of any disease whatsoever?

The measures to be taken fall into two classes: one tends to protect the animal from the action of pathogenic agents and the other has the objective of rendering the animals able to resist them. The first are hygienic (sanitary) prophylactic measures and the second are medical prophylactic measures and they complement each other.

Elaboration and understanding of the hygiene and prophylactic rules require a knowledge of the pathogenic agents, of the nature of their mechanisms and of their actions and also the optimum conditions for the upkeep of animals in good health, considered apart from climatic, viral, bacterial or parasitic factors that influence the animal.

The guidelines for animal husbandry (feeding, drinking, housing) are the starting point to ensure a satisfactory rate of reproduction and normal growth of healthy stock which will produce acceptable economic yields.

Feeding and drinking hygiene

Feeding of young stock

If young animals are well nourished, their later growth will be improved. This was seen in an experiment in which the genetic potential was manifested in young Gobra Zebus maintained on a Sahelian pasture and which were allowed to consume concentrate feed ad lib. In 2 years these reached 490 kg for males, 388 kg for females. These weights were 230 kg and 168 kg more respectively than those of a group of animals of the same breed which only had access to natural pasture and which only weighed 260 and 220 kg at the same age (Table 6.9).

Table 6.9 Weight of Gobra Zebus at different ages and different levels of nutrition (kg)

Age (months)	Males Level of nutrition High	Low	Females Level of nutrition High	Low	Differences in weight Males	Females
birth	21	25	23	24	−4	−1
1	33	39	36	36	−6	0
2	45	49	48	45	−4	+3
3	64	62	64	58	+2	+6
6	126	96	119	88	+30	+31
12	249	144	217	129	+105	+88
18	381	197	318	174	+184	+144
24	490	260	388	220	+230	+168

All the observations and experiments in the tropics have shown that feeding of calves poses no problems if they can suck milk from their mother: 400–800 kg per lactation in 210 days for cows maintained permanently on natural pasture, this being a lower production than that of cows of improved breeds but sufficient however for the requirements of the calf up to weaning at 80–100 kg.

But milk-drinking stockmen live as 'predators' and make demands along with calves. For one family alone, of 15 persons (one man, three women, five girls, six boys), about 20 litres of milk each day are required.

The amount of milk taken from each milking cow is less when there are a number of cows or when each cow produces more. The technique of drawing milk is fortunately favourable to calves. In the worst situations calves have access to the udder all the time because Zebu cows only allow themselves to be milked if their calf has initiated the process of milk let-down. If they disappear, then it is almost impossible to continue with the milking. The calf always drains the udder which takes the cow out of circulation until the next milking.

Tying young calves with a rope near the encampment (Plate 6.1), will not be prejudicial to their health if they receive a suitable feed supplement. Sometimes bran, from the preparation of meals, mixed with buttermilk is distributed to them but this is not sufficient. More often hunger forces them to eat absolutely anything. This unsatisfactory situation is the origin of terrible mortality among the young calves during their first year of life: from 20–35 per cent, or even 45 per cent in some regions. Obstruction of the abomasum by sand, diarrhoea and septicaemia engendered by micro-organisms normally present in a saprophytic situation, are the most frequent causes of morbidity and mortality.

The solution to the problem seems to be a gamble. However, by virtue of

Plate 6.1   Calves tied with rope

Plate 6.2   Development of a horn-like appendage following a traditional type of vaccination

Plate 6.3   Cattle dip

the adage 'money makes money', lowering of calf mortality happens with an improvement in the wealth of the stockman, either because he increases the number of milking cows or because he increases their production by better feeding. The proportion of the milk yield required for his subsistence will fall and the calves will have more milk at their disposal. The stockman might harvest or buy food for the calves and their mothers as means of providing improved rations.

The first solution is limited by the area of exploitable grazing and the capacity of the family to water and guard the herd. The second assumes that the family of the stockman possesses or has the use of an agricultural area where he cultivates forage crops as well as crops for home consumption. This is only possible in a semi-sedentary livestock rearing situation or better if there is a distribution network and a less onerous means of transport which allows carrying of indispensable food supplements to the dispersed herds.

If the cows with calf at foot are better fed, production will increase and the milk needed for the family will be relatively less significant.

In a trial lasting 3 months carried out on a herd of 80 milking cows, we have shown that, in distributing to N'Dama cows maintained permanently on a Sudanian pasture, food in sufficient quantity to avoid weight loss in the dry season, the mean monthly production of the herd of cows in lactation was from 421 to 491 kg. When the food was distributed all year round, production reached 830–840 kg.

Application of such a rationing plan assumes carrying 2.5–5 tonnes of food for a herd of 25 milking cows.

When distribution of supplementary food is not possible and if numbers are sufficient to allow half of the milk production to be given to the calf, a good technique is to let the calf drain the udder in the evening then take all the milk from the morning's milking, which stops the calf from being hungry while it is tied up and helps to stop the calf from eating non-foods such as earth.

Another technique, which requires very close herding, consists of forming a herd of young calves and leading them into areas where they can benefit from a certain amount of shade and can collect nuts etc. off trees and the straw of harvests.

For the other species of ruminants (sheep and goats), the problems are identical to those encountered by cattle with, however, a favourable difference; lambs are rarely suckled and in the humid zones goats only suckle in exceptional circumstances. As goats are very prolific it is not unusual for them to rear two, three or even four kids.

For animals raised indoors, errors in feeding are the most frequent cause of illness and mortality. There is a microbial and viral pathology of industrial livestock rearing, but there are also effective means of fighting these. Feeding factors are the determinants as soon as the herd numbers are above 100 calves, 50 pigs, 100 hens or rabbits. The logistic problems of raw materials supply become fundamental. Each supply stoppage of any of the elements of the ration has an effect on the economic yield of the rearing process and generally restricts its development.

Feeding standards were discussed in Chapter 5 – correct feeding is the way to success.

Drinking hygiene

The importance of water in the heat regulatory mechanisms has been noted (see Chapter 2). Lack of water is prejudicial to milk production, it leads to problems of intestinal movements, the faeces harden and are expelled covered in a blanched mucus sometimes containing traces of blood which can be signs of enteritis.

Animals on extensive pasture may only visit watering places every two days, travelling some 10 km to do so. This results in animals being in poor condition because the extra energy required for travelling is not provided by the available but inadequate forage.

The watering places, because of the quagmires and shallow pools which form around them, are favourable environments for the appearance of infective forms of parasites which come directly from eggs dropped with the faeces from the major or intermediate hosts. It is important, therefore, to avoid contamination of such places. Individual drinking prevents pollution of the water by excreta.

Spreading of molluscicides around drinking places breaks the major host/intermediate host cycle of liver flukes.

Transhumance and the temporary abandonment of pools due to drying out also breaks the parasite cycle.

When it is possible, laying down of more stone on the approaches to the pools and around the drinking troughs is an effective means of control.

Hygiene of rangelands and pastures

The first objective is to avoid their infestation or infection by parasites, other pathogenic agents and vectors of disease.

On open rangelands where the herds have unrestricted movement, protection is very difficult, however the very fact of a reduction in the number of watering points in the dry season is a natural means of sanitation, the dryness reducing the levels of intermediate hosts and even the encystment of eggs.

For bacterial diseases, sanitation can only concern enclosed pastures. Unfortunately there are soil-borne diseases whose agents can persist in the soil for very long periods in a state of suspended animation as endospores. Increase of the risks of infection can be avoided but sterilisation is almost impossible. It is necessary to have recourse to medical prophylaxis, which means the infested areas must be carefully identified.

This is particularly the case with anthrax, black-quarter, *Pasteurella* and Johne's disease.

For closed pastures in which animal movements can be very rigorously controlled, pollution can be avoided by subjecting newly introduced animals to a quarantine period during which they are given anti-parasite and prophylactic treatment.

If pastures become infested, their improvement by applications of fertiliser and ferrous sulphate are excellent means of sanitary prophylaxis, but the best protection consists particularly of eliminating stagnant water and avoiding quagmires around drinking places.

In humid regions, it is better to avoid bush land which is favourable to the swarming of insects and ticks.

Clearing of tree areas is an efficient means of controlling tsetse fly in rangelands which are infested (agronomic prophylaxis). It is better not to use live trees for field enclosure except where the branches can be regularly trimmed because, when they develop, they provide excellent shelter and routes for the movement of the tsetse fly, as do the trees planted along the sides of roads.

When toxic plants are found in pastures it is best to destroy them quickly. This would be done with *Harungana madagascariensis* and *Datura* spp. which can invade pastures.

Hygiene of livestock buildings

Since housing subjects the animals to the unfavourable factors of the artificial environment: heat, humidity, predators etc., it must not happen that the artificial environment created introduces insupportable constraints from the building's own characteristics or from its use.

Design of buildings

Exact knowledge of the variations in climatic characteristics should allow the design of appropriate buildings.

Protection against the sun, the force of wind and rain should not however lead to the design of 'fortified' buildings.

It is necessary to take account of the fact that cold months and cold nights can occur in the tropics.

Thus in pig and poultry rearing, good ventilation with protection against the direct sun is desirable in the warm season. During the cool season the same building should conversely protect against the wind and movable panels of palm leaf or straw-matting can be used to achieve this very economically.

The roof cover will be made of material with good reflective properties (corrugated iron or aluminium carriers) or with good insulation properties (thatch, weather-boarding).

All materials may be used. Wood should be treated with antifungal products and insecticides such as xylophene, tar, anthracene, copper sulphate etc.

When stone or breeze-blocks are used, it is important to make provision for well smoothed surfaces to avoid a build up of parasites: ticks, lice, fleas.

Floors should be impermeable and have sufficient slope for good drainage.

Use of buildings

Whatever the type of building or livestock housed might be, their cleanliness will assure success. Excrement should be removed regularly and any uneaten food should not be left in the mangers.

Disinfection with recommended antimicrobial chemicals and spraying with residual insecticides, carried out regularly, are indispensable methods in avoiding the build-up of commonplace micro-organisms or a few pathogens which can become dangerous because of their concentration (likely in piggeries).

Besides, when bedding is not regularly lifted, the ammonia concentration of the air increases and this leads to irritation of the mucous membranes of the primary respiratory tracts and of the conjunctiva which are factors favouring the appearance of serious infections.

Several guidelines on the construction and use of buildings according to species of animal are mentioned in Chapter 3.

Animal behaviour and hygiene

Domesticated animals generally have a gregarious (or herd) instinct and some breeds have this to a lesser degree. Thus Bororo Zebus graze pastures in herds while N'Dama bullocks more easily separate from each other and can live freely isolated from the others as happens in Guinea. The rules of herding should take account of these differences.

Among the animals which live in herds in extensive husbandry, rules of hierarchy are established between the animals. For example, when leaving the encampment or corral, it is always the same animals which take up the lead. It is useful to know which animals these are in order to direct them and lead the herd in the required direction should the need arise. The apprenticeship of young Peul herders begins by calling the lead animals which are generally bulls or old cows.

In an enclosed pasture in which the vegetation is not homogeneous (savanna, tree steppe), the animals always follow the same tracks to the drinking points. In order to rest, they always assemble in the same areas, but these are different for the day and the night. Usage of forage is therefore irregular, the material left tends to become overgrown and so it would have to be destroyed in order to encourage the animals to use the whole pasture.

Furthermore, cattle do not consume grass which has been soiled by their excrement and it is therefore necessary in enclosed pastures to spread the dung so that the rainfall and drying out processes will make it disappear into the soil.

Pigs raised on pasture behave very similarly to cattle as regards their areas of activity. As in the housed situation, they drop their excreta in a particular place separate from where they lie. Thus their housing should be of a sufficient size so that there is no mixing of the two areas.

In all livestock rearing systems, whether they be carried out in enclosed pastures with or without shelter or in housed accommodation, it is categorically imperative that each animal has free access to concentrate and forage and has sufficient living space. Not only design and construction of buildings and enclosures should be considered. It is necessary that herds or groups of animals are composed of animals of the same age, or at least of similar size, otherwise the weaker ones will be denied access to feeding troughs and their poor growth will be further retarded. Malnourished, they will be a source of contagious pathological problems.

It is necessary to avoid over-stocking which causes the animals to be aggressive because of their need to defend their territory and access to food. In addition to these inconveniences, the increased risk of transmission of normally commonplace and parasitic diseases, let alone contagious diseases, arises.

Finally, it is common for stockmen to dislike the practice of *culling*. When several animals in a herd or group of animals, although of the same age as the others, show sickly appearance and poor growth, they should be removed, primarily for health reasons but also for economic reasons. These stock do not economically convert the food they consume.

The latter rule should be strictly applied in poultry houses and piggeries.

Disease prevention measures

Tropical veterinary medicine, while it does not differ from that in other regions as regards technical means, differs in its methods of intervention and looks more towards prevention than cure. Prophylactic measures take the place of therapeutic ones.

Practical measures of sanitary prophylaxis

Practical sanitary prophylactic measures aim first of all to protect healthy herds. Each animal, before being introduced into the herd, should be subjected to a health inspection and isolation in quarantine.

If a sick animal is detected in a herd, it should be isolated and the herd, considered to be infected, should be isolated as well and kept in the area where it was when the disease was diagnosed. For certain diseases, this quarantine is accompanied by medical prophylaxis, a search for infected animals by immunological and serological methods and eventual vaccination of the healthy animals. For other diseases, statutory health regulations require slaughter of sick and contaminated animals.

Slaughter is an effective method of eradication when the disease is known to have only fatal consequences, when it attacks only a small number of stock in a limited area and when a new disease appears in a country.

Some countries systematically apply slaughter policies for both sick and contaminated animals e.g. foot-and-mouth disease in Great Britain and rinderpest in Europe.

The areas where the infected animals stay are equally considered to be infected and it is indispensable to apply surveillance measures or even to prevent stock movements both in and out of the area.

The carcasses of dead animals should be cremated or buried in the ground after having been covered with a sterlising agent (quicklime for example) in a place from which water sources will not become contaminated.

The locations where the sick animals and infected herds have stayed should be disinfected and this will sometimes include the pastures.

Administrative measures

Besides the practical measures there are administrative measures, which are directed by governments and which the staff of the veterinary departments have the responsibility of enforcing, with the aid of the police authorities if needs be.

The contagious diseases such as defined in the OIE Lists are generally considered as *legally contagious* and those in List A always are so.

When a case appears, the owner, the veterinary surgeon or any person who notices the disease are required to report it to the veterinary administrative authorities or the police.

According to the regulations the authorities invoke:

1. an *infection order*, which declares the limits of the infected area, defines the prophylactic and regulatory measures to be taken, indicates the authorities and departments which are charged with the responsibility and also the penalties to be incurred by those who contravene or obstruct their application;
2. an *infection lifting order*, which will annul the health regulation measures when the disease has not recurred in the infected area for a certain number of days or months.

Certain prophylactic measures included in the infection order can consist of the application of medical prophylactic measures (vaccination, see below).

Other methods of sanitary prophylaxis are applied to the vectors, in particular to the external parasites (ticks, horse flies, tsetse flies) which transmit the disease. The most effective method consists of making insecticides or residual acaricides penetrate into the skin or fleece of the animals.

This operation is carried out by spraying solutions of insecticide either with mobile sprayers or with fixed installations: spray races or dipping tanks (Plate 6.3).

The technique of sterile male (sterile insect technique: STI) successfully used for the eradication of screw worm fly (*Cochlomyia hominvorax*) from the USA and parts of Central America has been recently applied in Africa, for the control of tsetse flies.

Medical prophylaxis

From the epidemiological point of view, an historical perspective is useful in order to understand the current behaviour of stockmen. They have handed down stories of pandemics of rinderpest which decimated or annihilated herds at the end of the last century and in the first quarter of this century. More recently the epidemic of fowl pest (Newcastle disease) which, started in the Gambia in 1948 and spread across the continent of Africa killing hundreds of thousands of poultry.

In order to understand epidemics, one could recall La Fontaine who observed the rinderpest epidemic which ravaged Europe and who commented: *'everything did not die, but all were struck'*.

Stockmen understand the nature of contagion but have a clear idea of its effects, and therefore have but one aim . . . to flee before their herds could be contaminated. This rapid dispersion of herds may have been the cause of the rapid spread of epidemics.

With experience, stockmen noticed that animals which had been sick with rinderpest, pleuropneumonia and piroplasmosis did not suffer from these diseases a second time. One must see here one of the major motivations for stock-keepers to retain old cows and bulls in the herd: *'they have overcome the disease'*.

With pleuropneumonia, the association of the idea *disease and protection are linked with infection* has been taken a step further. For a long time, the Peuls and the Sahelian stockmen have known a method of vaccination which consisted of planting a small piece of the lung of a diseased animal in a wedge under the skin. The fragment was sometimes conserved for a day or two in acidified milk. When the reaction was too strong and had a tendency to spread to the cheeks and muzzle, they attempted to stop it by cauterising a lump of flesh around the point of implantation.

This type of vaccination was the origin of a legend. The inflammation of the skin and of the periosteum in a growth point close to that of the horns sometimes leads to the development of an horn-like appendage which can reach from 10–15 cm in length (Plate 6.2). It was thought in the eighteenth century to be a breed characteristic and could have been the origin of *Bostriceros* described by zoologists at the time.

This practical knowledge of the stockmen of immunoloy very often contributed to the success of medical prophylaxis campaigns using vaccines and serum and in the 1920s. Before the introduction of vaccines control was based solely on isolation of contaminated stock and on slaughter of the sick animals. Stockmen did not understand why they were compelled, often by force, to remain on pastures which they knew to be infected.

With each step forward in making vaccines, the attitude of the stock-keepers to the innovation was different. In the beginning, inactivated vaccines against rinderpest were made in the bush near to the encampment, by treatment with formalin of the pulp obtained by crushing the spleen and lymphatic glands of calves which had been inoculated by syringe with a virulent virus. It is easy to assume that the stockman, could relate this new method of vaccination to their own traditional practices.

When the vaccine treated with formalin was replaced by a live vaccine passaged through the goat, there was no difficulty in getting stockmen to use it. 'This is a good vaccine, the calves have wept' said a Peul from Niger. A scientific explanation which could be given by the veterinarian would be as follows: 'a viral induced septicaemia associated with congestion of the mucous membranes, therefore it will contain a high level of neutralising antibodies'.

When the virus-vaccine, obtained by culture in calf embryo cells, replaced the goat virus, its acceptance was more difficult to achieve because the stockmen doubted its value because there was no reaction after the vaccine injection. Consequently it was necessary for the staff of the Animal Husbandry Department to use all the trust which they had built up in order to have the system adopted.

Modern vaccination against pleuropneumonia was, until recently, little different from the traditional Peul method.

The virulent substance with was obtained from a pure culture of *Mycoplasma bovis*, the agent of the disease and was injected under a piece of skin. Animals were vaccinated at the head of the tail, a site recommended to avoid problems caused by the spread of the vaccinal inflammation. However, this practice ought to be abandoned because too many animals are losing their tail and, with it, the most practical means of holding them apart from by their horns.

The vaccinal reaction was limited initially by injecting animals with a chemical medicament, novarsenbenzol. More recently antibiotics of the tetracycline family have been used. A simple technique is to use cauterisation, a method used for a long time by the Peul.

For the control of trypanosomiasis in Africa what could be described as genetic means have been used. This technique does not call for the use of a vaccine but on specific qualities of African bullocks of the N'Dama, Lagune, and Baoule breeds. They are found in regions infested with tsetse fly, the vector of trypanosomiasis, but do not show clinical signs of this disease despite the presence of parasites in the blood and a greater number of polynuclear eosinophil than in other breeds. This characteristic was the reason why these breeds were exported to Zaire, central Ivory Coast, Central African Republic and Gabon. No other domesticated cattle existed in these countries at the beginning of this century because of their geographical isolation.

This 'trypanotolerance' is reduced in crossbreds produced by crossing their breeds with Zebus or humpless cattle not indigenous to Africa. The immunological mechanisms of this genetic trypanotolerance remain to be elucidated.

Reaction to viral, microbial or parasitic attack

During the life of a microbe, it produces soluble chemical products which if introduced in sufficient quantities into the bodies of infected animals, confers on them immunity against the fatal disease which the microbe provoked.

L. Pasteur

This observation by Pasteur is a good introduction to the study of the reaction of organisms to viral, bacterial and parasitic attack.

When antigenic viruses, bacteria and parasites develop in a host, whatever it might be, they stimulate defence reactions within it, which are cellular in origin. The white corpuscles, the cells of the reticulo-endothelial system and certain cells of the bone marrow, of the liver and of the spleen are called upon. They react as much to the presence of bacteria which they phagocytose or agglutinate, as to the toxins which they neutralise.

Very soon after the attack, *antibodies* appear in the serum of the host. These are complex protein substances which can be demonstrated by specific techniques. If the animal survives an infection or infestation, these antibodies could be shown to exist for a long time after its recovery. They will contribute to the protection of the patient from a new infection and therefore partial or complete immunity.

In medical prophylaxis phenomena are exploited.

Vulnerable animals, can be protected using the whole blood of recovered animals (foot–and–mouth disease) or serum of recovered animals followed by the serum of animals hyperimmunised, i.e. animals whose immunity was reinforced by repeated injections of virulent antigen .

The serum is either injected into healthy animals to protect them from the disease (this protection is relatively short and normally lasts less than 3 months) or into sick animals to reinforce their body defences and to neutralise the action of pathogenic agents (e.g. anti-poison serum, anti-tetanus serum).

The process of vaccination, uses the considerable capacity for reaction by the animal to the antigen which manifests itself even when the pathogenic ability of the antigen has been reduced by physical agents, such as heat, ageing or chemical (formalin, toluene).

The antibodies formed as a result of vaccination persist in the animal and protect it against infection by the virulent pathogen.

Laboratory methods exist that allow convenient means of identification and titre of the antibodies in the body fluids. Standardised methods of preparation of different biological products and methods of evaluation have been proposed by OIE and these are indicated in the International Health Code.

Different types of vaccine

Vaccines are classed in three groups:

1. inactivated vaccines;
2. toxoids;
3. live vaccines.

Inactivated vaccines come from cultures of viruses, bacterial or very virulent toxins whose pathogenic ability is activated by appropriate treatment,e.g. heat, formalin, phenolbetapropiolactone. Their injection into vulnerable animals causes practically no clinical reaction. At most an inflammation occurs at the point of inoculation.

Toxoids are antigens prepared from toxins isolated from cultures of toxigenic pathogenic agents and that have been inactivated with formalin. The best known of these are the diphtheria toxoid and the tetanus toxoid.

Chemical products are added to inactivated vaccines and toxoids. These moderate their resorption and increase the level of antibodies.

Inactivated vaccines confer an immunity which slowly develops in 7–15 days. This immunity lasts for more than a year in exceptional cases, but more generally from 6 to 9 months. In order to increase the effectiveness of these vaccines, adjuvants are added to them which increase the defence reactions of the animal and thereby confers on it a stronger immunity.

Live vaccines are obtained by culturing viruses or bacteria in such a way that they lose their virulence. When they are inoculated into the animals, they initiate the same reactions which a pathogenic virus would cause, but because their pathogenicity ability has been attenuated, any clinical signs of the reaction are very weak and sometimes not even apparent.

No antiseptic should be brought into contact with the vaccine, otherwise it will be killed and its activity will be destroyed. Therefore needles and syringes that are used for live vaccines should be sterilised by boiling or the action of dry heat and not disinfected with chemical products.

Vaccines are delivered ready for use in sealed vacuum flasks or in the presence of liquid nitrogen. The latter should be put in suspension in a liquid which is sometimes supplied by the laboratory. If this is not so available, physiological sterile saline solution should be used.*

The suspension should be prepared immediately before use and applied within half an hour of its preparation.

Doses and methods of introduction of vaccines are specific. It is important to follow the instructions scrupulously, if you do not want to run the risk of causing accidents or of not obtaining immunity.

Finally, each type of vaccine should be kept in its own prescribed condition. Liquid vaccines should be kept at about + 4° C in a refrigerated box; attenuated vaccines should be stored at − 18° C in a freezer if their efficacy is to be maintained for at least 1 year. If kept at + 4° C they will remain viable for between 15 days and 1 month.

Tables 6.10, 6.11 and 6.12 give a list of vaccines and biological products currently in use for the medical prophylaxis of contagious diseases.

---

* Physiological solution, often called 'physiological saline'; consists of a solution of 9 g of sodium chloride per litre of water sterilised by heating to 120° C for 15 min.

Table 6.10 Vaccines for viral and mycoplasma diseases of livestock

Disease and causal agent	Nature of vaccine	Dose and method of use	Duration of immunity	Observations
Rinderpest (virus)	attenuated live cell culture (freeze dried)	all cattle 1 ml subcutaneous injection	1–4 years	rinderpest Kabete O strain cultured on bovine kidney cells
	attenuated live virus from goats (freeze dried)	for Zebus only 1 ml subcutaneous injection	1–3 years	no vaccine reaction but not to be used on stock affected by progressive pleuropneumonia
Bovine pleuropneumonia (mycoplasma)	culture of Mycoplasma mycoides KH_3 or T_1 (strains freeze-dried)	humpless and Zebu cattle 1 ml injected subcutaneously on the side or in the neck	1 year	no reaction in Zebus; a little fever in humpless cattle
Rinderpest (virus) and pleuropneumonia (mycoplasma)	bivalent vaccine: Kabete O rinderpest strain attenuated by passaging in cell culture. Pleuroneumonia: live T_1 broth culture (freeze dried)	humpless Zebu of all ages and breeds 1 ml subcutaneous injection	rinderpest for 4 years pleuropneummonia: 1 year	
African horse sickness (virus)	cell culture vaccine (freeze dried)	subcutaneous injection in the neck	1 year	Two types of vaccine: monovalent when type of virus is known; polyvalent when type of virus not definitely identified. Do not vaccinate the foals of immunised mares before the age of 6 months. Keep the animal under observation for 15 days and treat digestive complications as they arise.
Infections of small ruminants (virus)	the same characteristics as the cell culture vaccine used in cattle for rinderpest	small ruminants	reactions to the vaccine vary with breed: before systematically vaccinating all animals test the virulence on a small number of animals.	

Table 6.10 continued

Disease and causal agent	Nature of vaccine	Dose and method of use	Duration of immunity	Observations
Sheep pox (virus)	Pox virus vaccine cultured on kidney cells of sheep, and attenuated by successive sub-cultures (freeze dried)	subcutaneous injection of 1 ml vaccine suspension into animals aged more than 3 months old	2 years	always make preliminary tests on a small number of animals
Swine fever (Hog cholera) (virus)	virus strain attenuated by successive passage on cell cultures. Freeze-dried vaccine	1 ml intramuscular injection	essentially life-long	possible to combine with vaccine against Teschen's disease. There is still no vaccine against African swine fever.
Teschen disease (pig) (virus)	inactivated vaccine	two subcutaneous injections of 5 ml at 15 day intervals, repeat injection 3–4 months later; the 5 ml are injected twice behind the knee in two different places	1 year	harmless vaccination
Rabies (virus)	*A. Living virus* Flury LEP strain of rabies virus adapted to culture on embryonated eggs and passaged 50 times; same strain passed 200 times (Flury HEP freeze-dried)	dogs more than 5 months old	1 year or less	strictly reserved for dogs more than 5 months old
		all animals given intramuscular injection in the thigh	1 year or less	subcutaneous injection totally ineffective
	B. Inactivated virus virulent viruses inactivated either by formalin or by betapropiolactone or by phenol after culture in animals or cells with or without adjuvants	conform strictly to specifications given by laboratories which make these vaccines	1 year	in dogs can be combined with vaccination against canine distemper and leptospirosis

Table 6.11 Vaccines for bacterial diseases of livestock

Disease and causal agent	Nature of vaccine	Dose and method of use	Duration of immunity	Observations
Anthrax (bacteria)	suspension of the Sterne strain of *Bacillus anthracis* spores (liquid or freeze-dried vaccine)	subcutaneous injections: • camel 1.0 ml • horse 1.0 ml • adult cattle 1.0 ml • calf 0.5 ml • sheep and goats 0.2 ml	1 year	shake flask well before use; do not vaccinate suckling young, pregnant females or animals in poor condition
Black-quarter (bacteria)	culture of *Clostridium chauvaei* in an anaerobic medium inactivated using formalin with alum of potash as adjuvant (liquid vaccine)	cattle: 1 ml subcutaneous injection	1 year	shake well before use; it is possible to vaccinate against anthrax at same time provided two different syringes are used
Pasteurellosis: haemorrhagic septicaemia of cattle and buffalo (bacteria)	cultures of Carter's type B or E *Pasteurella multocida* inactivated by formalin using alum of potash as adjuvant (liquid vaccine)	2 ml subcutaneous injection in neck or behind shoulder	6–8 months	do not vaccinate animals with fever or showing signs of pasteurella infection
Haemorrhagic septicaemia of small ruminants and pigs (bacteria)	culture of *Pasteurella multocida* types A and D	subcutaneous injection: small ruminants: 2 ml behind shoulder; pig: 2 ml behind ear in clean conditions, 4 ml in contaminated conditions	6 months	correct vaccination procedure to be supported by attention to good hygiene
Bovine brucellosis (bacteria)	A. *Inactivated vaccine* in (oil adjuvant) 1. non agglutinised 45/20 isolate 2. agglutinised H38 isolate extracted from stock B. *Live vaccine* Culture of strain B.19 *Brucella abortis bovis*	two injections at 15 day intervals vaccination repeated annually reserved for young stock between 4th and 7th month, single dose, repeat with inactivated vaccines after the first parturition	1 year 2–3 years	these vaccines are only used in setting up programmes for eradication by removal of infected animals and permanent veterinary surveillance of the herds
Botulism (bacteria and toxin)	toxoid obtained by culture and dialysis of *Clostridium botulinum* stock and inactivation by formalin with aluminium phosphate adjuvant (liquid vaccine)	horses and cattle two subcutaneous injections of 5 ml at 1 month interval; 1/2 dose for animals less than 1 year old	1 year	do not mix with a living vaccine 'in syringe'; combine the vaccination programme with an improved feeding regime

Table 6.12 Vaccines for diseases of poultry

Disease	Nature of vaccine	Dose and method of use	Duration of immunity	Duration and method of storage	Observations
Newcastle disease (fowl pest) (virus)	Newcastle virus of Hitchner B1 and Lasota strain cultured on embryonated hen's egg (live attenuated vaccine)	administer vaccine in drinking water, repeat at age 3 days, 3 weeks and 3 months otherwise: put a drop of vaccine preparation in each nostril	of short duration	for more than 1 year at − 18; C, for 4 months at + 4° C	HB1 isolate does not spread to non-vaccinated birds. Lasota strain spreads and transmits itself by contact with non-vaccinated birds
Fowl pox (virus)	live attenuated vaccine	inoculate vaccine into wing membrane twice with large needle previously plunged into the vaccine	6 months for first vaccination 1 year for following vaccinations	3 months at + 4° C	do not use in infected environment; do not vaccinate poultry less than 3 months old
Fowl typhoid (bacteria)	A. live attenuated vaccine of *Salmonella gallinarum* of 9R isolate (liquid vaccine)	1 ml intramuscular injection into the pectoral muscles	6 months	6 months at − 18° C 3 months at + 4° C	do not vaccinate younger than 1 month; contaminated stock can be vaccinated
	B. *Salmonella gallinarum* culture inactivated with formalin plus adjuvant (liquid vaccine)	1 ml subcutaneous injection	6 months	1 year in a cool dark place	possible to vaccinate in a clean or a contaminated environment
Newcastle disease (Fowl pox)	avian polyvalent vaccine	1 ml intramuscular injection into pectoral muscles	6 months	6 months at − 18° C 3 months at + 4° C	this vaccine is effective against Newcastle disease, fowl pox and fowl typhoid
Fowl typhoid	1. slightly pathogenic Newcastle virus of BANKOWSKI strain adapted using calf kidney cells 2. fowl pox virus strain BAUDETTE cultured on chorio-allantoic membrane of embryonated hen's egg 3. *Salmonella gallinarum* of 9R strain (attenuated vaccine)				
Fowl cholera (bacteria)	inactivated vaccine prepared from cultures of *Pastuerella multocida* type A plus variable adjuvant	1 ml injected under skin for birds over 6 weeks, 0.5 ml for young less than 2 months	life-long	to store for 1 year keep in cold store, to store for 1 month keep between + 4 and + 10° C	

Chemical medical prophylaxis

The term *chemical medical prophylaxis* is reserved for the protection of vulnerable animals by injection of synthesised chemical products. This method is mainly used in the prophylaxis of diseases due to protozoan parasites of the digestive tract (coccidiosis) and the blood system (trypanosomes, Table 6.13).

The products are scattered on the food at intervals of time from 1 day to a week, or injected under the skin or into the muscles. Their slow diffusion allows spacing of protective injections over several months and gaining of chemoprevention over a long period.

The latter method can create resistant pathogenic strains.

Biological tests used to reveal contagious diseases

Disease in the acute stage show symptoms which allow identification of the causal pathogenic micro-organisms. With diseases in the chronic phase, only the serological reactions permit revelation of the presence of antibodies which signal either the infection in the course of its attack or an infection from which the animal has recovered.

Serological reactions are of two types:

1. those which necessitate samples and their analysis by procedures requiring complex laboratory equipment and highly qualified staff;
2. those which can be carried out on site by simple clinical methods. The products necessary for the latter are described in Table 6.14.

In the case of a positive response, in particular for the diseases for which a medical prophylaxis programme should be applied, it is convenient to carry out the clinical screening by complete health examination by bacteriological and immunological laboratory methods (cultures, sero-agglutination, assessment of the group, haemagglutinations etc.).

Prophylaxis of nutritional diseases

Sanitary and medical prophylaxis gives the animals protection from microbial and parasitic diseases but not from nutritional diseases and the conditions of feeding can lead to catastrophic losses if the animals cannot obtain the nutrients, necessary for normal functioning of the body, in its ration.

In indoor livestock enterprises such as pigs and poultry, errors in the composition of rations are due to an insufficient knowledge on the part of the stockman or their advisers. The errors are corrected by a more realistic estimation of quantities and qualities of available foods all year round and of course by better informed stockmen.

Table 6.13 Chemical prophylaxis of trypanosomiasis

Name	Aqueous solution	Injection	Dose	Volume of solution injected	Trypanosoma species	Duration of protection	Affected animal species
Trypamidium	1–2 per cent cold water	IM deep	0.5–1 mg/kg	5–10 ml/100 kg	T. vivax T. congolense	2–4 months	cattle, small ruminants, horses, dogs
Prothidium		IM or IV	0.5–0.75 mg/kg	5–7 ml/100 kg	T. brucei	2 months	butchers animals
	2 per cent boiling water	IM deep	2 mg/kg	10 ml/100 kg	T. vivax T. congolense	2–4 months	cattle, small ruminants, dogs
Antrycide prosalt	3.5 g/15 ml cold water	SC	7.4 mg/kg	5 ml/100 mg	T. brucei T. evansi	2 months	horses, camels
Ethidium	2.5 per cent hot water	SC (in the dewlap)	1 mg/kg)	4 ml/kg	T. vivax T. congolense	1 month	butchers' animals
Suramine-antrycide (complex)	5 per cent cold water	SC	40 mg/kg of antrycide	4 ml/kg	T. simiae	3 months (piglets) 6 months (adults)	pigs

IM = intramusclar; IV = intravenous; SC = subcutaneous

Table 6.14 List of some serological tests used to reveal contagious diseases

Disease	Name of antigen	Method of use	Sign of reaction	Observation
Tuberculosis	tuberculin	simple intradermal tuberculination or only (ID1) 0.1–0.2 ml to the flat of the neck	after 72 h positive thickening of upper skin by 2 mm – clinical signs of inflammation exudation, necrosis, pain inflammation of the glands	commercial tuberculins are either those prepared on the classic Koch's medium or synthetic media
	special tuberculin for intradermal reaction	second intradermal (ID2) 0.2 ml injection in the fold under the tail, then 48 h later, 0.2 ml in the same place	48 h after the second injection: • positive reaction: rupture of skin surface whatever the size of the lesion or of the haemorrhage spot • negative reaction: no skin lesion, limited reaction, non-mobile oedema without local lesion	
Pleuropneumonia	antigen coloured for haemagglutination	haemagglutination reaction of a drop of blood mixed with a drop of antigen on a slide	result in 2 minutes (agglutinate coloured)	reserve for diagnosis of the herd – individual diagnosis made by assessment of the group
Brucellosis (cattle)	coloured brucellic antigen of *Brucella*	ring test: antigen mixed with milk from suspect cow(s) in clean test tube	appearance of coloured ring after 1 hour at 37° C	in a positive reaction, the agglutinated antigen adheres to fat globules and colours the cream which rises to the surface of the antigen/milk mixture – in a negative reaction, the milk remains coloured and unseparated
Pullorum (poultry)	pulloric antigen	haemagglutination reaction of a drop of blood mixed with a drop of antigen on a slide	immediate agglutination result, small coloured lumps	causative agent a bacterium *Salmonella pullorum*
Respiratory mycoplasmosis (poultry)	antigen coloured for haemagglutination	mix a drop of blood and a drop of antigen on a slide	result in 2 min (agglutinants coloured)	causative agents *Mycoplarna* spp.
Glanders	mallein of strain B *Pseudomonas mallei*	0.1 ml intradermal injection of crude mallein diluted to 1/4 in the eyelid	inspect 24–26 h after oedema and mucopurulent flow of the nasal passage	
		subcutaneous injection of 2.5 ml of 1/10 dilution in flat of the neck	increase in rectal temperature of at least 1° C, swelling local	

In a cattle rearing system that uses natural pastures, artificial pastures or even cultivated forage, the problems are less easy to resolve because, more than problems of quantity, there are those due to the composition of the forage itself. The quality of the forage that animals consume depends upon the quality of the soils upon which it is grown. If the animals find the necessary elements for their growth and reproduction in their forage, in sufficient quantity and without excess, they will remain in good health. If the opposite is true, their growth will be restricted, their reproduction will be disturbed and they will show pathological symptoms whose nature will depend upon the deficit or excess of the nutrients concerned.

The mineral elements of forage are the cause of a nutritional disease if one or more are in insufficient quantity and there is a deficiency or on the other hand there is an excess and they are toxic. This toxicity can be direct, for example intoxication by fluorine. Indirect toxicity develops by reducing the availability of another element, for example a copper deficiency caused by excess molybdenum or sulphates. Other examples of the latter are the antagonisms of copper/zinc, manganese/calcium, zinc/calcium and zinc/phytates.

The range of minimum and maximum levels of elements present in forage has been found to be considerable (Table 6.15). For example for calcium from lowest to highest the content is in the proportion 1 to 150, for phosphorus it is 1 to 20 and for sodium 1 to 1000. For the trace elements the difference is of the same order, iodine is 1 to 700, iron is 1 to 50, cobalt 1 to 200 and zinc 1 to 100. It is not surprising, therefore, to observe shortfalls when the animals consume deficient forage.

Table 6.15 Mineral requirements for ruminants in relation to mineral content of the pasture

Elements	Content of pasture		Desired content in pasture*	
	Limit of variation	Normal content of pasture	Fattening cow	Milking cow
	all values in percentage of dry matter			
Calcium	0.04–6.00	0.2–1.0	0.50	0.52
Phosphorus	0.03–0.68	0.2–0.5	0.25	0.42
Sodium	0.002–2.12	0.05–1.0	0.07	0.15
Chlorine	0.02–2.05	0.1–2.0	0.09	0.19
Magnesium	0.03–0.75	0.1–0.4	0.06	0.15
	all values in p.p.m. of dry matter			
Iodine	0.07–5.0	0.2–0.8	0.12	0.80
Iron	21–1000	50–300	30.00	30.00
Cobalt	0.02–4.7	0.05–0.3	0.10	0.10
Copper	1.1–29.0	2–15	5.00	10
Manganese	9–2400	25–1000	40	40
Zinc	1–112	15–60	50	50
Selenium	0.01–4000	0.03–0.15	>0.03	>0.03

* Data relating to a 40 kg sheep gaining 200 kg per day and consuming 1.36 kg of dry matter. Also for a 500 kg milking cow giving 20 kg of milk per day and consuming 14.3 kg of dry matter

Table 6.16 Trace elements in forage – thresholds of deficiency and toxicity for the plant and the ruminant

Elements	Forage			Ruminants		
	Threshold of deficiency p.p.m. DM	Threshold of toxicity p.p.m. DM*	Normal content and (extremes)	Threshold of toxicity p.p.m. DM in the ration	Threshold of deficiency in the ration p.p.m.	Known interferences
Copper Cu	2–4	> 20	4–15	adult cattle 4–10 young cattle + sensitive sheep hardy 4–6 Merinos 7–8	sheep 20–30 young cattle 40–100 adult cattle < 200	Cu–Mo Cu–SO$_4$ Cu–Ca Cu ? Cu–Zn
Cobalt Co	0.2 (legumes)		0.05–1.0	0.07	90–160 mg/100 kg live wt	
Iodine I		10–20	0.3 –0.4	lactating 0.12–12 others 0.12–1.3	non-lactating 8	I – goitrogenic substance
Manganese Mn		function of the relationship of Fe and Mn	15–200 (up to 600)	20–50	unknown	Mn–Ca
Zinc Zn	8–15	> 200	8–50	adults 40–45 young + sensitive	500–900	Zn–phytates Zn–Ca Zn–Cu Zn–Mn
Selenium Se		50–100 (except plant accumulators)	0.01–2.0 (up to 1500 in plant accumulators)**	0.1–0.2	5	Se–SO$_4$ Se–As
Molybdenum Mo	0.1		1–100	sheep 0.1 cattle unknown	> 3	Mo–Cu Mo–SO$_4$ Mo–K

* Cu–Mn–Zn toxicities are know in plants, but correspond more to a stunting of growth and specific symptoms rather than to precise concentrations in the plant
** Some plants accumulate selenium, e.g. *Astralagus bisulcatus*   SO$_4$ = sulphate; As = arsenic; Ca = calcium; K = potassium

Table 6.17 Zones of potential deficiency as a function of rock composition

Rock	Elements									
	Iron*	Manganese*	Nickel	Copper	Cobalt	Zinc	Molybdenum	Boron	Iodine	Selenium
Earth's crust (mean)	50 000	1 000	100	70	40	80	2.3	10	0.3	0.09
Volcanic rock†										
ultrabasic rock	95 000	1 500	2 000	20	200	30	0.2	1.0	0.01	0.05
basalt	85 000	2 000	160	87–100	48	105–130	1.4	5	0.5	0.05
granodiorites	27 000	600	8	35	10	60	1	15	0.4	0.05
granites‡	29 – 14 000	540–390	15–4	30–10	7–1	60–40	1–4	15	0.5	0.05
Sedimentary rocks										
clays	33 000	670	95	57	20	80	2	3–300	1	0.6
shales	47 000	850	68	45	10	95	2.6	100	2.2	0.6
gritstones	9 800	?	2	10	0.3	16	0.2	35	1.7	0.05
limestones	3 800	1 100	20	4–20	0.1	20	0.4	20	1.2	0.08

* Iron and manganese are not 'trace elements' in rocks but are given for comparison with the trace elements with which they are associated.
† The volcanic rocks are classified in the table in decreasing order of basicity.
‡ The two figures correspond to the two extreme series of granites; most alkaline to most acid

Table 6.15 gives the required mineral element content of pasture and Table 6.16 gives the thresholds of deficiency and toxicity levels of several trace elements for both the plant and the ruminant. In comparing them one can get an idea of the complexity of the problems.

In the same meadow, the mineral content of plants varies with botanical species. The Graminae are low in copper while members of the Compositae are richer in the element. It is interesting that certain natural species give an indication of the qualities of the soil; for example *Carex* species on acid soils and *Imperata* species on lateritic soils rich in iron and aluminium.

The trace element content varies in the course of growth. This has been observed in a monoculture forage crop, where it was the first cut which was the lowest in copper and yielding most significant tonnage of dry matter.

Correlations have been found between trace element content of the soil and that of forage, but their constancy is rare and up until the present day there is no general rule which can be applied.

One resorts, then, to defining the areas of potential trace element deficiency by the nature of the rocks (Table 6.17).

1. Sands, gritstones, quartzite conglomerates and most of the granites (particularly the leuco-granites) are low in copper.
2. The limestones (with little or no clay) are fairly low in copper but particularly low in cobalt.
3. The basalts, clays and shales, are rich in copper and cobalt. The latter are also well provided with molybdenum and selenium.
4. The most acid granites, the slate shales, the infraliassic black marls and certain marine alluvial soils are richer in molybdenum.

All the volcanic rocks are low in selenium which is concentrated in the clays (and shales). The gritstones and limestones are, on the other hand, low in zinc.

While the nature of the rocks allows an initial estimation of the areas of potential deficiencies, their intensity depends upon the nature of the chemical transformation of the mother rocks in the course of their creation. The leaching and binding by iron (of molybdenum and cobalt) in lateritic soils are two causes of the reduction of the trace element content in the soil layer accessible to plant roots.

Some economic aspects of disease

Veterinarians most often argue the following case:

The presence of a disease is an abnormal situation which should be returned to the normal.

This involves an error of economics which should be corrected thus:

> The presence of a disease is a normal situation and moving on from this normal situation one should look for ways of increasing productivity.

This reasoning should be modified, nevertheless, in the case of great devastating epidemics which appear in surges and whose impact on the basis of livestock productivity needs no further mention.

The fight against disease is, without doubt, a simple action to conduct and is economically attractive.

So far the fight against rinderpest (cattle plague) has been the one most discussed. Now an economic study has shown that:

> the success of PC_{15}* has restored the confidence of the producer and allowed him to concentrate more on the productivity of his livestock than on their mortality. The old females have started to be reduced significantly. In order to react to the ecological pressure, the structure of the herds has been modified towards a greater effectiveness. PC_{15} has reduced the impact of drought and has not provoked any tragic occurrence.

Vaccination campaigns allow the stockmen to gain confidence and prepare for future development efforts.

Not to fight large epidemics would be to deny a system of production where the young and the mother, that is to say the capital assets, could disappear at any moment.

In tropical countries, estimation of the cost of disease is, in general, very difficult because it is part of a complex situation from which it is practically impossible to separate out without experimentation (disease–nutrition–management complex of the herd-development . . .). For the large epidemics, the figure of cost is a little easier, and one meets it as soon as one works out the probability of disease appearance (this is the classic difference between *ex ante* and *ex post* estimates).

Nevertheless, the scale of economic losses can be shown:

1. The overall rates of herd mortality: about 10 per cent in cattle in Niger and about 14 per cent in small ruminants in Burkina Faso are scarcely smaller than the rates of offtake.
2. The annual herd production losses between the best and worst general situations (in Chad between February and the end of July) are of the same order of size as the total number of animals produced in a year. This is most certainly valid for the Sahel, but less so for the majority of developing countries.

* PC_{15} refers to the internationally financed Fonds Europeén Development (= European Agency for Development) (FED)– Fonds d'Aide et de Cooperation (= French Agency for Development) (FAC)–United States Agency for International Development (USAID)–African States) project for the fight against rinderpest: 70 million cattle from the tropical zone of Africa vaccinated between 1962 and 1976 under the aegis of OIE and OAU. It has been supplemented by an emergency campaign between 1980 and 1981. All vaccines used were made in Africa.

In general there is considerable under estimation of the cost of disease since published figures only effectively take into account *declared* mortalities. These represent about 10 per cent of meat production in cattle. A more realistic estimation is that disease is responsible for reducing the value of production by 50 per cent.

Some effects of disease on the economy of animal production

Mortality

Cattle

1. *Mortality due to large epidemics* is now relatively well controlled.
2. *Overall mortality.* Mortality rates in animals are very variable and the most affected, in climatologically normal years, are usually the youngest.

It is common to observe mortality rates of 25–45 per cent for the first age group, up to 1 year old.

Sheep

Mortality due to large epidemics such as small ruminant plague, sheep pox and anthrax in general has little bearing on the overall mortality (considered according to the country in question).

Mortality from other causes is probably higher than in cattle (in Chad, 98 per cent of sheep and 75 per cent of goats are parasitised).

Surveys carried out in recent years give the following mortality rates:

- 0 to 1-year-old stage   20–53 per cent
- 1 to 2-year-old stage   9–25 per cent
- over 2 years old   4–17 per cent

The figures show that every improvement programme in traditional stock rearing necessarily seems to have been by action against disease while neglecting the other problems (nutrition, housing etc.)

Morbidity

The causes of morbidity are often more difficult to define than those of mortality and they interact in a significant way. For East Coast Fever in Malawi, losses due to morbidity are estimated at about 10 per cent of production. On the other hand, the effect on reproduction is very strong – a high fertility rate of 65–70 per cent in cattle can drop to 45–50 per cent (in cases in the north Ivory Coast). Disease intervenes particularly in the form of brucellosis and trypanosomiasis.

In traditional livestock rearing in the north Ivory Coast, abortions have been estimated at 5.2 per cent of births, of which 1/3 would be due to brucellosis.

In Chad, the fertility rate of herds unaffected by brucellosis is 63.3 per cent and that of affected herds is 60.5 per cent (30 per cent of cows are infected and these have a fertility of 54.4 per cent).

A study has shown that the frequency of abortions due to brucellosis varies from 2.5 to 8 per cent of births.

In modern livestock rearing on the Dihesse ranch, where the females are from very diverse origins, the fertility rate was 52 per cent in 1976 and this rose to 58 per cent in 1977. Abortions, essentially from brucellosis, are of the order of 7 per cent.

Effects on other production parameters

On work

There are continual interactions between disease, malnutrition and over-work. Disease plays an even greater role in animals which have to work intensively.

The diseases from mites or ticks and trypanosomes play a significant role under this heading. Pleuropneumonia and dermatophilus can preclude any form of animal-drawn cultivation.

On rejection at the slaughterhouse

Tuberculosis, fascioliasis (fluke) and various abscesses are the cause of down-grading of meat which prevents, for example, exports from the Sahelian countries to coastal countries.

The most important reason for condemned meat remains cysticercosis. 40 per cent of carcasses of Bororo Zebus have cysticercosis in the Central African Republic and 31 per cent in Burundi. In Kenya, it is estimated that losses amount to 34 per cent of the value for infested carcasses and 3.3 per cent of the total value of slaughtered cattle.

On weight losses and mortality at the time of traditional trading

Examples of traditional trading are the transportation of animals from Chad to Central Africa or to Nigeria from Burkina Faso, Mali or from Niger to the Ivory Coast, Ghana or Nigeria. The losses due to trypanosomiasis are significant and those due to weight loss can reach 20 per cent (normally they vary between 0 and 10 per cent according to season and speed of transfer).

On markets and commerce

Weight losses have been observed in animals held in quarantine. Supplies of animals and their produce to local markets will be disrupted by the incidence of disease. Consequently commerce is interrupted. Income from sales will be less with futher financial implications of cash flow problems; and returns from investment in animal production and the rate of stock turnover will be reduced.

On the markets of developed countries

A number of attractive markets are closed because of the potential hazards of disease being introduced from the exporting country. Most certainly, the tropical countries need to produce proteins for themselves but the search for foreign exchange could be satisfied by the export of prime quality and prime category carcasses.

On extensive pastures

Trypanosomiasis is the major obstacle preventing the use of extensive pastures for livestock rearing. The following reasoning, although simplistic, puts its finger on the dimension of the problem. In Africa, 7 million km^2 of pasture are infested with tsetse flies. This vast area could provide for 120 million additional cattle, i.e. there is a lost potential production of 2 million tonnes. The reasoning is simplistic because it assumes that if trypanosomiasis were dealt with, then all the problems would be resolved. However the constraint remains very significant and this is why FAO has launched a large programme in which France and West Germany play a very active role.

Trypanosomiasis is not the only limiting factor to development of the humid zones where there is great potential for forage production. One should consider parasitism, the diseases due to ticks and the fairly obvious human factors such as the total absence of knowledge of the subject of animal production and the frequent presence of human diseases such as onchocerciasis.

On the introduction of improved breeds

Examples of indigenous breeds being acclimatised or resistant but of entire exotic breeds succumbing to a disease, are very numerous: streptothricosis, (*Dermatophilus congolensis*) trypanosomiasis, heartwater in cattle, tick-borne diseases and pox in small ruminants.

On zoonoses

Account is rarely taken of zoonoses, the diseases transmitted to man from animals. Often zoonotic diseases are more difficult to control in man. Economic losses of such diseases in man are calculated from the mortality and morbity rates. Such an estimation is made from the cost of loss of work (at market prices) by those who would otherwise be working plus the cost of medical treatment (or the medical insurance equivalent).

The economic approach to disease control

The basic measures of disease control already dealt with obviously do not need justification. Action which now needs to be carried out to increase productivity of the herd, will require economic justification.

The drugs which have appeared over the last twenty years allow prophylaxis to be undertaken (anthelminthics, trypanocides...) but they are expensive and must show a financial return.

Product prices have increased considerably and this has been brought about progressively by a change from stock rearing as a 'way of life' to stock rearing for 'speculation', that is to say where the costs of production, notably those concerning health, are cut down to the minimum.

Starting from a given health situation and the planned development of rearing conditions, one is seeking to obtain optimum productivity at minimum cost. In order to achieve this, one can certainly fight against diseases, but also choose other measures, such as improving nutrition, in order to look for the greatest possible net benefits (benefits being considered in the long term). Thus it is quite a wide husbandry policy which must be envisaged.

The measures taken will depend on the differing points of view of:

1. the farmer and his investment into his choice of agricultural enterprises;
2. the State – for example the decision to invest in either brucellosis control or make road improvements;
3. the investors who want signficant returns and to improve the overall financial situation of the country.

The role of international co-ordination

Globally the co-ordination is principally carried out by OIE who, by telex system, inform countries of the situation of epidemics. It is also carried out by FAO but in a more static and less detailed way.

At the continental level, there are also organisations: IBAR (International Bureau for Animal Resources) depending on Organisation of African Unity (OAU) for Africa.

Certain organisations are also charged with health co-ordination world-wide: CBLT (Lake Chad Basin Commission), CEBV (Economic Meat and Livestock Community).

Appendix

In this appendix will be found definitions of words and expressions most used in the international vocabulary, which are relevant to the health regulations for contagious diseases. Facsimiles of some animal health certificates approved by OIE are included.

International definitions and vocabulary relevant to health regulations

There are general health regulations and specific regulations for each disease. Some terms should be defined because, in development projects, one can be confronted with animal health problems.

Administrative division a section of territory clearly delineated and having a veterinary organisation suited to taking the appropriate measures which the animal health code allows or prescribes.

Animal health bulletins the periodic reports established by the national veterinary services and which give information in table form weekly, fortnightly or monthly, on the animal health situation observed in each country in the course of the corresponding period.

Animal products meat, fish products and animal products destined for human consumption, animal consumption or pharmaceutical, agricultural or industrial purposes.

Animal products destined for animal consumption meat fats, fish, liver, bone, blood, feather and tissues.

Animal products destined for human consumption egg products, milk and milk products, honey.

Animal products destined for industrial use skins and coarse hides, body walls, wool, hair, hooves and horns, bones, blood, guts, animal manure, guano.

Animal products for pharmaceutical use organs, organ tissues and liquids destined for the preparation of pharmaceutical products.

Area of epidemic disease indicates the agricultural holding, livestock rearing group or the locations, including the buildings and attendant structures, in which one of the diseases registered in the OIE list has appeared.

In a situation where this delineation is not possible, what is considered as the 'area' is the part of the territory in which, taking account of the local conditions, one cannot guarantee that the animals, receptive or not, would have no direct contact with diseased animals or animals suspected of contamination, which they might encounter.

In the particular case of certain parts of Africa, the area is defined as one-sixteenth of a square degree (i.e. 1/16th of the area between 1 degree of latitude and 1 degree of longitude) in which the disease is present. There is little need to mention that it is a single area, even if the disease appears in several places in the same sixteenth of a square degree.

Approved collection centre   a building or site in which are gathered rearing and commercial stock or butchers' animals, which come from different farms or from various markets officially approved and satisfying the following conditions:

- to be placed under the control of a veterinary official;
- not to be situated in an infected area, and to be disinfected before and after use;
- to serve only rearing and commercial stock or butchers' animals which meet the conditions of the current Code.

Biological products

- biological reagents used for the diagnosis of certain diseases;
- sera capable of being used in the prevention, treatment and possibly in the serovaccination of certain diseases;
- vaccines, inactivated or modified, capable of being used in the preventive vaccination of certain diseases.

Butcher's animal   an animal of the cattle, buffalo, camel, goat, horse, sheep and pig species, as well as the domesticated reindeer, destined to be transported or conducted from the time of arrival in the importing country and under the control of the responsible veterinary authority, to an officially approved abattoir to be slaughtered there after some delay.

Case   an individual animal affected by one of the infectious or parasitic diseases recognised by OIE.

Imported case   a case introduced into a territory from another country.

Disinfection   the operation designed to destroy the infectious agents of animal diseases, including zoonoses. It applies to animals as well as to buildings, vehicles and various objects which could have been soiled directly or indirectly by the animals or by the animal commodities and products.

Disinfestation the operation designed to kill insects, vectors of animal diseases, including zoonoses, present in boats, trains, road vehicles and other means of transport or containers.

Farm an establishment in which rearing, commercial or butchers' animals are raised or kept.

Fresh meat indicates meat which has not been subjected to any treatment which would irreversibly modify its organoleptic or physio-chemical characteristics. In the context of the Code, meat simply refrigerated or frozen is fresh meat.

Health slaughter a control measure to prevent animal disease consisting of slaughtering the animals infected by an epizootic disease, those suspected of being affected or those simply in danger of infection from a new outbreak of the epidemic, taking every necessary health precaution at the same time.

Import and export health controls the group of health control measures for animals, fish, bees, animal products, embryonated birds' eggs, embryonated fish eggs, semen, stocks of bees, biological products, pathological products. These controls are applied on entry and departure from a country.

International animal health certificate a certificate established by a veterinary official from the exporting country, attesting to the good health of the animal or animals, fish as well as bees and possibly specifying the biological proof or proofs of the tests to which the animal or animals have been subjected. The certificate can be individual, or collective according to the species of animal in question or the particular conditions of the shipment. These certificates conform to the standard forms entitled '6–1 of the Code'.

International health certificate a certificate established by a veterinary official attesting to the cleanliness of meat, fish products or animal products destined for human consumption, and possibly specifying the precautions taken to avoid the transmission of epidemics. This term also indicates a certificate attesting to the precautions taken to avoid the transmission of epizootics for embryonated eggs, semen, stocks of bees and animal products destined for animal consumption, industrial use or pharmaceutical purposes. These certificates conform to standard forms entitled '6–1 of the health Code'.

Meat all the parts of the animal deemed to be edible.

Monthly epidemic circular the circular (trilingual: English, French, Spanish) established and distributed each month by OIE.

Observation   surveillance effected by the veterinary authority to ensure that the animal is not carrying the diseases covered by the Code. It can call for clinical examination, allergy tests, laboratory tests and, in a general way, any procedure which would allow the demonstration of infection which the animal could be carrying.

Officially approved market   a market meeting the following conditions:

- to be placed under the control of a veterinary official;
- not to be situated in an infected area and to be disinfected after use;
- to serve only rearing, commercial or butchers' animals which meet the conditions laid down by the Code.

Officially approved refrigerated warehouse   an establishment using cold to preserve meat and animal or fish products destined for consumption and meeting the recommendations of the International Institute of Refrigeration, insomuch as they concern the management, equipment and its functioning and approved by the veterinary administration and placed under the control of a veterinary official.

Officially approved slaughterhouse   an establishment approved by the veterinary administration and satisfying international standards approved by OIE or, if not, those imposed by the importing country.

Pathological products   stocks of infective agents as well as the samples of infectious or parasitic materials taken from living animals, excreta, tissues and organs taken from corpses, to be sent to a specialist or reference laboratory recognised by OIE, World Health Organisation (WHO), Food and Agricultural organisation (FAO) etc.

Prepared meat   products obtained by subjecting meat to treatment either by cooking or by dessication, salting, pickling in brine or smoke-curing.

Quarantine controls   the group of measures concerning the entry and stay of animals in quarantine establishments or stations, as well as their departure from these establishments.

Quarantine establishment or quarantine station   a building or group of buildings where animals are kept in complete isolation, without direct or indirect contact, for the purpose of allowing the official veterinary service to assure that the animals are not carrying certain diseases.

Rearing and commercial animal   an animal of the cattle, buffalo, camel, goat, horse, sheep and pig species, as well as the domesticated reindeer, which is not destined for the abattoir immediately.

Veterinary authority the veterinary service directly responsible for the application of appropriate animal health measures in an administrative division.

Veterinary official a veterinary surgeon, official or commissioned, designated or approved by the veterinary administration of his country.

Following these definition, there are two concepts which require particular clarification and these are: *infected area* and *indemnified area*.

The definitions of indemnified areas and infected areas may concern the following diseases from List A:

Foot-and-mouth disease
Rinderpest
Contagious bovine pleuropneumonia
Sheep pox
Hog cholera
African swine fever
Enzootic swine encephalomyelitis
Fowl pest
Newcastle disease

Indemnified area within a country, a clearly delineated area in which no case of the diseases specified above has been reported during a defined period which is indicated for each disease in the animal health code, and within and up to the limits of which an official veterinary control is exercised on the animals, on the products and on their transport.

Infected area within a country, a territory in which one of the diseases specified above has been verified, and whose extent, which should be clearly delineated, is fixed by the veterinary authority, taking account of the environment, the different ecological and geographic factors, as well as all the epidemiological factors and the manner of stock rearing.

The territory should have a radius of at least 10 km in areas of intensive rearing and of at least 50 km in areas of extensive rearing, the focus of the disease being the centre of the circle.

Within and up to the limits of the infected area, an official veterinary control is effectively exercised on the animals, on the animal products and on their transport.

The duration of the period in which the area remains infected varies according to the health measures and the methods of prophylaxis used.

Examples of international animal health certificates

ANIMAL HEALTH CERTIFICATE* FOR DOMESTIC ANIMALS (REARING OR COMMERCIAL) OR WILD OF THE SPECIES CATTLE, BUFFALO, SHEEP, GOAT OR PIG** FOR THE PURPOSE OF INTERNATIONAL EXCHANGE

Exporting country: ....

Ministry: ....

Department: ....

Area or district etc.: ....

I. – Identification of the animal

Official ear tag	Breed	Sex	Age

II. – Origin of animal

Name and address of exporter: ....

Place of origin of the animal: ....

III. – Destination of the animal

Country of destination: ....

Name and address of consignee: ....

Nature and identification of means of transport: ....

IV. – Health information

The undersigned veterinary official certifies that:

a) the animal indicated above and examined this day presents no clinical sign of disease and;

b) the animal has satisfied all the requirements below.

(These conditions are established from a common accord between the responsible veterinary services of the importing and exporting countries and chosen from the options provided in the Code.)

Official stamp: Made at .... date ....
Veterinary official (name and address)

....

Signature:

* It is recommended that individual certificates are issued
** Delete species not applicable.

ANIMAL HEALTH CERTIFICATE FOR BUTCHERS' ANIMALS OF THE SPECIES CATTLE, BUFFALO, SHEEP, GOAT OR PIG FOR THE PURPOSE OF INTERNATIONAL EXCHANGE*

Exporting country: ....

Ministry: ....

Department: ....

Area or district etc.: ....

I. – Number and identification of animals

Official ear tag	Breed	Sex	Age

II. – Origin of the animals

Name and address of exporter: ....

Place of origin: ....

III. – Destination of the animals

Country of destination: ....

Name and address of consignee: ....

Nature and identification of means of transport: ....

IV. – Health information

The undersigned veterinary official certifies that:

a) the animals indicated above and examined this day present no clinical sign of disease; and

b) the animals have satisfied the conditions below.

(These conditions are established from a common accord between the responsible veterinary services of the importing and exporting countries and chosen from the options provided in the Code.)

Official stamp: Made at .... date ....

                         Veterinary official (name and address)

                         ....

                         Signature:

* Delete species not applicable.

HEALTH CERTIFICATE FOR THE MEAT OF DOMESTIC ANIMALS OF THE
SPECIES CATTLE, BUFFALO, HORSE, SHEEP, GOAT OR PIG OR POULTRY*

Exporting country: ....
Ministry: ....
Department: ....
Area or district etc.: ....

I. – Identification of the meat

Nature of pieces: ....
Nature of packing: ....
Number of pieces or packing units: ....
Net weight: ....

II. – Origin of the meat

* Address(es) and number(s) of veterinary approval of approved abbatoir(s): ....

....

* Address(es) and number(s) of veterinary approval of approved butchering
   establishment(s): ....

III. – Destination of the meat

The meat is being dispatched from: ....
                                                                                (place of dispatch)

to ....
                                                                           (country and destination)

Nature and identification of means of transport: ....
Name and address of exporter: ....
Name and address of consignee: ....

IV. – Certification of health

The undersigned veterinary official certifies that:
   a) the meat*, the packages of meat* indicated above carries the stamp of approval that
      the meat has come entirely from animals slaughtered in approved abbattoirs;
   b) the meat is suitable for human consumption;
   *c) the meat has been butchered in approved premises; and.
   d) the meat has satisfied the requirements below.
(These conditions are established from a common accord between the responsible
veterinary departments of the importing and exporting countries and chosen from the
options provided in the Code.)

Official stamp: Made at .... date ....
                          Veterinary official (name and address)
                          ....
                          Signature:
* Delete species/parts not applicable.

HEALTH CERTIFICATE (INDIVIDUAL) FOR SEMEN OF THE SPECIES CATTLE, BUFFALO, SHEEP, GOAT OR PIG* FOR THE PURPOSE OF INTERNATIONAL EXCHANGE

Exporting country: ....
Ministry: ....
Department: ....
Area or district: ....

I. – Information on the sire**

Species: ....
Breed: ....
Name: ....
Date of Birth: ....
Place of Birth: ....
Details on breed form: ....
Date of approval for artificial insemination: ....

II. – Information on the semen**

Date and time of production: ....
Quantity and packaging of semen exported: ....

III. – Origin of the semen

Name and address of exporter (Artificial insemination centre or participating exporter): ....

IV. – Destination of the semen

Name and exact postal address of consignee: ....
Name and identification of means of transport used: ....

V. – Health information

The undersigned veterinary official certifies that:
a) the sire, identified above, that produced the semen did not show any clinical sign of disease on the day of production of the semen; and
b) the sire has satisfied all the conditions below.

(These conditions are established from a common accord between the responsible veterinary departments of the importing and exporting countries and chosen from the options provided in the Code).

Official stamp: Made at .... date ....
                        Veterinary official (name and address)
                        ....

                        Signature:

* Delete species not applicable
** Technical information supplied by ....

PART II

THE ANIMALS

7
Animal production and genetics

The concepts of species, breed and varieties have very clearly evolved since the beginning of the century due to discoveries in genetics.

Species is still defined as a population of individuals which resemble each other and can reproduce and produce fertile offspring, the latter ability being essential in order to be able to define a species.

In domesticated animals the reality of species is quite clear and yet some people consider the humpless cattle *Bos taurus* and the Zebu *Bos indicus* to be different species even though crossing them gives fully fertile offspring. Thus one can say that the concept of breed is more intuitive than objective. There are pure breeds only because the actions of man are added to environmental factors to produce populations which have in common some morphological, physiological or biological characteristics the expression of which varies with a greater of lesser degree around a mean.

Standards describe morphological characteristics sometimes with a great deal of detail. They are still often used for judging and the selection of animals for breeding.

With regard to physiological characteristics, the intensity of milk production, fattening ability, speed of growth, egg-laying ability etc., which govern the economic return of the animals, are considered to be essential in the field of animal production.

Biochemical characteristics, blood groups, the nature of the blood proteins and above all immunological attributes are increasingly taken into account in estimating the qualities of blood-lines.

A review of some concepts of genetic factors

Stockmen used the ability of domesticated animals to transmit their characteristics to their offspring well before genetics, biometrics and cytology enabled an understanding of the detailed mechanisms of heredity to estimate the economic value of populations and to establish programmes for the genetic improvement of production.

In a living organism, all the cells come from the multiplication of the initial cell, the fertilised egg (or zygote) which, in higher animals is the result of fusion of a spermatozoon (male gamete) and an ovum (female gamete).

The young developing from the zygote manifests a group of specific characteristics, some of which are identical to those of its parents. Thus, in the egg, there must be structures which support the programme of organisation of the cell which, in the course of embryogenesis, determine the manifestation and then the transmission of these hereditary characteristics.

In the absence of an exact knowledge of the nature of these structures, they were known as characters, and in 1911 they became known as genes. Later, two concepts were introduced: phenotype which groups the apparent hereditary or non-hereditary properties of the individual, and genotype, which is the group of apparent or non-apparent hereditary properties and which can be transmitted in part to the offspring. The phenotype is the result of genotypic and environmental effects.

In 1863, Naudin, who effected inter-species crossing with *Datura,* primrose, flax, tobacco and petunias, proposed these ideas. He observed *a great uniformity of appearance in first generation hybrids . . . these are intermediate mixed forms between two parental species; starting in the second generation the appearance of the hybrids is modified in a most remarkable way in the majority of cases (and perhaps in all of them) and this dissolution of hybrid forms, which seems to me to be beyond all reason, begins to occur.*

Naudin, having recognised the separation of temporarily united characters of species explained it by *the separation of two specific ingredients in the pollen and the ovule of hybrids.*

Mendel, carrying out inter-specific hybridisations with breeds of pea at about the same time (1865), continued the analysis of transmission of characters further, because the plants which he used belonged to the same species and the products of crossing were completely fertile.

Effecting cross-fertilisations between plants which only differed in one or a few simple characters such as the appearance of the seed (smooth or rough), the colour of the endosperm (yellow or green) or the colour of the flowers, Mendel could trace the distribution of them through successive generations.

However, on their publication, neither the works of Naudin nor those of Mendel attracted the attention of scientists, whose preconceptions did not allow them to foresee the importance of hereditary phenomena in the mechanisms of evolution.

At the beginnings of the century, three researchers working independently from each other — de Vries in the Netherlands, Correns in Germany and Von Tchermak in Austria — rediscovered and confirmed Mendel's laws. In 1924, Cuenot demonstrated the validity of the Mendelian theory of inheritance in mammals. From 1910 to 1945, Morgan and his collaborators working on *Drosophila* (fruit fly) developed the consequences of Mendel's laws and showed that the chromosomes must be the vehicle of the hereditary transmission of characters, while Fisher and Snedecor provided geneticists with method for the mathematical analysis of hereditary phenomena in populations and in particular of the variability of characters.

More recently, biochemists have proposed coherent explanations for the nature and functioning of the detailed mechanisms of embryogenesis and the hereditary transmission of characters (Watson and Crick, Monod, Jacob and Lwoff).

The mechanisms of hereditary transmission of Mendelian characters

Mendel's laws have received such widespread coverage that it seems unecessary to treat them in detail.

The law of segregation (Mendel's first law)

The most simple case is that of crossing two breeds or varieties which only differ in one qualitative character. This latter property, is frequent in plants but occurs much less in animals.

In the same species, when the parents differ only in the manifestation of one given character, all the hybrids of the first generation (F_1) are similar.

In the second generation (F_2), resulting from the random crossing of F_1 individuals, there is a ratio of $\frac{1}{4}$ of individuals like the father, $\frac{1}{4}$ of individuals of the maternal type and $\frac{1}{2}$ of the individuals being hybrid and identical to the F_1 hybrid. If the latter are crossed, they give offspring among which an identical breakdown ($\frac{1}{2}$, $\frac{1}{4}$, $\frac{1}{4}$) is observed.

If, in the F_1 generation, all the individuals have the character of the father, this character is said to be *dominant* over the *recessive* character of the mother and *vise versa* if, in the F_1, it is the character of the mother which appears.

In the F_1 generation all the subjects may, for the character under consideration, be intermediate between the father and the mother. This is so in the cross between Shorthorn cattle of the red-coated type and those of the white coated type, where the offspring have uniform roan coats.

Separation of characters occurs at the time of random mating of the first generation crosses to give the proportions of $\frac{1}{4}$ red, $\frac{1}{4}$ white and $\frac{1}{2}$ roan.

Polyhybridism – purity of gametes (Mendel's second law)

Mendel's second law relates to the independent assortment of characters or the law of segregation.

In crossing two pure-bred individuals which differ by two allelomorphic characters, the offspring will all be identical in the first (F_1) generation.

In random crossing independent recombination of the two characters is obtained in the F_2 offspring, according to the proportions:

$$\frac{9}{16} : \frac{3}{16} : \frac{3}{16} : \frac{1}{16} \quad \text{i.e. a ratio of } 9 : 3 : 3 : 1.$$

Thus in crossing pure breeding white long-haired rabbits with pure breeding brown short-haired ones of the Rex type whose pelts are used in the fur trade, in the F_1 generation one only obtains brown short-haired rabbits, the white long-haired characters (bb ss) being dominated respectively by the brown short-haired characters (BB SS). The F_1 offspring have the genotype Bb Ss, they are *heterozygous* for the two characters, of which they produce gametes BS, Bs, bs, bS which by random combinations of the F_2 give the genotypes of the F_2 shown in Table 7.1.

Table 7.1 Genotypes of the F_2

Gametes of the F_2 BS		Bs	bs	bS
BS	BS BS	BS Bs	BS bs	BS bS
Bs	Bs BS	Bs Bs	Bs bs	Bs bS
bs	bs BS	bs Bs	bs bs	bs bS
bS	bS BS	bS Bs	bS bs	bS bS

Phenotypically, there are 16 combinations as follows:

- 12 are dominant brown, of which three have long hair and thus are homozygous for this recessive character, and nine have short hair;
- four are white and thus homozygous for this recessive character; of these three have short hair and one has long hair and is thus homozygous for this recessive character.

These proportions are found amongst animals as well as in plants when crosses bringing together two pairs of dominant and recessive alleles, are made.

One must therefore admit that in the inheritance of characters, there are entities responsible for the manifestation of characters and that they are transmitted independently from each other in the way that Guyenot described:

> one cannot, in effect, separate and recombine that which does not have an objective existence.
>
> Hereditary material is thus necessarily finite and formed from parts of hereditary units. The concept of hereditary units is not a hypothesis *a priori* . . . it stems from this indisputable argument that the various pairs of characters are subject to independent segregation.

Each character is controlled by a pair of genes (alleles) and if the two genes are identical, that is to say if they induce the same character, there is homozygosity for the gene under consideration. If the two genes of the pair are not identical and correspond to different characters of the phenotype, there is heterozygosity and the phenotypic character which appears is that induced by the dominant gene.

At the time of gamete formation, each gamete carries only one element of the pair of alleles. This is the hypothesis of the purity of gametes, which is based on the study of the segregation of characters in polyhybridism.

In the early research, it was evident that a gene A corresponded to an allele a, but it soon appeared that sometimes a whole series of allelomorphic genes correspond to the same gene, each of the elements of the series controlling the degree of expression of the character. Such a group of genes are called *polygenes*.

Even without the polygenetic effect, when two individuals which differ by three, four or five characters are crossed, the number of possible sorts of gametes increases rapidly by 2^n where n is the number of characters envisaged (Table 7.2). The number of recombinations possible in F_2 is equal to the square of the number of different types of gametes, which led some to say that genetics was the mathematics of the number two (in fact that of the number three since certain recombinations are identical).

Table 7.2 F_2 combination numbers

Allelomorphic characters	Number of different types of gametes	Number of combinations in F_2
1	2^1	$(2^1)^2 = 4$
2	2^2	$(2^2)^2 = 16$
3	2^3	$(2^3)^2 = 64$
4	2^4	$(2^4)^2 = 256$
n	2^n	$(2^n)^2$

This introduces into genetics the concept of population variability because, in the same species, the different individuals differ by so many characters that the probability of two organisms born from the same sexual union, being identical is most unlikely (with the exception however of true identical twins). Mendel's laws are statistically exact and have been successfully used to explain anomalies in theoretical proportions. Recent progress in biogenetics and genetic engineering would not have been possible without them.

In animal breeding, the game of possibles is exploited to the maximum, according to Francois Jacob, one above all makes use of the within species and within-breed variability of quantitative characters. Crossing is practised either to conserve an average type, or to obtain a new type which deviates most from the mean, or to combine the different characters of breeds or varieties.

It was Weismann (1885–1892) who, studying reproduction and having noticed that the ovum and the spermatozoon resemble each other only in their nuclei, supposed that they must play the same role in the transmission of hereditary characters, the determinants being found in the nuclei and the protoplasm only playing a somatic role.

He put forward the idea of a privileged germinal line (*germ*), unalterable, omnipotent and transmitted by the organism to its descendants, and a purely somatic, vegetative line totally independent of the *germ*. This explained the non-heredity of characters acquired in the course of a lifetime, which only involve the *soma*, only that attached to the germinal stock being transmissable.

As in the fertilised egg, half of the *determinants* come from the father, half from the mother, and each fertilisation would double the number of them unless, in the course of gametogenesis, there was a reduction of half before fusion.

In 1903, Sutton developed the hypothesis that genes were particles linked to the chromosomes, the segregation of the Mendelian characters being due to chromosomal reduction which becomes evident in the germ line. He based his hypothesis on the fact that, in a given species, the number of chromosomes and their form are constant. This is known because, even though the chromosomes cannot be seen during the working life of a cell, they reappear in the same form as the originals when cells divide.

The research of Morgan and his school, on *Drosophila*, supported Sutton's concept and the establishment of the irrefutable fact of the correlations which exist between the abstract entities of their predecessor (Weismann's determinants, Guyenot's hereditary units, Mendel's characters) and the perfectly defined cytological structures, the chromosomes, which are present in all cells of living beings. In organisms which reproduce sexually, the chromosomes show different behaviour from that of their homologues in other cell lines during the series of cell divisions which result in gamete formation.

The chromosome theory of inheritance rests on a certain number of experimental arguments:

- specific constancy of the chromosome number;
- mechanism of heredity and of the determination of sex;
- existence of linkage groups (consistent transmission of certain groups of characters *en bloc*).

However this theory does not explain everything and it required research into explanations for its weaknesses. This enabled progress in biological genetics.

Chromosome theory of heredity

Specific constancy of chromosome number

The chromosomes are seen when they separate during cell division. In the same species they are constant in number and form and it is possible to match them in pairs.

The higher the number of chromosomes, the more difficult it becomes to observe them but, in comparing the works of those who have counted them, one notes that the results fluctuate round a mean with very little deviation.

The numbers of chromosomes in some species of animal is given in Table 7.3.

Table 7.3 Chromosome number of domesticated animals

Domesticated animals		Chromosome number
Mammals:		
Bos taurus	humpless cattle	60
Bos indicus	zebus	60
Bubalus bubalis	water buffalo	48 or 50
Capra hircus	goat	60
Ovis aries	sheep	54
Camelus dromaderius	camel	74
Lama glama	lama	74
Sus scrofa domesticus	pig	40
Equus cabalus	horse	60
Asinus asinus	ass	64
Oryctolagus cuniculus	rabbit	44
Birds:		
Anas platyhrinchos	duck	80
Meleagris galloparvo	turkey	82
Gallus gallus	hen	78

Experimentally, it was demonstrated that the sex chromosomes were certainly the carriers of the genes responsible for sex determination and moreover, that certain heredity characters were controlled by genes located on these sex chromosomes.

It is in the poultry industry that *sex linked* hereditary characters are systematically employed, particularly to differentiate males from females at hatching by colour of the plumage. The breeds or hybrids to which this refers are called *autosexable* (Figure 7.1).

From the pathological point of view, certain heritable diseases are characteristically controlled by genes located on the sex chromosomes. In man, haemophilia is a classic example.

The phenomenon of linkage

A little after the discovery of Mendel's laws and the independent assortment of characters, it was frequently observed that the segregation of characters was atypical and that they had a tendency to remain associated in the offspring in the same way as they were in the parents.

Thus in uniform coloured Angora rabbits, the characters *angora coat/ uniform colour* were transmitted together, as were the characters *short coat/ white spots*.

The anomalies in the Mendelian separation of characters in the F_2 generation led to the thinking that if the genes were located in the chromosomes, they should have as many linkage groups as there were pairs of chromosomes. Thus Sturtevant, of Morgan's school, in collating all the works which had been carried out on *Drosophila*, which has four pairs of chromosomes, brought together the some 400 known characters into four

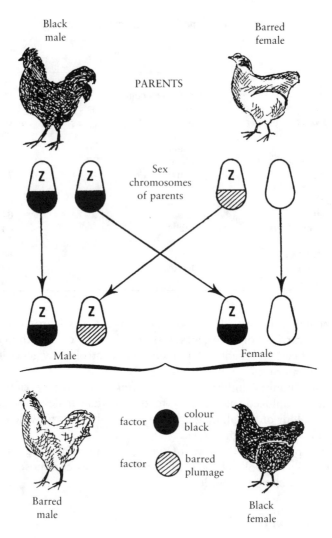

Figure 7.1 Sex-linkage in the hen
When a speckled hen is crossed with a black cock, all the cocks are speckled and all the hens black
(after Hammond, J. Jr, Mason, I. L. and Robinson, T. S. (1971) *Hammond's Farms Animals* London, Edward Arnold)

groups – in other words as many groups as there are pairs of chromosomes.

However, in systematically studying the case of linkage, it appeared that this phenomenon is not absolute; there is a probability of linkage, only gene A being linked to gene B in *n* per cent of cases.

In the same linkage group, the frequency of *linkage* is highly variable, but in taking the genes two at a time, the mean of the frequencies observed has a low variability. Furthermore, if the genes are classed in increasing order of frequency of linkage, their relative positions are constant; finally, the linkage of two genes A and B in relation to a third gene C are such that:

If A is linked to B in n_1 per cent of cases,
B is linked to C in n_2 per cent of cases,
A is linked to C in n_3 per cent of cases,

one finds that $n_3 = n_1 - n_2$. Also it is possible to work out the linear arrangement of the genes from the same group and to estimate their *position*.

As the link between characters in the same group is not absolute, it is at meiosis that there must be an exchange of genetic material between chromosomes from the same pair and, if the genes are positioned linearly in the chromosomes, the probability of seeing two separate from each other will be much higher the further they are apart on the chromosome (and the lower their percentage linkage will be). Thus from a statistical standpoint, one has established *chromosome maps* whose validity has been demonstrated by cytological information.

Figure 7.2 explains the mechanism of this exchange; in case A, the segregation demonstrates absolute linkage: in case B hereditary material is exchanged.

Estimation of linkage percentages requires a very large number of offspring in each generation. Also, the larger the number of chromosomes in the species under consideration, the greater the number of offspring needed in order to estimate linkages. This is why in domesticated animals the linkage groups have mostly been studied in rabbits and poultry.

The linkage groups of sex-linked characters are better known, as the mathematical analysis of the results is far simpler.

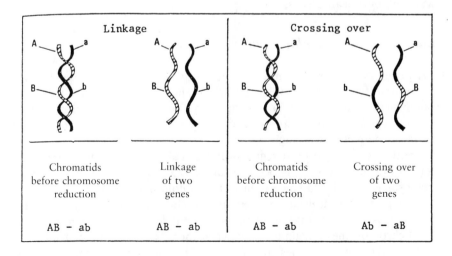

Figure 7.2 Explanatory diagram of linkage and crossing over

Figure 7.3 Karyotype from an animal of the Baoule breed having the 1/29 translocation (the fused chromosome is marked with an arrow)

Most of the animals studied have a normal karyotype, $2n = 60$. Five animals (three of the Baoule breed and two Zebu × N'Dama crosses) show centric fusion, which probably involves chromosomes 1 and 29 and which reduces the diploid chromosome number by one ($2n = 59$)(Figure 7.3). Pure Zebus and Zebus crossed with other breeds have an acrocentric Y (Figure 7.4), whereas the N'Dama and Baoule breeds show a submetacentric Y, identical to that of the European breeds.

Translocations – polyploidy, aneuploidy and mutations

In *crossing over* there is an exchange of genetic material whereby one chromosome loses and the other gains, but there is also transfer from one chromosome to another without reciprocity, and there are total or partial fusions (*translocations*), which are demonstrated by staining cells during meiosis at the metaphase stage.

In cattle from the tropical regions, in particular in the Baoule breed and Zebu × N'Dama crosses, Popescu *et al.* (1979) found a centric fusion of chromosomes 1 and 29, which reduces the diploid number from 60 to 59.

Crossing over and translocation are limited chromosome alterations. There are more significant alterations when there is a *deletion* or *addition* of one or several chromosomes (aneuploidy) or when there is a doubling or tripling of the number of chromosomes (polyploidy). These anomalies crop up in the course of irregular mitoses occurring at the first stages of gamete maturation or

Figure 7.4 Karyotype of Zebu × N'Dama cross animal having the 1/29 translocation (after Popescu *et al.*, 1979)

at egg division. Polyploidy is largely used for genetic improvement of plants and is widespread in the plant kingdom.

Chromsome alterations are not the only means of modifying the action of genes. The internal nature of the genes can be modified (*mutations*), and this involves profound modifications of their phenotypic manifestation.

The existence of mutations has been proven as much in the animal as in the plant kingdom. Table 7.4 gives some examples found in domesticated animals.

Table 7.4 Some known mutations in domesticated animals

Nature of mutation	Description	Affected species
Castor-Rex	absence of leg hair	rabbit
Porcupine	feathers without barbs	pigeon
Anury	absence of tail	dog, cat, sheep
Atrichosis	absence of hair	mouse, rat, dog, rabbit, cattle, man
Hypertrichosis	abnormal development of certain types of hair	guinea-pig, cat, rabbit (Angora)
Albinism (seven types)	absence of pigments in the skin and hair (coat, feathers).	birds, mammals
Achondroplasia (17 types)	shortening/thickening of long, flat bones, dwarfism	cattle, sheep, dog, man
General ankylosis (four types)	locking of the limb and body joints	cattle

Mutations and chromosome alterations are the means of evolution, but they will only have a chance of perpetuation if, in the course of the meiosis, fertilisation or of embryogenesis, they do not lead to problems such as might cause the death of the cells, that contain them (lethality) or which might be eliminated by the phenomenon of autoregulation.

The exceptions to formal Mendelian genetics and above all the mathematical study of variations have thus led researchers to consider the chromosomes not as chains of intangible genes, between which the relationships are unalterable, but as structures which can be modified.

Research into physiological genetics and molecular biology has led to the proposition of a structural model in which the whole of the cell participates in the expression of characters, the nuclear structures playing the role of organisers, having the dual role of auto- and heterocatalysis. This signifies that, at one and the same time, they control their own reproduction and, by the intermediary of the biosynthesis of enzymatic proteins, they control the organisation and regulation of the whole of the organism.

Some classic examples of the heredity of biochemical characters

Heredity of blood groups

General – example of man

When samples of blood from individuals of the same species are mixed, an agglutination of the red blood cells is sometimes produced. This agglutination can equally be produced when the red blood cells of one individual and the plasma or serum of another individual are used.

Everything happens as if each organism had the capacity to defend itself from an intrusion of foreign red blood cells. This capacity is in fact much more general and concerns not only the red blood cells but all the cells and certain chemical substances.

With regard to the red blood cells (antigen), an agglutinogenic property is present in the red blood corpuscles and an agglutinin (antibody) is present in the plasma.

In man, in the first system, two agglutinogens designated by the letters A and B, and corresponding agglutinins designated α and β, have been demonstrated. Their distribution in individuals has enabled the definition of four blood groups (Table 7.5).

An organism never has a situation where the agglutinins correspond to the agglutinogens of its blood cells.

The accident which is most feared in a blood transfusion is that which is caused when the red blood corpuscles of the donor are agglutinated by the agglutinins of the recipient.

Thus, group O, having no agglutinogen, is a universal donor. Group AB is a universal recipient.

Table 7.5 Blood groups in man

Groups	Agglutinogen of red blood cells	Agglutinin of plasma	Type of blood compatibility
O	none	α and β	universal donor
A	A	β	group A or O
B	B	α	group B or O
AB	A and B	none	universal recipient

An individual of group A can only receive blood from groups O, or A.

An individual of group B can only receive blood from groups O, or B.

The heredity of blood groups (Table 7.6) follows the laws of Mendel and it is due to the effect of polygenes:

Codominant gene I^A
Codominant gene I^B } responsible for the presence of agglutinogen

Ressesive gene I^o } the individuals homozygous for I^o do not have agglutinogen.

Table 7.6 Genotypes and phenotypes in the heredity of ABO blood groups in man

Groups	Genotypes	Phenotypes	
		Agglutinogen (cells)	Agglutinin (plasma)
O	$I^o I^o$	none	α and β (anti A and B)
A	$I^A I^A$ or $I^A I^o$	A	β (anti B)
B	$I^B I^B$ or $I^B I^o$	B	α (anti A)
AB	$I^A I^B$	A and B	none

Other systems in man

There are other agglutinogen/agglutinin systems in man but, contrary to agglutinins which are natural, those of other systems have an immunising effect: they correspond to agglutinogens which have been genetically acquired.

Thus following a transfusion which has introduced into the body agglutinogens D, E, c or C, derived from erythrocytes of an individual who does not have them, the recipient reacts by synthesising immunising agglutinins anti-D, anti-E, anti-c or anti-C.

In man, the Rhesus system is the best known because of its implications in the aetiology of jaundice in new-born babies.

Individuals have or do not have the Rh agglutinogen factor: they are either

(Rh+) or (Rh−). If, due to a transfusion, a (Rh−) patient is injected with (Rh+), he will develop anti-(Rh+) agglutinins and at the time of a later transfusion will agglutinate the red blood corpuscles of (Rh+) blood.

If a (Rh−) woman successively carries several (Rh+) (father positive) fetuses, the anti-(Rh+) agglutinins which her body will produce against the erythrocyte agglutinogens of these fetuses will end up destroying their red blood cells. These babies will die in the uterus or, if they live, will suffer with the exception of the first of them, from serious jaundice. Death can generally only be avoided if total replacement of the blood of the fetus in the uterus or of the new-born baby is carried out.

In animals, jaundice of the young mule has the same aetiology. It is due to the destruction of the red blood cells of the young mule by haemolysin produced by the mare in the course of gestation.

Blood group systems in animals

The presence of ABO and Rh blood groups in man is only one particular example of blood group systems that are found in all animals.

The number of blood group systems in domesticated animals is much greater than in man.

In cattle 10 blood group systems have been identified. In blood group system A there are only three factors, and in blood group B there are 15; and almost each year new ones are found.

Practical use of blood groups

Blood transfusions

The existence of blood factors responsible for red blood cell or erythrocyte incompatabilities necessitates determination of the blood type of the recipient before all transfusions in order that the injected blood does not agglutinate.

In emergencies in man, only the groups within the ABO and Rhesus systems are used.

Identification of parents

Each agglutinogen or group of agglutinogens corresponds to a dominant gene and the absence of such agglutinogens corresponds to a recessive gene. An individual only has an agglutinogen if one or other of its parents has it.

In practice, if the blood groups of the parents are known, the possible blood groups of the offspring can be predicted. However the reverse cannot be done with 100 per cent accuracy and one can only affirm, for example, the impossibility of a supposed parent being the father of such a child; one cannot confirm that a child has as its father an individual who has the same blood groups as itself.

Extension of the research to groups, other than ABO and Rhesus can reinforce this system of exclusions.

Blood typing is sometimes used in legal medicine in court cases (in paternity suits). It is also used in veterinary medicine for the identification of offspring of elite breeding stock whose pedigree value enters largely into the determination of the sale price.

The great number of blood groups and factors increases the precision of determination. As indicated in Table 7.7, one can say which is the possible sire of a given calf but also affirm that it is not the son of a known bull. This system is only capable of determining paternity with certainty if there is a finite group of supposed parents.

Table 7.7 Determination of the actual father of a calf born to a known cow

								Blood factors													
Bull S_1	A	B		F		J	O					X_2			Z			I		I	
Bull S_2	A	B	C_1	F		J	O	R	S	V	W	X_2	Y_1	Y_2	Z	$A'E_2$	H'		JK		
Mother S_3	A				H	J	O			V		X_2					H'		J'K'	L'	
Calf S_4	A				H		O	R		V	W	X_2		Y_2	Z		H'	J	K'	L	

Calf S_4 has the bull S_2 as its father and cannot have the bull S_1 as its father, the factors R, V, W, Y_2 being common to S_2 and S_4 and not being present in S_1.

Frequency of blood groups in populations

The distribution of different blood groups in populations is used in anthropological research because the frequency of the genes is different in different human groups (Table 7.8). Similar data has been produced for genes of blood groups in cattle (Table 7.10).

Table 7.8 Examples of the frequency of ABO blood groups in man (percentage values)

Blood groups	World average	France	Japan	Bantu Congo	Arborigines Australia
O	38.81	45	31.5	51.6	38.7
A	31.41	44	37.3	25.1	61.3
B	22.81	8	22.1	19.6	0
AB	6.97	3	9.1	3.7	0

Laboratory determinations of the frequency of blood factors in different breeds of cattle have been made, but it should be noted that the complexity of anti-serum preparation necessary for identification has, till now, limited their use.

Table 7.9 Absolute difference of the frequencies of certain genes characterising the blood groups in cattle

Blood group system	Number of genes	Difference (absolute) in frequency						
		BZ–JRT'	BZ–JRK	BZ–JB	BZ–JS	BZ–M	BZ–K	BZ–FY
A	2	0.119	0.034	0.171	0.271	0.424	0.071	0.267
B	15	0.433	0.467	0.045	2.523	1.646	0.327	0.408
C	4	0.691	0.501	0.937	0.380	1.011	0.359	0.378
FV	2	0.326	0.436	0.390	0.502	0.782	0.592	0.820
J	2	0.318	1.000	0.120	1.140	0.580	0.240	0.244
L	2	0.910	0.722	0.766	0.632	0.744	0.860	0.476
SU	5	0.392	0.111	0.324	1.065	0.009	0.313	0.088
Z	2	0.468	0.890	0.490	1.400	1.556	0.642	0.054
R'S'	2	0.545	0.568	0.165	0.536	–	0.536	0.484
Tf	5	0.327	0.511	0.544	0.630	0.485	0.329	0.424
Hb	3	0.700	0.706	0.830	0.860	–	0.706	0.232
A1B	3	1.690	–	1.690	1.684	–	1.650	0.070
Total	47	6.101	5.946	6.727	9.571	6.715	6.408	3.785

Studies of genetics of the blood systems of Brazilian Zebus of the Nellore and Gir breeds and Nellore/Gir crosses gave the results shown in Table 7.10. It will give an understanding of the complexity of the work involved.

Nevertheless, if one simply considers the heredity of blood groups in cattle, one notes that although its analysis is technically delicate, it poses no problem from the point of view of its logic.

Other hereditary blood factors

Haemoglobins

In cattle, several types of haemoglobin have been identified. The haemoglobins HbA, HbB, HbC, HbD, HbG and Hb Khilari are distinguished and these exist in the red blood cells, alone or combined, in variable proportions according to breed.

Research workers studying the distribution of haemoglobins HbA and HbB in samples of Zebu and humpless cattle in West and Central Africa and Madagascar, found the frequencies of the genotypes $Hb^A Hb^A$, $Hb^A H_b^B$ and $Hb^B Hb^B$ given in Table 7.11.

The rarity of haemoglobin HbB in the samples of Ivory Coast and Gabon N'Dama cattle should be noted. The frequency in the sample of Montbeliarde cattle is given for comparison.

Haemoglobin HbC is present in the Indian Kankrej and Dangi breeds and the African Angoni breed. It was found in the Afrikander breed by Osterhoff (1975).

In the Zebu populations of East Africa, Braend (1971) gave the following haemoglobin frequencies: HbA: 0.52; HbB:0.32; HbC: 0.14; HbD: 0.01.

Table 7.10 Frequency of factors responsible for blood factors in Brazilian Zebus

Blood group system	Factors	Frequency		
		Nellore	Gir	Cross
A	A_1 (2)	0.731	0.625	0.708
	A_2	0.877	0.813	0.857
	Z' (37)	0.354	0.438	0.369
B	B (24)	0.631	0.625	0.625
	C (70,102)	0.431	0.563	0.452
	K	0.246	0.313	0.250
	I_2 (66)	0.446	0.438	0.452
	O_1 (51)	0.515	0.594	0.524
	O_3 (72)	0.307	0.063	0.262
	O (24)	0.654	0.625	0.637
	T (30)	0.477	0.563	0.500
	Y_2	0.631	0.813	0.655
	D'	0.108	0.188	0.199
	E_1' (70)	0.646	0.250	0.548
	I' (66)	0.077	0.063	0.071
	J'	0.138	0.063	0.131
	K' (67)	0.138	0.063	0.131
	O_2' (54)	0.762	0.625	0.720
C	C_1 (22)	0.502	0.625	0.542
	W_1 (59)	0.785	0.688	0.762
	X_1 (14)	0.954	0.938	0.952
	R (12)	0.169	0.125	0.155
F	F (36,81)	0.577	0.344	0.536
	V_3	0.223	0.188	0.208
J	J_1 (120)	0.231	0.313	0.250
L	L (57)	0.677	0.875	0.710
SU	S_1 (62)	0.931	0.965	0.940
	H' (103)	0.938	0.938	0.940
	U_1 (15)	0.115	0.125	0.113
	U_2 (60,2)	0.308	0.281	0.292
	U' (7)	0.223	0.125	0.196
Z	Z (71)	0.969	1.000	0.976
R'S'	R' (8)	0.446	0.750	0.488
	Number of animals	65	16	84

Figures in brackets are number of antisera

Genetic markers

When the heredity of blood groups or haemoglobins is studied, one is dealing in fact with particular cases of the heredity of biological factors which are involved in the functioning of living organisms.

Table 7.11 Frequency of haemoglobin genotypes of cattle

Breeds of cattle	Frequency		
	Hb^AHb^A	Hb^AHb^B	Hb^BHb^B
Zebu – Arab	0.35	0.45	0.20
Zebu – Bororo	0.40	0.43	0.17
Zebu – Madagascan	0.16	0.44	0.40
Zebu – Gobra	0.40	0.60	0
Zebu – Soudan	0.40	0.48	0.12
Zebu – Brahman	0.19	0.50	0.31
Zebu – Rénitélo	0.56	0.37	0.07
Humpless – N'Dama (Gabon)	1.00	0	0
Humpless – N'Dama (Ivory Coast)	0.90	0.05	0.05
Humpless – Montbéliarde (France)	0.97	0.02	0
Humpless – Kouri (Chad)	0.38	0.47	0.14

Laboratory techniques now enable large scale determination of the structure of blood and tissue substances such as albumins, transferrins, esterase, alkaline phosphatase, immunoglobins G1 and G2 etc., which are true genetic markers. It is in effect possible to determine, within animal populations, the frequencies of the variants of these markers and, in the same species, to estimate the divergencies and convergences between populations or breeds which constitute them. Knowledge of the genetic structure of populations for certain biochemical characters of known determinism thus enables elaboration of hypotheses relating to the origin of these populations and the reconstitution of the history of migrations and crossing between populations.

In the future, it is probable that the use of similar markers will develop, as research discovers relationships between certain of these easily detectable characters and characters which are of major economic interest but of complex genetic determinism.

Concepts of the genetics of populations and of quantitative genetics

General

The individuals (with the exception of identical twins) making up a population of a given species are not identical to each other. This variation comes from several origins. On the one hand, all the individuals of the population do not live in exactly the same environmental conditions and thus do not present the same physiological and morphological characteristics. On the other hand, they do not all have the same genetic make up and there is a certain variation within the whole population.

The genetics of populations aims to study the genetic variation of populations and their variations in the course of time, with particular reference to the case of natural selection. This discipline has enabled the drawing up of a certain number of concepts which have been used in the scientific approach to methods of artificial selection of plants and domesticated animals which man has practised for millenia.

The phenotypic characters which have been discussed above present modest, qualitative variations which arise from simple genetic causes i.e. the discontinuous nature of Mendelian factors reconciles well with the modest expression of such characters. Biochemical characters, in particular, are elementary characters which depend, in general, upon a very small number of genes – often only one – in accordance with the 'one gene, one enzyme' hypothesis. However, it is frequently the case that one gene has an effect on several characters at the same time (pleiotropy) or conversely that a group of genes situated or not situated on the same chromosome, simultaneously contribute to the expression of a complex character for which the variation might be continuous and very large i.e. polygenic.

In the subject of animal genetics, the characters of economic interest, whose purely operational definition often has no biological basis, are mostly of a synthetic nature and arise very generally from a polygenic determinism. It concerns quantitative measurable characteristics whose genetic interpretation, in the light of Mendelian models, appears much less evident. Their study is the subject of quantitative genetics, on which the methods of animal selection rest.

These characteristics are categorised by:

1. the actions of a large number of genes with small individual effects which interact together (although the existence of some major genes is known whose expression dominates a polygenic group and which are evidently particularly interesting to the geneticist);
2. the superimposing of environmental influences which themselves have continuous variation.

In this case it is not possible to reveal the particular contributions of each gene, nor to identify them more conclusively. Artificial selection, which aims to modify the mean value of a characteristic in a population almost by guesswork, can only therefore use methods which depend on the deduction of the genotype of individuals from the observation of phenotypes. It depends on complex statistical methods, whose principles will be shown after a brief review of the genetics of populations.

Genetic evolution of natural populations

Hardy and Weinberg (1908) established that in a large random-mating population (that is to say one in which the crosses are made at random, without deliberate choice of partners), with an infinite population size, in the absence of mutation, migration and immigration, and without selection, the proportion of genotypes remains absolutely identical from one generation to another i.e. the genetic structure of this ideal population will be in equilibrium.

On the contrary, the genetic structure of real populations evolves under the combined influence of mutations, a finite population size, selection, and the deliberate choice of partner at the time of mating.

Natural populations constitute more or less isolated groups which each exploit a territory whose resources are limited. The indefinite expansion of these populations is thus prevented and, taking account of the theoretical possibilities of the phenomena of reproduction, this implies that extremely severe processes of elimination come into play in order to limit population size. Thus almost all of the male gametes are eliminated, as is a variable number of the female gametes (99 per cent in the human species). Likewise, from very large numbers of fertile eggs, most of the larvae and some of the adults will not reach reproductive age and therefore will not contribute to the perpetuation of the species. Part of this process of elimination is haphazard and therefore independent of the genome of individuals that are eliminated or preserved; the remaining part constitutes the reverse, namely selective elimination, which depends on the characteristics presented by each individual – characteristics which are partially determined by the genotype of these individuals.

The number of direct offspring of an individual of given genotype is a random variable the expected value of which in relative terms, represents the selective value of this genotype, or *fitness*.

Working thus essentially through the balance between mortality and fertility, natural selection tends to increase over successive generations the frequencies of alleles producing genotypes that confer selective advantages, and tends to reduce or even destroy the genetic polymorphism of populations. This polymorphism is maintained in natural populations because it is maintained by different mechanisms operating simultaneously:

1. mutations resulting in the appearance, once or continually over time (recurrent mutations), of new alleles;
2. variation of selective value as a result of variations in the environment;
3. divergence from random mating, i.e. the non-random formation of mating pairs in the case where the choice of partner is a function of the individuals' genotypes or phenotypes, or inbreeding in small populations where mating occurs between related individuals;
4. migrations and interbreeding occurring on contact with populations of different genetic structure.

In 1930 Fisher demonstrated that natural selection always tends to increase the mean selective value of populations, that is to say it increases their degree of adaptation to environmental constraints. This being so, human intervention in the genetics of animals runs the risk of reducing this adaption, and is only justified because it is accompanied by profound environmental modification and because it is intended to produce, in a character or group of characters, advantages that are considered important enough to make the risk acceptable.

Of the methods capable of modifying the genetic structure of populations, four have been or are currently used by man for the genetic improvement of domestic animals:

1. artificial selection, which relies on the estimation of individual genetic values and the choice of the breeding stock;
2. systematic inbreeding;
3. organisation of crosses between populations or lines;
4. hybridisation between related species to a lesser extent, which will not be discussed here.

These methods are generally combined, particularly the two most important method – selection and crossing.

Principles of selection

The object of artificial selection is to increase the mean value of a population for one or several characteristics chosen a *priori*, by improving the genetic potential of the animals of this population. The process consists of estimating the individual genetic value of the animals then choosing the breeding stock which will produce the next generation and do this in the most judicious manner possible. Putting it into practice necessitates, in a general way, relatively important measures which consist of the following operations:

1. measurement of individual performance;
2. processing of recorded data and assessment of animals;
3. choice of breeding stock and organisation of their use.

These operations have for a long time been carried out on a purely empirical basis, starting by ascertaining the resemblances between relatives i.e. the stockmen chose as breeding stock those animals which showed the best performance or which came from the best lines. They then organised breeding in such a manner as to ensure the greatest possible number of offspring from the animals thus selected. For obvious reasons, given the nature of physiology of reproduction, the selectors have almost always been forced to use the male line since the males are able to fertilise a large number of females and to sire a large number of offspring. It is thus possible to eliminate a significant proportion of them, that is to select them more effectively than the females. It can be intuitively understood, that the effectiveness of selection depends directly upon the stringency of selection.

These very old techniques have seen constant improvements over the centuries and developments accelerated in Europe from the eighteenth century onwards. However it was necessary to await the synthesis model proposed by Fisher in 1918 before the bases of quantitative modern genetics could be created and this discipline could be linked to the chromosome theory of heredity.

Fisher's theory enabled the explanation, in the light of Mendelian analysis, of the nature of the biometric relations between relatives and provided breeders with an essential operational tool, which was later perfected by other workers.

Without entering into details of the theory and its often very complex mathematical and statistical development, one can say that under this model the action of the genes on characteristics can be resolved into several effects:

1. an additive effect;
2. non-additive effects (or interaction), which concern alleles present at the same locus (the effect of dominance, which explains the fact that the value of the heterozygote frequently differs from – and usually exceeds – half the value of the two corresponding homozygotes), at alleles present at different loci (effects of *epistasis*), or effects associated with recombination between loci (effects of *linkage*).

To these genetic effects are added environmental effects. These include, in certain cases, maternal genetic effects, the maternal phenotype constituting an essential element of the environment of the young. The phenotype of the offspring depend in part on the genotype of the mother, which is not independent of that of the offspring.

In the population, the phenotypic variation is itself broken down, according to the same model, into additive genetic variance, non-additive genetic variance, environmental variance and into different terms of covariance which cancel each other out under certain hypotheses. This breakdown, which relies on the distinction of different classes of related individuals, is exactly analogous to that practised in the statistical models for the analysis of variance.

The relationship between the additive genetic variance and the total phenotypic variance is particularly interesting. This is the hereditibility (h^2) of the character considered in the population.

The chromosome model provides a statistical expression of the resemblance between related animals as a function of the nature of the relationship, and resemblance is generally expressed in terms of covariance between related animals.

Moreover, Fisher's model provides a statistical expression of the relationship between two characters, which is generally expressed in terms of phenotypic correlations and genetic correlations between characters. The heritabilities and genetic correlations between characters constitutes the 'genetic parameters' of the population.

All things considered, quantitative genetics enables:

1. forecasting the extent to which a character to which selection, the value of its hereditability in the population considered being a determinant in this respect (Tables 7.12 and 7.13);
2. considerable improvement in the estimation of the genetic value of candidates for selection, by allowing combinations of all available information, obtained from measurements taken on the individual itself or on its relations;
3. the working out of selection schemes, by (a) the evaluation from past performance of the genetic and phenotypic progress that one can expect from a selection programme, (b) estimation of indirect effects on the characters linked to the selected character, and (c) comparison of the effectiveness of different selection methods.

The practice of selection

General

On the ground, setting up a system of evaluation of the animal's individual performance constitutes the first stage of building the selection programme. Its objective is twofold since the information recorded is needed for.

1. the evaluation of the genetic value of candidates for selection by differences in indices of selection, which are estimators calculated from phenotypic measurements made on these candidates and/or on their relatives;
2. the prediction, from phenotypic covariances measured between relatives, of genetic parameters of the population.

Evaluation of genetic parameters

The heritability of a character and the genetic correlations which link it with other characters are estimated from the measurement of 'parent-offspring' covariances (father-offspring, mother-offspring or average parent-offspring), of covariances between half-cousins (half-brothers and half-sisters) or between cousins and half-cousins.

The choice of factors relative depends upon theoretical factors (certain relatives give more useful information than others) and practical factors, in particular the system of mating and the structure of families which characterise the species under consideration, and the system of animal production, which determine the type of possible arrangements for crossing.

It must be noted that the values of genetic parameters, and in particular the heritability, both of a characteristic depend on the variance of environmental effects and on the genetic structure of the population under consideration, i.e. the values are relative values, which are modified, notably by changing the system of animal production. This is currently practised by changing for

	0.1	0.2	0.3	0.4	0.5	0.6	0.7
Cattle		- Milking time	- Milk let-down	- Growth rate after weaning - Age at first oestrus - Index of consumption	- Carcass grading - Tenderness of meat - % muscle ⎫ - % fat ⎭ 11th rib		- Conformation of udder - Areas of Longissimus dorsi muscle - Position of quarters (teats)
Pigs		- Technical yield of hams - Colour and pH of the meat	- Growth rate from weaning to slaughter - Index of consumption - Weight of ham		- Thicknes of fat - Loin and back bacon weight		- Weight of fat
Goats		- Kidding interval	- Butter-fat content - Protein content - Milk let-down	- Index of consumption	- Ability to retain water - Carcass length - Age at first kidding - Quantity of milk		- Content of coagulable proteins
Rabbits	- Size at birth and at weaning - Mortality rate from birth to weaning - Individual weight at weaning			- Weight gain from weaning to slaughter - Index of consumption - Weight at 11 weeks - Muscle/bone ratio of the carcass	- Yield at slaughter	- % fat content of the carcass	

Table 7.12 Principal heritability values measured in research stations

Heritability scale: 0.1 — 0.2 — 0.3 — 0.4 — 0.5 — 0.6 — 0.7

Cattle
- Calving interval — 0.1
- Birth weight — 0.1
- Weaning weight — 0.1
- Birth rate — 0.1
- Growth rate from birth to weaning — 0.1
- timing of weaning — 0.2
- Timing of maturity — 0.2
- Quantity of milk — 0.2
- Timing of age-pattern — 0.2
- Butter-fat content — 0.55

Pigs
- Size at birth — 0.1
- Size at weaning — 0.15
- Average birth or weaning weight — 0.1
- Conformity of the live animal — 0.2
- Growth rate from weaning to slaughter — 0.45

Sheep
- Fertility–Fecundity of ewes — 0.1
- Prolificacy — 0.1
- Growth rate from birth or weaning — 0.1
- Age at first lambing — 0.2
- Adult weight — 0.35
- Growth rate after weaning — 0.35
- Weight of fleece — 0.35
- Length of leg of mutton — 0.5
- Length of wool fibre — 0.55

Table 7.13 Principal heritability values measured on the farm

example when animals being evaluated are put into a common environment so as to reduce the environmental variance (e.g. animals transferred to a tropical environment).

On the other hand, in the genetic structure of the evolving population – in particular under the influence of selection – the value of genetic parameters, and above all that of the genetic correlations between characteristics, is liable to vary. This evolution is in a way a general way unfavourable to the effectiveness of selection, i.e. lowering of the heritability, appearance of negative correlations between characteristics etc.

Definition of the objectives and criteria of selection

Theory would like the choice of selection objectives to rely on a previous study of the production systems in such a way as to determine objectively the respective contribution (the economic weight) of each of the characters with an overall economic function synthesising the results of the system. This would allow optimisation of the choice of characters for simultaneous improvement, account having been taken of their genetic and phenotypic relations. In reality, this complex process is rarely practised and selection programmes are only concerned with one or a very small number of characteristics. They thus tend

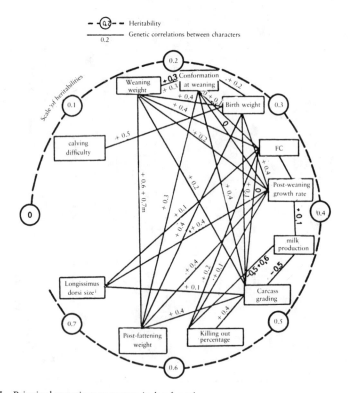

Figure 7.5 Principal genetic parameters in beef cattle

to instigate the creation of lines or strains, improved for a particular use, which are part of the wider group of participents of a genetic improvement programme; they are then involved not only in selection but also in crossing.

The selection of breeds or lines specialised for milk production and meat production etc., and of paternal (for example the doubled muscle type) and maternal (whose reproduction qualities are improved) blood-stock, are pursued in this way.

This specialisation allows the breeder to circumvent the problems raised by negative relationships between characters which often occur, or develop — for example between the meat production, or growth rate, conformation and reproduction – fertility, ease of calving, production of milk etc. (Figures 7.5 – 7.8).

Once the objective of selection is clearly defined, the problem is to choose one or several selection criteria that correspond to this objective, that is to define the characteristics which one or more animals will be judged. A good criterion for selection has two essential qualities; first and quite evidently, it must show a strong correlation with the objective so that the effects obtained by selection on this criterion represent an improvement in the objective, and second it must be easy to measure with standard methods, be reliable, precise and cheap (Table 7.14)

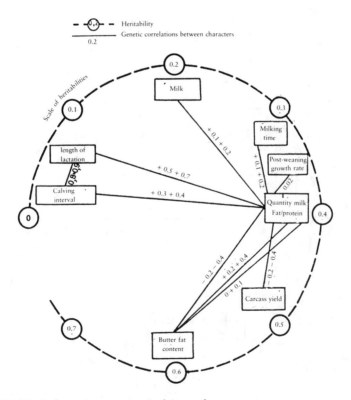

Figure 7.6 Principal genetic parameters in dairy cattle

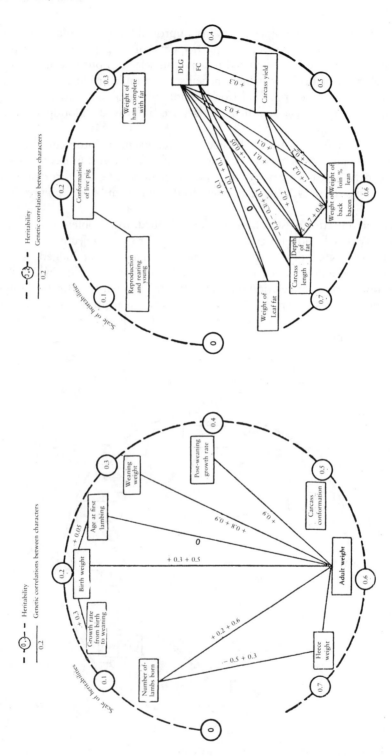

Figure 7.8 Principal genetic parameters in pigs

Figure 7.7 Principal genetic parameters in meat sheep

Table 7.14 Examples of characteristics considered suitable for selection

Species	Production	Reproduction	Growth	Carcass

Cattle	longevity
	duration of lactation
	persistence of lactation
	quantity of milk per
	  lactation, per day of
	  life
	quantity of fats
	quantity of protein
	butterfat content
	nitrogen content
	teat conformation
	milking time
		age at first calving
		calving interval
		calving capacity
		fertility
		
		sexual precocity
		sperm production
		quality and fertility of sperm
			weight at birth
			weight at weaning
			weight gain over different
			  periods
			weight for age/type
			conformation at different
			  stages
			adult weight
			consumption index in
			  different periods
				killing value
				carcass yield
				meat yield
				conformation (cuilinary)
				area from long dorsal to
				  side
				  isle
				weight of different cuts
				conformation of different
				  cuts
				thickness of fat cover
				quality of meat: colour
				  (calves)

Sheep	weight of fleece fineness of wool duration of lactation quantity of milk butterfat content nitrogen content	age at first lambing fertility prolificacy anoestrus period weaning rate quality and quantity of sperm	weight increase from birth to weaning weight at weaning adult weight conformation consumption index	carcass yield conformation significance of kidney fat thickness of back fat leg length

Pigs	maturation period
	quantity and quality of
	meat
		age at first heat
		prolificacy
		farrowing interval
		litter mortality rate
		weaning rate
		milk production
		
		sperm quality
			speed of growth at
			different
			  stages and
			corresponding
			  consumption index
			conformation
			resistance to stress
			liveweight at different ages
				carcass yield
				weight of bone
				length of carcass
				weight of complete ham
				thickness of dorsal and
				  cervical fat
				back bacon weight
				fat weight
				loin weight
				meat colour
				meat tenderness and
				  flavour

Poultry	age at point of lay
	number of eggs laid
	per
	  season
	intensity of lay
	broodiness
	persistence of lay
	egg weight
	shell colour
	shell strength
	internal egg quality
		egg fertilisation ratio
		fertile egg
		hatching ratio
		chick mortality
		
		sexual vigour
		sperm fertility
			vitality of young
			resistance to stress
			consumption index
			speed of growth
			angle of breast
			length of leg
			liveweight at different ages
				carcass yield
				ease of plucking
				skin colour
				length of trunk
				'drumstick' leg length
				angle of breast
				thickness of wing skin
				proportion of breast bone
				  muscle
				bone/meat ratio
				meat juices

The choice of selection criteria depends largely on the way the characteristics held as the objective are manifested:

1. Certain characteristics are only manifested late in the life of the animals. One chooses a criterion which manifests itself more clearly (for example if one wishes to increase adult weight, one could choose to predict it by the weight at one year of age). This is done in such a way as to increase the speed of selection and thus its efficiency, since one cannot keep all the candidates up to adulthood, and one can then test more for the same cost.
2. Certain characteristic manifest themselves in one sex only. This is the case with egg production in poultry and with milk production in mammals. The prediction of the genetic value of a sire can only be based on the

performances of the females which are related to him (mother, sisters, half sisters, daughters, grandmothers etc. . . .).

3. Certain characters have sequential manifestation, spread over the life of the animals, and it is then convenient to gather discontinuous information (such as in milk production, when each lactation provides new information), in such a way as to improve progressively the precision of the data and to be able to compare performance with those animals which have had a similar background.

Construction of selection indices and rationalisation of selection programmes

Selection indices, which are the predictors of the individuals' own genetic value, will enable comparison between them and then enable a choice of the breeding stock to produce the following generation. Their construction first of all assumes that each individual, or each performance in the case of sequentially expressed characteristics, has a phenotypic record which in general can only be a rough measure of the character under considerations, but which describes performance more accurately after corrections for environmental factors (even if all the animals measured are in a common environment, which is quite exceptional). In other words one should correct the performances to take account of the effects of the year, the farm, the herd, the group etc. . . . These corrections are generally effected using the statistical technique of least squares.

The individual records should then be combined in order to use all the available information. The genetic value of each candidate is thus predicted from its own performance and also from the performance of its relatives. We will not enter into the details of the methods used (aggregation of indices methods), which are extremely complex. Nevertheless, this short presentation enables one to understand that one will not, in general, have comparable information at one's disposal on all points for each animal. The more numerous the relatives of a candidate the more precise is the information relating to that candidate. Each index will therefore be accompanied by a value calculated for its accuracy, which is none other than the square of the correlation (R) between the genetic value of the candidate and its predictor, the selection index. This value, written R^2, is often designated by the term *coefficient of determination* (CD).

Theory predicts that the *annual genetic progress* which it is possible to achieve with a selection programme depends on:

1. The intensity of selection, which is a standardised measure of the difference between the mean of the population and the mean of the sub-population of selected individuals, which is obviously superior to it – this value is linked to the selection ratio, which represents the proportion of animals selected in the population. The greater the selection intensity (i.e. the lower the selection ratio), then the greater the expected genetic progress.

2. The precision of the index, which itself depends upon the amount of information relating to the genetic value of each candidate which it has been possible to record – quite obviously, the higher the coefficient of determination of the index, the more effective will the selection be.
3. The interval between generations (mean age of the parents at the birth of their offspring in the population under consideration) – the larger this interval is, clearly that the less effective will be the selection. It is helpful therefore to reduce this interval to the minimum.

Unfortunately there are opposing forces between these variables. Thus for example, to increase the precision of indices will often lead to an increase in the interval between generations (if for example one wishes to progeny test a male, one delays the time when the animal could be used for breeding and increases the generation interval). Similarly, for material reasons, to increase the intensity of selection (that is to say for example to test more candidates in order to select the same number of breeding stock) amounts to reducing the precision of selection, because one will have to relax the controls or collect a smaller amount of genealogical information.

All these problems should be taken into account when setting up appropriate schemes to give maximum potential annual genetic progress. Table 7.15 gives an example of this, and shows that it is not satisfactory to record genealogical information high on ancestors other than the parents when the heritability of the characteristic under consideration is strong and that, even if it is weak, the improvement of the value of R^2 is hardly perceptible beyond three generations.

Table 7.15 Value of R^2 (coefficient of determination) at the time of the choice on the individual phenotypic values of ancestors as a function of the number of generations considered

Heritability h^2	Number of generations				
	1	2	3	4	5
0.1	0.050	0.070	0.079	0.082	0.085
0.2	0.100	0.133	0.144	0.147	0.149
0.3	0.150	0.188	0.199	0.202	0.203
0.4	0.200	0.239	0.248	0.249	0.250
0.5	0.250	0.286	0.292	0.293	0.293
0.6	0.300	0.329	0.333	0.333	0.333
0.7	0.350	0.371	0.373	0.373	0.373
0.8	0.400	0.412	0.412	0.412	0.412
0.9	0.450	0.454	0.454	0.454	0.454
1.0	0.500	0.500	0.500	0.500	0.500

Figure 7.9 shows that, although it is worthwhile to increase the progency of the candidate in order to improve the precision of selection on the progeny, the heritability of the character is reduced (but it must be remembered that in this case, one will undoubtedly reduce the intensity of selection since one cannot test an unlimited number of animals and one must then limit the number of candidates).

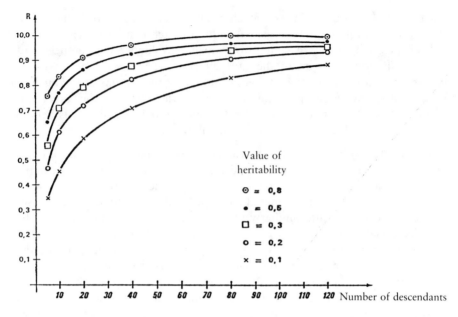

Figure 7.9 Change in R as a function of the number of progeny and of h² in selection of offspring

Principal methods of selection

Selection on one character

The simplest and oldest method practised is mass selection or individual phenotypic selection, where the genetic value of the candidates is predicted purely on their phenotypic value, which can be measured once or several times in the life of the animal (in the case of animals with sequential expression). In the latter case, the effectiveness of selection depends on the repeatability of the measurement of the character, which constitutes a higher limit for the heritability. Thus one cannot easily select cows on the length of the interval between calving (criteria of fecundity), because the repeatability of this characteristic is almost nil. This indicates that the correlation between its successive values is nil.

The coefficient of determination of mass selection indices presents the peculiarity of being equal to the heritability:

$$R^2 = h^2$$

It follows that this method gives excellent results when it is applied to highly heritable characters and that it is unusable for characters with low heritability.

It will be noticed that the practice of selection is possible independently of all theoretical considerations. Knowledge of the value of the genetic parameters is not necessary, nor is the testing of progeny, which explains the historical success of this method.

The other methods are selection on the value of phenotype of previous generations, selection on progeny, selection on siblings and combined selection, which integrates information relating to the individual's own performance and that of its family. The attraction of family selection or selection on progeny, previous generations or siblings is obvious when no information is available on the candidate itself (as in the case of selecting bulls for milk production). The combination of information of a diverse nature always necessitates previous estimation of the genetic parameters of the population and poses delicate problems of correction of the data for environmental factors.

Combined methods of selection are frequently used which measure the character in the candidates (if that is possible) and in a contemporary sample of the progeny placed in a common environment (progeny test). This necessitates very significant resources and can only be envisaged on a national or regional scale.

Selection on several characters

These methods are essentially used, in the industrialised countries, to improve meat production (poultry, pigs, cattle) and thus combine characters such as speed of growth, consumption index and killing out performance (yield, composition etc). Three methods are classically distinguished:

1. *Tandem selection,* which consists of alternating the selection of each character in phases over time. The effectiveness is fairly poor and it is not voluntarily used on a large scale, although the history of selection shows that changes in the objectives of selection has led to the adoption of a policy of this type.
2. *Selection by independent culling levels,* which consists of eliminating all the animals whose selection indices, calculated independently for each character, are inferior to thresholds fixed a *priori.*

   This method is particularly easy to use, but its effectiveness is very variable according to the character considered. It has the inconvenience of eliminating certain animals acceptable for one character but not for the others.
3. *Selection on index.* Selection indices are a linear combination of values calculated for each character. One can show that this method is the most effective of the three. It requires relatively complex calculations. This method is used essentially for the improvement of species reared under standardised conditions (poultry, rabbit, pigs etc. . .), and facilitates the calculation of weightings for each of the characteristics in the index; the

effects of variations in each character on the economic result of production are easily measured.

In the case where cannot be determined economic weights cannot be determined, one can introduce a variant of the system by introducing constraints on certain characters. One may thus want to improve the adult size of the animals without increasing their weight at birth and one can then talk of selection on index with restriction.

Selection for crossing

In actual fact most genetic improvement schemes integrate selection and crossing at the same time. Specialised bloodstocks are thus selected classically on a given trait before being crossed with other bloodstocks, themselves selected in another direction. Recurrent selection relies on the observation of the performances of progeny obtained by crossing two lines i.e. in each of them, selection is operated on the crossbred progeny. On the other hand, numerous selection methods used with success in plants, have led to experimentation on animals, however they have not become widely used, especially for species with long cycles. They mostly require complex operations for the creation of inbred lines for later crossing (divergent selection intended to recreate variability). This can hardly be envisaged in large animals for technical and economic reasons.

Systematic use of inbreeding

Inbreeding results from matings between related individuals. It is inevitable in populations whose numbers are limited. Genetically it tends to reduce the frequency of heterozygotes in the population, by increasing differences in gene frequencies between the different inbred lines (the phenomenon of genetic drift). It equally exerts effects upon quantitative characters; on the one hand it reduces the mean of the phenotypic value of the population. This is linked to the phenomenon of dominance and the diminution of the number of heterozygotes – this is inbreeding depression. On the other hand the additive genetic variance is split up into variance within lines and variance between lines, of which the sum can be higher than the initial additive variances, particularly if this is weak. One has an idea here of the possibility already suggested of recreating genetic variability by selection then by the crossing of inbred lines. On the other hand, inbreeding always seems to increase the variance of effects due to the surroundings, perhaps because the homozygosity which it favours does not permit individuals to adapt themselves to variations in the environment as easily as heterozygotes.

These effects increase as the mean level of inbreeding in the population increases. Despite the risk – well known since antiquity – of inbreeding depression, inbreeding has been much used to improve domesticated animals, principally for the purpose of 'fixing animal types' by reducing the frequency of heterozygotes. This sort of worry having damped the spirit of the breeders, the systematic practice of inbreeding has been little used in recent improvements of quantitative characters. Nevertheless there is a revival of interest in these methods to the extent that the standardisation of common farm species (mainly poultry) has become a significant concern, and in the research already cited relating to crosses between inbred lines there is hope of genetic gains from heterosis (see below).

The most classic example of the systematic use of inbreeding is that of the creation, in the eighteenth century, of the breed of horse called the *English Thoroughbred*. All the animals of this breed, which is specialised for racing, descend from a very small number of Arab stallions which were crossed with about thirty English mares (the Norfolk breed). Another example is the creation of the Santa Gertrudis breed of cattle in which all the members descend from the bull 'Monkey'.

The use of crossing

Crossing consists of the introduction of breeding individuals from another population into the population under consideration. Originally, the term indicated exchanges between breeds, but its actual acceptance is wider since it equally concerns lines and bloodstock.

Diffusion of genetic progress

A particular case of crossing is represented by diffusion in the foundation population (production herd) of individuals from a selection nucleus, a subgroup of the population in which selection involving continuous genetic progress is practised. It is possible to show that the flow of individual breeding stock enables this genetic progress to diffuse into the whole of the population, with a delay which varies with the proportion of improved animals introduced into the breeding group of the population.

This situation is fairly frequent. It has been studied in detail, notably by Bichard and Smith (1971), because it relates to the impossibility of setting up selection schemes on the scale of whole populations of a given breed.

It also happens that between the two levels noted above (selection stage and production stage), there is a multiplication stage intended to produce breeding stock in sufficient numbers from animals selected at the first stage and destined for the production stage.

These aspects, linked to the exploitation of the genetic progress obtained by selection, must be to considered at the time of conception of a genetic improvement plan, because it is clear that the effectiveness of selection should be envisaged not only at the nucleus, but also on the scale of the population as a whole.

The practical application of these principles has led ranchers to create elite herds for multiplication and herds for diffusion (King Ranch, etc., Norris Cattle Co.).

The effect of crossing on quantitative characters

The term crossing will be reserved for the case where, in the new population, matings are only made between immigrants and the population which receives them. This situation is artificial and in nature one can observe the fusion of two populations. In this case there is mating at random in the new population and the genetic structure evolves more slowly.

It has been known for a long time that, for certain characters, mixing populations, lines or breeds gives results superior to the mean of the parental population or even to the best of these populations, and that all of the individual effects recorded on different characteristics combine to confer remarkable vitality on the crossbreds. This known as *hybrid vigour*.

The difference observed on a characteristic with monogenic determinism between the mean of its value in heterozygotes and half of the value of the means of two corresponding homozygotes is called heterosis. It depends on both the difference of gene frequencies of two inter-bred populations and the level of the effects of dominance at a given locus. In the case of polygenic characters, the total heterosis is the sum of the heterotic effects of individual genes (with interactions), and it expressed only to the extent that the dominance effects at each locus act predominantly in the same direction; otherwise they would cancel each other out.

Now, due to the action of natural selection, it is argued that the genes favourable to vigour and to fertility are very generally dominant in all species. This explains why these characteristics almost always show the most marked effects of heterosis. It will be noticed that the results of crossing are not always superior to the best of the parental populations (although they are almost always superior to the mean of the parental populations). The practical attraction of heterosis increases as the means of the initial populations approach each other more closely.

The attraction of crossing is essentially linked to this phenomenon, but it is not limited to it. Crossing also allows combinations of complementary characters in the new generations (the simultaneous selection of which would have been much more difficult and would have taken longer to achieve), thanks to the introduction of new alleles and to the radical modification of gene and genotypic frequencies which it brings about.

Crossing plans

There are different crossing systems — simple and multiple according to whether they concern two populations or more (Tables 7.16, 7.17 and 7.18):

Simple cross (two populations)	$A \times B$
Triple cross (three populations)	$(A \times B) \times C$
Return cross or back cross (two populations)	$A \times (A \times B); A \times [A \times (A \times B)];$ etc.
Alternate cross or criss-cross (two populations)	$A \times (A \times B); B \times [A (A \times B)];$ etc.
Rotating cross (three populations)	$A \times (B \times C); B \times [A \times (B \times C)]; C \times (B \times [A \times (B \times C)]);$ etc.

The theory of heterosis does not allow the prediction of the advantage of the cross made by a male A on a female B over that of a male B on a female A, because its value is identical. Now in practice, due to the combination of direct effects and maternal effects, this is not so and one can see all the advantages of practising a commercial cross of the male meat breed

Table 7.16 Respective roles of two parental populations in the cross and effect of heterosis: alternate cross

Generation	A	B	Heterosis (in units of H_{AB})*
$F_1 = A \times B$	0.50	0.50	2
$F_2 = A \times F_1$	0.75	0.25	1
$F_3 = B \times F_2$	0.375	0.625	1.5
Fn $= A \times$ Fn $- 1$	0.666	0.333	1.333
Fn $+ 1 = B \times$ Fn	0.333	0.666	1.333

* Heterosis is expressed in units whose value is equal to half of the heterosis recorded in the simple crossing of two breeds. For multiple crosses, the measure refers to the heterosis of each of the elementary crosses.

Table 7.17 Rotary cross of three breeds

Generation	A	B	C	Heterosis		
				H_{AB}	H_{AC}	H_{BC}
$F_1 = B \times C$	0	0.5	0.5	0	0	2
$F_2 = A \times F_1$	0.5	0.25	0.25	1	1	0
$F_3 = B \times F_2$	0.25	0.625	0.125	1	0	0.5
$F_4 = C \times F_3$	0.125	0.3125	0.5625	0	0.5	1.25
Fn $= A \times$ Fn $- 1$	0.5715	0.1428	0.2857	0.5714	1.1429	0
Fn $+ 1 = B \times$ Fn	0.2857	0.5715	0.1428	0.1429	0	0.5714
Fn $+ 2 = C \times$ Fn $+ 1$	0.1428	0.2857	0.5715	0	0.5714	0.1429

Table 7.18 Value of heterosis of different systems of crossing

System of crossing	Generations				
	1	2	3	4	... n
Two breeds					
simple cross	2 HAB	HAB	HAB	HAB	HAB
back cross	HAB	$\frac{1}{2}$ HAB	$\frac{1}{4}$ HAB	$\frac{1}{8}$ HAB	$\frac{1}{2^{n-1}}$ HAB 0
alternate cross	2 HAB	HAB	$\frac{2}{3}$ HAB	$\frac{3}{5}$ HAB	
Three breeds					
triple cross	2 HBC	HAB + HAC	HAB + $\frac{1}{2}$ HBC	$\frac{1}{2}$ HAC + $\frac{5}{8}$ HAB	$\frac{6}{7}$ H mean
rotating cross	2 HBC	HAB + HAC	HAB + $\frac{1}{2}$ HBC		$\frac{4}{7}$ H mean
crossing between successive generations	2 HBC	HAB + HAC	$\frac{1}{2}$(HAB + HAC) + HBC	$\frac{3}{4}$(HAB + HAC) + $\frac{1}{2}$ HBC	
Four breeds					
quadruple cross (A × B) × (C × D)	HAB + HCD	2 H mean			
rotating cross order A, B, C, D	2 HCD	HAC + HAD	HAB + $\frac{1}{2}$(HBC + HBD)	HBC + $\frac{1}{2}$ HAC + $\frac{1}{4}$ HCD	$2\bar{H} - \frac{1}{15}$(HAC + HBD)
crossing between successive generations	2 HCD	HAC + HAD	HAB + $\frac{1}{2}$(HBC + HBD)	$\frac{1}{2}$(HAB + HAC + HAD) + $\frac{1}{4}$(HBC + HBD + HCD)	$\frac{2}{3}$ H mean

(After Ollivier)

type × hardy female, when the reverse cross would be unthinkable. One has thus managed to introduce the idea of complementarity between populations, which relies on the measurement of the difference between reciprocal crosses. This idea stresses the advantage of distinguishing the male lines from the female lines and is often used in practice, certain meat types in particular being selected for crossing in cattle, pigs and poultry.

The improvement in reproductive techniques, and especially the use of artificial insemination, has radically changed selection and crossing schemes notably by considerably simplifying the problem, of the maintainance of purebred parental populations for use in crossing schemes. It allows a much greater and faster diffusion of genetic progress and an increase in the intensity of selection of males. Research into the subject of fertile egg transplantation partly aims to obtain similar results with females.

The introduction of artificial insemination, it should be noted, raises other problems. On the one hand, it may reduce the genetic variability of the population, while on the other hand, and this has already happened on several occasions, it introduces the risk of increasing the incidence of heredity anomalies of which selected males will be unaffected carriers (lethal recessive genes, chromosome anomalies, etc.). The risks are reduced, however, by the practice of selection on the offspring.

Genetic improvement of tropical breeds

Putting genetic improvement plans for tropical breeds into operation brings difficulties which arise both from peculiarities in the natural environment and from the stage of production of the animal considered.

Organisation of selection

The first difficulty will be to establish an effective performance testing system. This necessitates a certain technical mastery on the part of the stockmen (milk recording, for example) and fits in very badly with certain realities of tropical herds (transhumance, nomadism etc. . . . .). The recording of reproduction, which affects knowledge of descendants and relationships in general, is indispensible (except in the case of mass selection), although recent work has shown that it could be reduced if a certain degree of uncertainty was acceptable.

The treatment of recorded information cannot be dissociated from the organisation which collects it. It also poses problems in a number of countries which lack the means for adequate calculation. It must be understood that the collection of data alone involves considerable expense.

Estimation of the genetic parameters of populations is still difficult at this stage due to the lack of close control of environmental factors i.e. in most

Table 7.19 Analysis of the effects of heterosis (%) on weaning performance in beef cattle (crosses between two British breeds)

Character	Weaning rate	Weight at weaning	Overall
Type of effect			
direct	4.1	4.6	8.7
maternal	4.7	5.4	10.1
total	8.8	10.0	18.8

(Source: National Institute for Agronomic Research)

Table 7.20 Classification of characters determining the profitability of meat production

Characters acting on the productivity of meat		Genetic influences linked:	
		To the mother	To the offspring
Numerical productivity	fertility and prolificacy	– sexual precocity – ovulation rate – quality (fertility or fecundity) of the eggs – uterine effects on implantation rate and viability of embryos	– fertility of the mating (union of the gametes) – implantation rate and viability of the embryos
	viability	– maternal instinct	– vigour/vitality
	aptitude for calving	– pelvic opening – behaviour (or preparation) before and at the moment of parturition – uterine effect on the dimensions of the fetus	– dimensions of the fetus (stature and morphology)
Production productivity	growth before weaning	– maternal aptitude (milk production and maternal instinct) (particularly)	– potential for growth (high) – aptitude to milk let-down mode (maternal or artificial)
	growth after weaning	– (poor) growth potential	– potential for growth (high)
	feed conversion efficiency	– (low) requirements for maintenance (above all) and growth	– (low) maintenance and growth (above all) requirements
	carcass and meat quality	– body and tissue composition (cast cow)	body and tissue composition

* At the level of the father, the fecundity of the sperm will constitute 'the paternal effect' on the numerical productivity, in comparison to the maternal effect

Table 7.21 Heterosis and heritability

Genetics	Aptitude for reproduction	Aptitude for growth	Carcass conformation
Heritability	weak 0–0.15	average 0.20–0.40	high 0.50–0.70
Genetic progress achievable by selection	weak	average	high
Effect of heterosis	high 10–20%	weak 5–8%	practically nil
Improvement by crossing	high	average	nil

tropical conditions, the animals are totally subject to an extremely severe environment (cyclical food stress, irregular watering, high disease risks, excessive temperature and humidity etc.) which is very variable in time and space. Correction of these environmental effects – annual effects, regional effect, herd effect etc. – is very difficult. Moreover the variance of environmental factors, which is very high, indirectly reduces the contribution of genetic effects and thus the heritability of the characteristics (Table 7.19 to 7.22).

Table 7.22 Effects of heterosis expressed by superiority in relation to the average of the parental breeds

	Simple cross – pure-bred mother, crossed offspring (per cent)	Double cross – crossed mother, crossed offspring (per cent)
Cattle		
number of calves at birth	1	5
number of calves weaned	4	5
weight of calves weaned	5	5
weight of heifer at 1 year	5	–
weight of adult males at slaughter	1	–
growth after weaning	5	–
quantity of milk	–	5
quantity of fats	–	8
butterfat content	–	0
food conversion efficiency	1	–
carcass composition	0	0
Pigs		
number of piglets born alive per litter	2	2
number of piglets weaned	8	16
weight of litter: born	4	10
weight of litter: weaned	15	25
weight of piglet at weaning	6	7
DLG after weaning	6	7
individual weight at 154 days	10	10
food conversion efficiency	3	3
percentage lean cuts in carcass	0	0
percentage fat cuts in carcass	0	0
Sheep		
ewes lambed per ewes put to the ram	0	2
number of lambs per ewe at birth	0	10
number of lambs weaned per ewe put to the ram	2	15
individual weights of weaned lambs	5	5
weight of lambs weaned per ewe put to the ram	10	35
Rabbits		
ratio of deaths to births	40	–
number of live-born young per litter	12	18
number of young weaned per litter	15	26
viability rate of young at weaning	3	7
weight of litter at weaning	8	18

DLG = daily live – weight gain
(Source: National Institute of Agronomic Research)

The choice of selection objectives is difficult in the context of agricultural systems that are undergoing change and often poorly understood, since the economic weights of different characters depend on the structure of the agricultural systems. These change rapidly as the production, marketing and price structures evolve: forecasting as one proceeds is problematical in this respect.

The environment being very severe, natural selection has conferred on tropical breeds adaptation qualities which should not be neglected (resistance to stress and in particular to diseases . . .). Now these characteristics are very complex as regards their genetic determination and are quantifiable with the greatest of difficulty. This prohibits taking them into account in selection, with certain exceptions.

Historically, the first moves in selection were developed in situations which enabled partial control of the environment and the management of herds, i.e. on ranches or research stations.

In this context, the qualities of hardiness in the animals lost their importance in relation to the rural environment, and thus one could argue that the animals selected in research stations could not always resist the stresses met in non-improved rearing situations, and that this hampers or prohibits the spread of genetic improvements.

At the present time, ideas are evolving in favour of selection schemes rooted in the production environment itself, and this enables the characteristics of hardiness to be taken into account without having to quantify them, but again raises difficulties in the organisation of work (obtaining data) and management of the herds (in particular the organisation of mating).

In conclusion, it must be remembered that the most rapid improvements will come at first from improvements in the environment (feeding, prophylaxis, shelter etc.), then on preselection activities which are easy to set up (culling of unproductive females, castration of males which have visible faults), and finally on mass selection, at least with regard to the most heritable characteristics (conformation, speed of growth, adult size). One can assume, without too much risk, that the hierarchy of heritabilities is similar to that in other parts of the world.

Setting up sophisticated selection schemes at project conception and calculation stage is in no way excluded, but should be kept for the most favourable situations (sufficiently large sedentary herds for example) and should be accompanied by a thorough consideration of the production systems and their development. The simple transfer of technology does not seem to meet the needs of developing countries any more than in other fields.

Crossing and the introduction of foreign breeds

Because the difficulties of selection, recourse was taken to the introduction of blood from breeds already selected in developed countries. This has been carried out since the nineteenth century by importation of male breeding stock,

Table 7.23 Populations obtained by crossing Zebu with humpless cattle to increase the production of meat and milk in the tropics

Name of breed	*Bos taurus* (humpless)		*Bos indicus* (Zebu)	
	Name of breed	% genes	Name of breed	% genes
Bambara	N'Dama		Sahelian Zebu	
Parzoma	Aberdeen Angus	25	Afrikander	25
	Hereford	25	Santa Gertrudis	25
Beefmaster	Hereford	25	Brahman	50
	Shorthorn	25		
Belmont Red	Hereford		Afrikander	
	Shorthorn			
Bonsmara	Hereford	19	Afrikander	62.5
	Shorthorn	19		
Braford	Hereford	50	Brahman	50
Brangus	Angus	62.5	Brahman	37.5
Brown Sind	Brown Swiss	62.5	Red Sindhi	37.5
Canchimy	Charolais	62.5	Indian Zebu	37.5
Charbray	Charolais	75 −87	Brahman	12−25
Charford	Charolais	50	Brahman	12.5
	Hereford	37.5		
Drakensberger	Dutch Friesian		Afrikander	
Droughtmaster	Shorthorn	50 −52.5	Brahmah	37.5−50
Jamaica Black	Aberdeen Angus	62.5−75	Zebu	25 −37.5
Jamaica Hope	Jersey	37.5−87.5	Zebu	12 −62.5
Jamaica Red	Devon		Zebu	
	Red Poll			
Jersind	Jersey	62.5	Red Sindhi	37.5
Pitangueiras	Red Poll	62.5	Kankrej	37.5
Renitelo	Limousin		Afrikander	
			Brahman	
Santa Gertrudis	Shorthorn	62.5	Brahman	37.5
Thibar	Brown Atlas	50 −60	Ongole	40 −50
	Charolais		Red Sindhi	
	Tarentais			
	Montbeliarde			

or more recently by semen, with very variable results (Table 7.23). The success of such operations depends above all, on the level of mastery of stock rearing in which crossing is practised, on the capacity for adaptation of the breeds imported into the new environment and on the health situation in the receiving region.

The crossing operations practised in research stations have seen varied technical success and have made possible the creation of useful types, but have generally reached their limit at the stage of distribution of the improved animals outside these favourable situations.

It appears more and more that an essential condition of the success of a crossing operation is the prior setting up of a selection programme in the pure indigenous breed which will provide the support of the cross. Performance testing then enables estimation of the suitability of crossbreds and judicious orientation of the crossing programme. Organisation of production systems in advance of crossing is a prerequisite to success.

The practice of crossing between tropical breeds is also attractive. It is often used, particularly between Zebus and humpless cattle, and this cross benefits from very high levels of hybrid vigour and from obvious complementary factors, particularly in the case of humpless females tolerant to trypanosomiasis. The development of communications and trade greatly favours these practices, notably by the organisation of markets for production animals and the regularisation and development of demand.

The general run of crossbreeding poses the important problem for the future of maintaining variability and safeguarding local breeds in the regions. In effect, crossing exploits variability, which tends to disappear as a result, and it is this which condemns it in time (heterosis declines rapidly, then disappears in the case of random fusion between populations).

Species reared under standardised conditions

The case of 'factory farming' of pigs, poultry, and eventually of rabbits, should be separated from that of rearing ruminants. The standardisation of these farming activities, which are largely independent of the natural environment and are mastered perfectly from a technical point of view, have enabled the establishment in a number of tropical countries of modern production units, based on the model of farming practised in the industrial countries. In this case, as long as they can withstand the difference in climate, the direct use of breeds selected from a variety of sources can often be envisaged, especially since the transport of semen or chicks in one day, for example, does not pose an insurmountable problem and can relieve these units from part of the burden of selection. Thus for example the Large White pig breed, is widely distributed in the tropics with excellent technical results.

Introduction to the origins of the domesticated animals of the tropics

General

The Americas and Oceania were lacking in domesticated herbivores (with the exception of the lama) at the time of their discovery by the great navigators in the fifteenth and sixteenth centuries. The animals actually exploited in the tropics thus originate from the old continents.

Epstein, in 1971, published a thorough study on the origins of domesticated animals in Africa. In two volumes and nearly 1300 pages, this author brought together the knowledge accumulated on the subject through palaeontology, anatomy, biochemistry and most of the scientific disciplines.

It seems, as a result of this detailed documentation that, with only a few exceptions such as the donkey which is of African origin, all the species of domesticated animals have been domesticated by man from Asia Minor and Western Asia.

In the case of cattle, the oldest to be associated with man is the Hamitic type with long horns, which was domesticated 8000 years ago in Mesopotamia. The chronology of its expansion towards Africa on the one hand, and to Europe and Asia on the other, seems to have been established with relative clarity. In the different regions of the ancient world the domesticated form of wild oxen would have given types different from one another by crossing with local varieties of these wild animals.

The long-horned Hamitic cattle were the first occupants of Africa, Southern Asia and Europe.

In Africa, this long presence is confirmed in its descendant, the N'Dama breed, by hereditary resistance to the bovine trypanosomiasis.

The long-horned Hamitic animal was a creature of average to large stature, lacking a hump, endowed with developed horn, and sometimes very large in length or girth. This characteristic of recognition by the horn is debatable since it is now known how often herdsmen are influenced by differences in the growth of horns. Osteologically, it seems to be established, nevertheless, that the remaining ancient domesticated cattle belonged to a type with well developed horns.

In the same region of Mesopotamia about 2000 years later, a new type of animal appeared in association with man. This was an animal of much reduced stature, with smaller horns similar to those of Jersey, Holstein or Baoule cows nowadays. Appearing about 6000 years ago, this type of animal spread rapidly across three continents, where they coexist and sometimes replaced their long-horned Hamitic predecessor. Nothing indicates that they have a particular advantage and the two types have been used for traction, milking and meat.

Finally, 4000 years ago, or about twenty centuries after the short-horned cattle, the Zebu appeared in a region corresponding to present day Afghanistan. According to Epstein, this humped beast represented a form adapted to desertified areas from earlier cattle, and there would be no proof of the existence of a wild form nor of crosses with a closely related species. The Zebu, an animal of the warm steppes, would have spread in preference towards the tropics and would have been favoured by the growing aridity of the latter millenia, and thus by a resistance to rinderpest superior to that of other animals.

India, today considered as the birthplace of Zebus, would only have been colonised by this species 3000–3500 years ago, along with the migrations of man.

These theories, based on numerous documents, and which are widely discussed by Epstein in all their aspects, are supported by the actual distribution of cattle types, notably in Africa, and by the first results of studies on genetic markers (blood groups, haemoglobins etc.).

The Americas have been stocked with three types of cattle in the same order as the ancient world. As regards Oceania, the first cattle introduced into Australia came from the Cape of Good Hope (i.e. from Africa). Then, for more than a century, only Great Britain provided sires, and it was during the second quarter of the twentieth century that Zebus were imported, but this was from the United States.

According to Epstein, sheep and goats have always been domesticated in this same region of the Middle East. It is considered that the domestication of the goat took place in Anatolia 9000 years ago and that this is the same for sheep. The wild species from which they are derived are not known with certainty. There again, the considerable period of time in which small ruminants have been in the tropics is attested by the existence of African forms tolerant to trypanosomiasis.

The horse orginates from Caucasia and was only completely domesticated 4000 years ago. Different diseases have thwarted its expansion in the tropics, notably in Africa where it only exists in the areas not affected by tsetse.

Finally, pigs were already domesticated in Anatolia 9000 years ago and in different places in the tropics. About 4000 years ago, Islam caused a reduction in number or total disappearance of this species in parts of Asia and Africa.

History tells us that peoples effected their migrations over the course of centuries and took their domesticated animals everywhere with them. These constituted and often still constitute part not only of the technical inheritance but also of the cultural inheritance. The movements and exchanges from the distant past will remain largely unknown. Those of the latter centuries, and notably since 1750–1800, are linked to the present.

A bibliography relating to all the tropical breeds of domesticated animals would fill an entire book by itself and it is not proposed to make an exhaustive list here.

It can be said that all the authors who have described tropical breeds are each preoccupied with the animals that they have occasion to see regularly. Thus animals having the same ethnic characteristics (basic form, appearance and aptitudes) have been described as belonging to different breeds, whereas they are only at most geographic variants in which the secondary characteristics are found in the populations in slightly greater frequencies. Thus animals described in West Africa as belonging to the Azawak breed have great resemblances to, if not the same characteristics, as those observed in certain Ethiopian Zebus.

At the moment, the domesticated animals and in particular the cattle of the tropics fall into three large categories:

1. the animals of local breeds which are more or less modified;
2. the animals of foreign breeds (generally originating from temperate countries) which were introduced by a European population;
3. the animals of new breeds originating from crossing then crossbreeding of the first two types and which now constitute stable populations which satisfy particular requirements.

Among the tropical breeds and the new breeds, three types of animal are found: humpless cattle (*Bos taurus*), Zebus (with a hump – *Bos indicus*) and half-breeds, which are intermediate and result from the crossing of humpless breeds and Zebus.

If it were necessary to categorise the tropical breeds, it would be necessary to show their very great heterogeneity, and this can be considered a shortcoming if one confines oneself to a search for uniformity of ethnic groups. It is surely an advantage because it is the manifestation of a genetic variability from which much progress is possible.

Among the domesticated tropical breeds, one now finds types whose origin is lost in time and which have left their traces in archaeological sites or their images in pre-Pharaonic art. Also found are new breeds created by cross-breeding with stock which do not belong to the tropical breed.

The systematic use of modern reproductive methods (artificial insemination, heat synchronisation, embryo transplants) gives hope for a considerable development of animal production, when feeding problems are overcome.

It is not possible in this book to deal with all the breeds of domesticated animal. This chapter relating to ethnology will be limited to the description of 20 breeds of cattle and five breeds of sheep and goats, which will give some idea of the characteristics of the tropical animal.

Aviculture, like pig rearing, will be the subject of specialised works.

For those who wish to have a more detailed knowledge, we recommend reading the works and publications of Maule (1953), Mason (1951), Mason and Maule (1960), Joshi *et al.* (1957) and Cockrill (1974), the last work treating buffaloes and their husbandry in great detail.

Cattle breeds of the tropics

Zebu breeds

American Brahman

Origin and history

The American Brahman is an example of a modern breed created by crossing then crossbreeding and selection. The present population is the issue of 266 Zebu bulls and 22 Zebu females imported into the United States between 1854 and 1926. Apart from some individuals coming directly from India, the majority were imported from Brazil via Mexico. The breed essentially came from breeding stock of the Guzerat and Nellore types as well as some Gir stock. These animals were used principally in Texas and in the States of the sub-tropical zone of the United States (Louisiana, Florida), around the Gulf of Mexico.

Plate 7.1   American Brahman bull – Texas (USA)

Plate 7.2   American Brahman bull born and raised in Madagascar (Kianjasoa)

In 1964, the American Brahman Breeders Association of Houston recognised 340 000 registered animals and the presence of the breed in every State in the United States and in 57 other countries.

The American Brahman has been imported in considerable numbers into Australia, Cameroun, Madagascar and Thailand.

Description

The American Brahman (Plates 7.1 and 7.2) is a stable breed managed by an Association of Stockmen founded on 28 February 1924, which defined a standard of which the following is a resume:

General appearance: two colours are accepted: red and grey, uniform or progressively mixed. Depigmented hide is downgraded. The muzzle and hooves are darkened. The animals should have a physique as follows: 1600–2200 pounds for adult males (about 750 – 1000 kg); 1000–1500 pounds for adult females (about 450–700 kg), in good condition.

The conformation is heavy, large, moderately deep and close to the ground. The back is straight with slightly round hindquarters. The hump should be well developed in males and positioned above the shoulders in a bean shape. The forehead is large, flat and moderately prominent; the short face is slightly

Plate 7.3 'Arabe', Azawak bull – Filingue, Niger

'Arabe', Azawak cow – Filingue, Niger

dished towards the nose. The eyes show the influence of the predominant bloodstock. Temperament is alert but docile.

Rearing techniques and type of production

Generally, the Brahman is a free ranging animal in tropical ranching and the frequent type of production is the 24—30 month steer finished on intensive pasture.

Utility

The milking abilities of the Brahman have apparently not been developed to any extent, except in Madagascar (Miadana) where lactations in ¾ Brahman ×Madagascan Zebu have been compared with those of the Sahiwal (see the Sahiwal section, Utility paragraph, page 376).

Although modest, the milking ability of Brahman cows does ensure satisfactory growth in the calf which is superior to that in a number of other Zebu breeds.

The Brahman is used for draught in Madagascar and in South-East Asia. Its principal aptitude is for open range production of meat. A number of results are available in the literature. We will cite here those relating to the works of Serres *et al.* in Madagascar, 1968 (Table 7.24 and 7.25).

Compared with the earliest known Madagascan Zebus, the Brahman represented a considerable improvement, unfortunately offset by an excessive sensitivity to streptothricosis. In Cameroun, the offspring of the crossbreeding of ½ Brahmans was hardly better than Foulbé Zebus of Adamawa. More recently, it appeared that the improved Boran also has performance close to that of the Brahman.

The Brahman thus constitutes a methodological model and can be used to improve the productivity of cattle populations in the semi-arid zones where the level of performance is particularly poor.

Genetic improvement

Genetic improvement is actively sought by the American Brahman Breeders Association and its affiliated bodies in other countries (notably Australia).

Azawak

Origin and history

The Azawak Zebu is classed in the largest group of Sahelian Zebus, of which it is an evolved type.

Azawak Zebus are reared by the Tuareg tribes in the valleys of the Azaouak.

Table 7.24 Growth rates in males Zoological Research Centre of Miadana

		Birth	3 months	6 months	12 months	18 months	2 years	3 years
Madagascan Zebu	kg	19.9	75.6	116.6	136.5	151.6	161.4	226
	No.	(21)	(20)	(20)	(19)	(14)	(13)	(11)
3/8 Brahman	kg	20	70	104	140	168	184	233
	No.	(26)	(24)	(20)	(20)	(20)	(20)	(20)
1/2 Brahman	kg	22.4	73	122	169	237	282	342
	No.	(88)	(75)	(72)	(48)	(40)	(35)	(39)
5/8 Brahman	kg	25	90	138	186	229	244	297
	No.	(14)	(14)	(12)	(12)	(12)	(12)	(12)
3/4 Brahman	kg	24	92	148	193	235	261	343
	No.	(68)	(65)	(58)	(52)	(42)	(35)	(15)
7/8 Brahman	kg	24	100	157	193	218	234	–
	No.	(7)	(6)	(4)	(18)	(18)	(7)	–
Brahman (pure)	kg	25	91	150	209	246	303	410
	No.	(49)	(50)	(48)	(44)	(35)	(30)	(18)

Table 7.25 Growth rates in females Zoological Research Centre of Miadana

		Birth	3 months	6 months	12 months	18 months	2 years	3 years
Madagascan Zebu	kg	19.4	66.6	102.8	128.4	158.6	172.9	226
	No.	(27)	(27)	(27)	(25)	(20)	(29)	(13)
3/8 Brahman	kg	20	67	103	132	172	176	246
	No.	(19)	(18)	(15)	(14)	(14)	(14)	(13)
1/2 Brahman	kg	22.7	66.5	109.9	158.6	201.3	232	321
	No.	(110)	(82)	(61)	(82)	(67)	(66)	(36)
5/8 Brahman	kg	22	84	131	178	225	242	310
	No.	(12)	(22)	(10)	(9)	(9)	(9)	(8)
3/4 Brahman	kg	22	90	138	181	222	241	310
	No.	(61)	(61)	(58)	(51)	(42)	(37)	(27)
7/8 Brahman	kg	24	91	144	186	214	252	–
	No.	(5)	(5)	(3)	(12)	(5)	(5)	–
Brahman (pure)	kg	22	89	138	192	227	267	335
	No.	(35)	(39)	(35)	(32)	(33)	(32)	(26)

North Tadist and Azah and by some Peul tribes. This region is situated between longitudes 3° and 7° east and latitudes 15° and 20° north, close to the borders of Mali and Niger. It is an undulating plateau with a mean altitude of 500 m. The term Azawak signifies 'sandy country without marked relief'.

The Azawak Zebu would have been brought into this region to escape from an epidemic on the edge of the river Niger. It seems to have been introduced by a white race of stockmen arriving in the Sahel between the seventh and eleventh century AD.

Importance and distribution

Populations of shorthorned Zebu cattle was estimated at 2 660 000 head in Niger, during the early eighties; most were Azawak Zebus. The Azawak Zebu breed is little known beyond the indigenous home of the breed although it exists in the whole of the Sahel in shorthorned Zebu cattle which manifest strong similarities and which are reared, either by Arab and Moorish peoples (Kreda Zebus, Moorish Zebus) or, rarely, by Peul people.

Description

The Azawak Zebu (Plates 7.3 and 7.4) is an animal of average stature, stocky and fairly close to the ground. All types of coat are found. A study made in 1956 showed 34.5 per cent red pied with red dominant, 16.5 per cent with white dominant, 16 per cent black coats, 8.5 per cent white or beige coats. The remaining animals, Bororo Azawak crossbreds, have not been taken into account.

The hump is developed and erect but less marked in the female. The head is fine with a straight profile and small ears. The horns are short, cupped or rounded, sometimes asymmetric and sometimes absent. (See Tables 7.26 and 7.27).

Table 7.26 Dimensions of the Azawak breed: bulls

	29–36 months	42–50 months	50 months and more
Height at withers (cm)	123.25	127.20	131.40
Perimeter of thorax (cm)	158.50	164.60	169.80
Perimeter of anterior canon (cm)	16.50	17.25	18.60
Height of brisket (cm)	60.25	61.40	57.60

Table 7.27 Dimensions of the Azawak breed: cows

	Number of observations	Mean	Type divergence
Height at withers (cm)	119	123.3	0.43
Perimeter of thorax (cm)	111	155.7	0.70
Perimeter of anterior canon (cm)	125	15.2	0.08
Height of brisket (cm)	125	60.6	0.32

Rearing techniques and types of production

The herders of Azawak Zebus are nomads and they move to other pastures (transhumance) in the rainy season at the northern limits of the Sahel, and towards the south in the dry season after the harvest in the millet, sorghum and groundnut growing areas. They spend part of the year in the areas where the water supplies are saline. The animals are exploited for their milk and for transportation, and are traded for meat. The hides are tanned and used by artisans (shoes, sandals, saddles etc.).

Utility

The aptitudes of Azawak Zebus have been studied by Pagot at the Toukounouss station in Niger.

The milk production observed, from animals kept in conditions very close to the traditional, were as shown in Table 7.28.

Table 7.28 Milk production of Azawak cows

Numerical order of lactation	Production (theoretical) in 270 days (litres)	Production (theoretical) in 300 days (litres)
First lactation	445.5 ± 9.7	484.7 ± 10.4
2nd lactation	477.5 ± 10.9	517.7 ± 11.8
3rd lactation	564.8 ± 14.3	613.5 ± 15
4th lactation	624.2 ± 17.7	672.5 ± 20
5th lactation	539.9 ± 20.9	585.2 ± 22.6
6th lactation	537.1 ± 32.6	595.89 ± 35.7

It has been calculated that, if the feeding conditions were corrected to the mean annual level (feeding during the worst months), one could obtain 768 litres instead of 687 litres per annum per cow in the milking herd and 917 litres by correcting the feeding to the level of the best 5 months of the year.

The ability of the draught animal has not been studied experimentally, but the ox is an excellent carrier which can transport loads of 80, or even 100 kg over a distance of 15–20 kg at a speed of 3–4 km/h.

The aptitude for meat production has been made the object of diligent analyses at Toukounouss. The growth rates shown in Table 7.29 have been recorded.

Table 7.29 Weights of Azawak cattle

	Birth	1 month	3 months	6 months	1 year	2 years	3 years	4 years
Average weight of males (kg)	20.7	38.6	69.5	100.4	124.6	204.8	303.1	392.8
Average weight of females (kg)	19.8	–	–	–	129	195.1	264	292.3

Genetic improvement

This is carried out at the Toukounouss station in Niger where the bulls are selected by trials on the offspring.

A herd is located in Nigeria at the Gumel station, 120 km north-east of Kano.

A transfer to the central delta of the Niger near Segou in 1942 to 1944 was abandoned in failure.

An acclimatisation trial has been run in Burkina Faso.

Boran

Origin and history

According to Joshi 1957, the Boran originates in an area stretching from the plateau of Lebanon to southern Ethiopia, from where it was introduced into the arid zones of Kenya half a century ago. There, it has been improved by selection in farming enterprises managed by Europeans. In their original form, these Zebus represent a type wide-spread in the Horn of Africa.

Importance, distribution and numbers

Numbers are unknown. However, the breed is the most numerous in East Africa. Boran Zebus have been introduced into Tanzania and Zaire.

Description

The Boran (Plates 7.5 and 7.6) is a widespread breed in semi-humid to sub-humid East Africa and is known under different local types.

It is an animal with a stature slightly superior to the average. Pale, white or grey coats are the most frequent; the cost may also be biscuit coloured, red or sometimes dappled.

The dewlap, the umbilical fold and the hump are well developed in the bull, but in the cow the hump can be almost absent.

The head is long, the forehead generally convex and the muzzle large. The horns are variable, usually short and cup shaped, but sometimes long.

Average dimensions are shown in Table 7.30.

Plate 7.5   Boran bull (Kenya)

Table 7.30 Dimensions of the Boran breed

	Cows		Bullocks	
	Range	Mean	Range	Mean
Weight (kg)	346–417	380	539–653	615
Scapulo-ischial length (cm)	132–144	138	146–166	158
Height at withers (cm)	118–122	120	133–147	140
Depth of chest (cm)	60– 65	62.5	73– 81	76.4
Width of hips (cm)	36– 47	42.8	52– 56	53.3
Thorax perimeter (cm)	153–173	165	195–220	208

Plate 7.6   Boran herd (Ethiopia)

Plate 7.7   Bororo cow (Central African Republic)

Plate 7.8   Bororo bull (Central African Republic)

Rearing techniques and types of production

Like most African cattle, the Boran is above all a free-ranging grazing animal.

Traditionally the animals are exploited for their milk and meat. The improved forms found in modern operations have been exploited in ranching for their meat but also for milk in intensive situations.

The development of intensive pasture has shown growth potential comparable with that of the best blood-lines of tropical Zebus.

Utility

With regard to milking ability, lactations in extensive situations have been estimated at 1673 kg in 295 days.

This does not seem to justify specialisation towards milk production, which in East Africa remains the prerogative of European (Jersey, Ayrshire, Friesian) and Indian (Sahiwal) breeds.

The use of the Boran for draught has not been assessed. The true vocation of the breed is meat production. Different systems co-exist. In traditional herds, butchers' animals are traded at an advanced age. In modern operations, the young animals are sometimes raised on intensive pasture. Growth rates have been recorded (see Table 7.31).

For the Malya, Tanga and West Kilimanjaro stations, Tanzania, the live-weights were estimated from data on body weight and girth. Results obtained on intensive pasture have testified to the potentials of the Boran breed (Table 7.31).

The rations used correspond to the requirements shown in Tables 7.32 (a) and (b).

Table 7.31 Mean liveweight of Tanzanian Boran at different stages of growth

	Birth		18 mth.		30 mth.		Adult	
Females								
Malya (dairy enterprise)	37	23.5	42	166	13	268	52	307
Tanya (dairy enterprise)	38	23.8	8	215	7	262	33	350
West Kilimanjaro (ranch)	91	23.7	76	206	10	250	82	335
Matamondo (ranch)	4	19	3	203	26	258	43	293
Bulls								
Malya (dairy enterprise)	31	24.2	23	190	17	311	7	384
Tanga (dairy enterprise)	18	25.3	1	190	–	–	1	427
West Kilimanjaro (ranch)	62	24.8	17	238	9	269	7	413
Matamondo (ranch)	7	21.5	3	205	3	263	2	494
Bullocks								
Malya (dairy enterprise)	–	–	2	142	3	315	5	393
Tanga (dairy enterprise)	–	–	–	–	–	–	–	–
West Kilimanjaro (ranch)	–	–	37	233	30	295	3	387
Matamondo (ranch)	–	–	6	204	29	258	45	302

Table 7.32(a) Observations taken from private establishments in Kenya showing the daily liveweight gain by breed and by type of ration

Breed	Boran (any)			Boran (improved)		
Ration used	No.	Duration (days)	Daily liveweight gain (kg)	No.	Duration (days)	Daily liveweight gain (kg)
R3	213	93.1	993	627	126.5	734
R4	2857	87.8	1012	1208	97.5	1044
R5	276	89.6	906	320	109.0	915
	3346	88.3	1002	2155	107.7	919

Breed	Large cross			Total		
Ration used	No.	Duration (days)	Daily liveweight gain (kg)	No.	Duration (days)	Daily liveweight gain (kg)
R3	264	123.2	855	1104	119.2	803
R4	980	114.8	1077	5045	95.4	1035
R5	880	112.4	1200	1476	107.4	1092
	2124	114.8	1098	7625	101.2	1007

Table 7.32(b) Rations used in the observations of Table 7.32(a)

	R3	R4	R5
Maize grain	20.61	36.66	52.83
Urea–molasses	9.93	10.52	11.10
Cotton seed cake	2.65	2.65	2.65
Forage of which:	66.81	50.17	33.42
Crude protein	10.09	10.61	11.13
Metabolisable energy (Mc per kg)	2.74	2.87	3.00

Genetic improvement

In Kenya, a Boran Stockman's Society has been created which controls the selection of the breed.

M'Bororo, Red Fulani or Rahaji

Origins and history

The Bororo Peuls of Central Africa are a branch of the Peul people, less Islamic and less sedentary than the others. Bororo Zebus are animals characteristic of the semi-arid zones, particularly suited to long journeys and to searching for water and food. Their presence in the Sahel is historic and this is confirmed by the cave drawings of Tassili.

Importance, distribution and numbers

Bororo cattle numbers are estimated at 7 898 000 head. They share the pastures of Cameroun with Foulbé (Fulani) cattle, those of Chad with Kreda and Kouri cattle and those of Niger and Azawak cattle.

Description

The Bororo Zebu or Red Fulani (Plates 7.7 and 7.8) is an animal of average stature or slightly superior to the average and has highly developed horns. Three principal types are distinguishable: the Red Bororo or Djafoun (Nigeria, Niger, Chad, Central African Republic, Cameroun); the White Bororo, Akou or White Fulani (Nigeria, Cameroun, Niger); the Wodabe, red pied, dappled or mottled, which is the most common in Chad and Niger.

Apart from the differences in coat, used for selection by the Bororo Peul herdsmen for a thousand years, these animals have in common their stature, their 'sprightly' bony appearance, their large horns and their hardiness.

The dimensions recorded in Central African Republic are shown in Table 7.33.

The corresponding data by Kassoum Kone (1948) for the animal of eastern Niger differ a little.

Rearing techniques

Bororo Zebus are open range animals – transhumant or nomadic. They receive no supplementary feeding apart from minerals (natron). The females are milked for family consumption and for sale and the bullocks are often used for transport.

The principle type of production is for butchering at more than 4 to 6 years of age.

Table 7.33 Dimensions of Bororo Females

Dimension: October 1967	Average age 2½ years		
Weight (kg)	248.66 ± 6.77	v =	14%
Height of withers (cm)	120.56 ± 0.69	v =	3%
Height of brisket (cm)	63.06 ± 0.54	v =	4%
Width at chest (cm)	25.03 ± 0.41	v =	9%
Perimeter of thorax (cm)	142.73 ± 1.33	v =	5%
Scapulo-ishchial length (cm)	126.50 ± 1.14	v =	5%
Average length (cm)	59.06 ± 0.69	v =	6%
Length of pelvis (cm)	42.20 ± 0.36	v =	4%
Width of pelvis (cm)	39.26 ± 0.52	v =	7%
Length of head (cm)	48.36 ± 0.34	v =	4%
Width of head (cm)	19.16 ± 0.15	v =	4.4%
Perimeter of canon bone (cm)	15.10 ± 0.12	v =	4.4%

v = coefficient of variation

Utility

The characteristic aptitude of the Bororo Zebu is that of utilising the natural vegetation of the range-lands. Milk production from the females, although poor, is exploited; it has been measured at Bambul (Cameroun), and compares with that of Jersey and Holstein – Fresian cows (Table 7.34).

The butchering capacity of the Bororo Zebu has not been studied. Taking into account its large size, it is considered that it provides heavy carcasses but with poor meat yield.

Genetic improvement

Genetic improvement of the Bororo Zebus was undertaken in 1967 at Bouar (Central African Republic) and seems to have been subsequently abandoned.

Foulbé

Origin and history

The Foulbé breed co-exists in Central Africa (Cameroun and eastern Nigeria) with the M'Bororo Zebu. These animals are raised by two branches of the Peul people who differ in the history of their migrations, their degree of Islamisation and their way of life.

The Foulbé Peuls arrived in Adamaoua in the eighteenth century from West Africa, and they brought their cattle, which had the same origin, with them. Adamaoua is a high region (1200–1500 m) which lies between latitudes 6° and 8° north and longitudes 12° and 14° east. The altitude-modified climate ensures that this region, which is so close to the equator, is unaffected by the tsetse fly and, due to this fact, suitable for raising Zebus. The rainfall is relatively high (1600 mm) and it is estimated that 2 500 000 ha are suitable for Zebu rearing.

Table 7.34 Average milk production of Bororo Zebus and European breeds

Breeds	Groups	Length of lactation 70 days (10 weeks)			Complete lactation		
		Average class of lactation	Average production (kg)	Average daily production (kg)	Average length (days)	Average production (kg)	Average daily production (kg)
Bororo Akou	C	3	277.86	3.97	173	465.10	2.80
Bororo Akou	T	3	286.93	4.10	200	554.90	2.87
Bororo Djafoun	C	1	174.54	2.49	126	294.70	2.40
Bororo Djafoun	T	1	283.50	4.10	114	392.60	3.30
Jersey	9 cows	1	551.20	7.90	210*	1 685.70	8.03
Holstein-Friesian	10 cows	1	946.10	13.50	278*	3 202.40	11.52

* Late but incomplete lactation

Importance, distribution and numbers

The Foulbé breed of Zebu is represented in Nigeria under the name of Adamawa Gudali. Numbers are estimated at 2 942 000 head.

Description

Several local types are generally distinguishable (Banyo, N'Gaoundéré etc.) in the Foulbé Zebu group (Plates 7.9 and 7.10). These diverse blood lines have in common an average stature, a relatively stocky and 'close to the ground' appearance, with short or relatively short curved horns.

Plate 7.9   Foulbé (or Goudali) cow (Cameroun)

Plate 7.10   Foulbé (or Goudali) bull (Cameroun)

Plate 7.11 Gir cow (Brazil)

Plate 7.12   Gir bull (Brazil)

Coats are varied, generally pied or red-pied and frequently dappled or speckled. The hump is well developed in both sexes looking like a conical hat in the males. The horns of the bulls are short and bulky while those of the female are fine and little developed.

The dimensions shown in Table 7.35 were recorded at N'Gaoundéré, Cameroun.

Rearing techniques and types of production

In Adamaoua, the herds are sedentary for the major part of the year. At the end of the dry season they undertake a short transhumance into the flood valleys (Yaeres) of the tributaries of the Benoue. At this time, there is least risk of

Table 7.35 Average dimensions for the Foulbé–N'Gaoundéré breed

Dimensions	Bulls	Cows
Weight (kg)	563	335.4
Height of rump (cm)	142.2	131.8
Height of withers (cm)	132.8	123.2
Height of brisket (cm)	62.7	59.7
Length of pelvis (cm)	68.1	48.3
Width of pelvis (cm)	50.6	43.6
Scapulo-ischial length (cm)	178.5	145.2
Thorax perimeter (cm)	193.9	169.6
Length of head (cm)	58.6	51.9
Width of head (cm)	27.6	20.5

contamination by trypanosomiasis. At the time of the transhumance, the lactating females remain in the village.

The herds are exploited for their milk and meat. They are starting to be used for draught purposes (25 000 ploughs are now in use).

The types of production are typical of those in the rest of Africa i.e. bullocks of 4–6 years.

Utility

The milking capacity of Foulbé cows, traditionally exploited by stockmen, has been measured. The average and maximum recorded production per month of lactation is shown in Table 7.36.

Table 7.36 Lactation data for Foulbé cows

Lactation period	Average (litres)	Maximum (litres)
1st month	92.7	177
2nd month	85.1	174
3rd month	78.5	154.5
4th month	70.1	135
5th month	70.3	122.1
6th month	63.9	111
7th month	59	96
8th month	50.5	81
9th month	49	69
Average lactation (9 months)	619.1	

This capacity is modest as is generally the case in the tropics for animals under extensive systems.

The aptitude of Foulbé bullocks for draught purposes has not been measured. The principal known use is for meat production.

Table 7.37 Growth of male and female Foulbé cattle at Wakwa, Cameroun

Ages	Males		Females	
	Average weight (kg)	Range	Average weight (kg)	Range
Birth	24.5	–	23.4	–
Weaning (8 months)	143	–	133	–
1 year	155	100 –215	141	95–190
2 years	210	140 –270	196	130–250
3 years	330	(220)–400	307	240–350

Table 7.38 Dimensions of the Foulbé breed of cattle

		Height to withers (cm)	Height to hips (cm)	Perimeter of thorax (cm)	Height to chest (cm)	Width of chest (cm)	Scapulo-ischial length (cm)	Weight (kg)
	6 tooth	120.53	127.13	154.41	59.09	30.55	130.04	321.37
	n = 43	± 0.44	± 0.52	± 0.71	± 0.31	± 0.31	± 0.58	± 3.91
	4 tooth	120.13	127.20	152.42	58.72	30.25	128.00	308.45
Average	n = 116	± 0.30	± 0.30	± 0.48	± 0.23	± 0.20	± 0.43	± 2.8
	2 tooth	118.53	125.83	148.60	57.66	29.56	126.00	296.76
	n = 30	± 0.64	± 0.67	± 1.0	± 0.44	± 0.43	± 0.74	± 4.3

The growth rates shown in Tables 7.37 and 7.38 were observed by Dumas and L'hoste at Wakwa station near to N'Gaoundéré.

The Foulbé Zebus are well adapted to intensive grazing and daily liveweight gains of 600–1000 g over periods of 3–4 months have been noted.

Good butchering yields have been observed in the course of an experiment based on the principles shown in Table 7.39. The results are shown in Table 7.40.

Genetic improvement

In 1932, the genetic improvement of the Foulbé Zebu was undertaken by crossing with the Montbeliarde breed. Despite giving satisfactory results, the operation was discontinued until 1970 when the trials were re-started.

From 1950 to 1966, crossing with the American Brahman was undertaken at the Wakwa station with the objective of creating, by cross-breeding, a Brahman half-breed. It is apparent that the results were less significant than those hoped for and that the Brahman breed was excessively susceptible to streptothricosis.

Since 1975, genetic improvement by selection by progeny testing has been carried out at Wakwa.

Table 7.39 Method of animal maintenance: feeding trial with Foulbé cattle

Lots	I	II	III	IV	V
Animals (numbers at the start)	16 Foulbé bullocks	16 Foulbé cross Brahman bullocks	11 Foulbé bullocks	5 Foulbé bullocks	8 Foulbé bullocks
Regime	intensive		semi-intensive		extensive
Method of maintenance	loose housing		at pasture		savanna
Ration	silage and hay plus concentrate		pasture hay plus molasses and urea	pasture hay plus cotton seed	pasture only

Table 7.40 Liveweight gains of Foulbé cattle; five experimental lots

	Lot I (13 head)	Lot II (13 head)	Lot III (10 head)	Lot IV (5 head)	Lot V (8 head)
Initial weight (kg)	346.3 ± 17.8	337.2 ± 20.2	343.1 ± 42.5	363.6 ± 105	345.3 ± 53
Final weight (kg)	410.5 ± 15.2	407.5 ± 5.7	363.7 ± 41.1	411.5 ± 106	317.7 ± 45
Overall variation (kg)	+64.2 ± 7.2	+70.4 ± 10.9	+20.6 ± 9.5	+47.9 ± 14.4	−27.6 ± 10.6
Average daily variation g/day	729.1 ± 83	799.8 ± 125.5	231.3 ± 107	537.6 ± 164	−310 ± 120
Extremes: Max.	972	1080	+483	685	−551
Min.	517	(324)*602	−11	393	−129

Gir

Origin and history

The Gir breed originates from the highlands and forests of the southern part of the Kathawar peninsula on the west coast of India. This region is situated to the south of the Tropic of Cancer between latitudes 25°5' and 22°6' north and longitudes 70°6' and 72° east. In this region, the Gir Forests cover almost 4000 km². It comprises a landscape of average altitude (140–640 m), broken by small valleys which are frequently submerged by flood waters. All the hills are volcanic in origin.

The climate is temperate with moderate rainfall (500–700 m), with abundant dews and thick mists. The Gir Forest, despite its density, is exploited more for grazing than for timber production.

Importance and distribution

Gir cattle have been used to improve the populations of the neighbouring regions of India. Moreover, as long ago as 1890, they were exported to Brazil where they continue to be reared as a pure breed and have contributed to the creation of the Indu Brazil breed.

Description

The Gir (Plates 7.11 and 7.12) is a breed of average stature or slightly larger than average. Unlike the Krankej and Nellore, its coat is a speckled red, sometimes uniformly red. The speckles are of varying density, from light wheat coloured to an almost black tint, and the varied size of them can often be classed as spots or flecks.

The most remarkable peculiarity of the Gir is a prominent and very large forehead, forming a massive shield on the head which extends to the eye sockets to the point where 'the eyes appear to be half-shut giving the animal a sleepy look'. Moreover, the ears are very long and drooping, turned towards the front, resembling a rolled up leaf and having characteristic notches at their

Table 7.41 Dimensions of the Gir breed

Dimensions	Male adult			Female adult		
	Max.	Min.	Mean	Max.	Min.	Mean
Weight (kg)			544.3			385.0
Length from the point of the shoulder to the point of the hips (cm)	167	130	152.6	162	122	139.7
Height of withers (cm)	142	122	136.0	145	114	128.0
Height of chest (cm)			60.2			56.1
Width at hips (cm)	61	30	45.2	53	30	43.2
Perimeter of thorax (cm)	203	152	182.4	188	147	167.6
Weight at birth (kg)			25.4			24.0

extremities. The forehead is linked to very particular short bulky horns developing like those of buffaloes, at first downwards and back, then upwards and towards the front.

The dewlap is only slightly developed. The hooves are black, of average size and hard. Dimensions of the breed are given in Table 7.41.

Rearing techniques

In the region from which they originate, Gir cattle are reared not only by farmers but also by nomadic herders (Habaris, Bharwads, Maldharis). From the end of the rainy season, the herds transhume to the forest. The bullocks and milking cows remain in the village and receive complementary feed based on wheat bran, legume straw and cereals. The males are used for draught.

In Brazil, Gir cattle are reared on ranches exclusively for meat.

Utility

The milking capacity of this breed is mediocre to average (Table 7.42).

The principle use, essentially developed in South America, is for meat production. The growth rates are shown in Table 7.43.

Table 7.42 Mean milk production of the Gir cow in approved Indian farms

Years	Number recorded	Average production per lactation (kg)	Average duration of lactation (days)	Average duration of dry period (days)
1936/37	5	1 249	295	197
1937/38	22	1 746	378	120
1938/39	33	1 707	347	138
1939/40	46	1 576	324	123

Table 7.43 Weights of Gir cattle held at the Udereba livestock experimental station (Brazil)

Age	Males (kg)	Females (kg)
At birth	24.6 ± 0.9 (27)	23.8 ± 0.6 (31)
3 months	64.1 ± 2.9 (32)	61.1 ± 1.7 (46)
6 months	113.4 ± 5.6 (36)	105.6 ± 2.9 (45)
9 months	159.6 ± 6.0 (28)	145.9 ± 3.5 (43)
12 months	191.3 ± 7.4 (19)	173.3 ± 4.1 (39)
15 months	233.1 ± 14.3 (8)	194.8 ± 6.1 (36)
18 months	275.0 ± 1.6 (7)	219.9 ± 4.8 (33)
21 months	323.3 ± 12.0 (7)	250.9 ± 4.2 (29)
24 months	360.4 ± 15.8 (5)	273.0 ± 5.1 (28)
Daily liveweight gain in kg from birth to the age of 24 months	0.211	0.157

The figures in brackets indicate the number of stock observed

Genetic improvement

Rational selection of the breed for meat production is carried out in Brazil.

In India, selection for milk production is conducted in government for centres for animal production.

Gobra

Origin and history

The Gobra Zebu is raised by the Peuls in the Djollof region of Senegal.

It is related to other Peul Zebus of the Sahelo-Soudanian zone, in particular to those raised in the West of Mali, the Sudanese Peul Zebu and that from Niger. It is considered, in the absence of objective data (genetic markers), that these cattle are the product of the incorporation of the Hamitic long-horned type into Zebus from the East.

The Gobra Zebu has occupied its present grazing lands for several centuries.

Importance, distribution and numbers

The grazing lands of the Gobra lie between longitudes 12° and 16° west and between latitudes 13° 5′ and 16° 6′ north, and cover West Senegal from the low plateau up to Mauritania.

The breed numbers are estimated at 1 720 000 animals of which there are 1 409 000 in Senegal, 287 000 in Mauritania and 24 000 in the Gambia. Only one acclimatisation trial has been carried out outside its home grazing lands and this was in the north of the Ivory Coast, but unfortunately with no great success.

Plate 7.13   Gobra cow (Senegal)

Plate 7.14   Gobra bull (Senegal)

Description

The Senegalese Peul Zebu or Gobra Zebu (Plates 7.13 and 7.14) is of superior stature to the average. The head is long, the forehead bulging and the nose straight. The horns are long in the bullock and the cow, but short in the bull in the shape of a lyre. Wavy horns are also found. The neck is short, the dewlap very prominent and the hump developed in the bull. The coat is generally white and in rare cases red pied or wheat coloured. The dimensions shown in Tables 7.44 and 7.45 are those reported by Joshi.

Plate 7.15   Kankrej cow (Brazil)

Plate 7.16   Criollo cow (Brazil)

Table 7.44 Average dimensions of Senegalese Peul Zebus in Senegal

Dimensions	Adult cows	Adult bulls	Adult bullocks
Weight (kg)	322 (34)	415 (8)	348 (56)
Scapulo-ischial length (cm)	142 (34)	140 (8)	135 (56)
Height at withers (cm)	139 (34)	143 (8)	137 (56)
Depth of chest (cm)	72 (34)	78 (8)	74 (56)
Width of hips (cm)	45 (34)	42 (8)	43 (56)
Perimeter of thorax (cm)	183 (34)	192 (8)	180 (56)

The figures in brackets indicate the number of animals measured

Table 7.45 Average dimensions of Senegalese Peul Zebus in Mauritania

Dimensions	Adult cows	Adult bulls	Adult bullocks
Weight (kg)	250–300	300–350	300–350
Scapulo-ischial length (cm)	104	124	126
Height at withers (cm)	124	130	137
Depth of chest (cm)	63	70	71
Width of hips (cm)	41	45	41
Perimeter of thorax (cm)	149	160	162

(Source: The Livestock Service of Mauritania, personal communication)

Rearing techniques and types of production

Senegalese Peul Zebus are the ultimate free-ranging animals which exploit the natural Sahelian pasture in practising transhumance. They are not allowed into the valleys until after the harvest. The herds are raised in complete freedom and are only restrained for milking, and this is usually every 2 days.

The type of production is the bullock over 4 years of age traded on the market at Dakar. For some years, different forms of intensive pasture have been developed enabling, with the aid of harvest residues (haulms and shells of groundnuts), the improvement of the condition of animals destined for slaughter.

Utility

The milking ability of the Gobra Zebu is estimated at 500–600 kg of milk per lactation and is exploited purely by traditional stockmen.

The principle aptitude is therefore meat production. In the traditional conditions of livestock keeping, this is limited by resources and the feeding regime. The potential is nevertheless attractive and has been demonstrated experimentally (Tables 7.46 and 7.47).

Table 7.46 Growth of Gobra Zebu cattle under traditional livestock husbandry

		6 months	12 months	18 months	24 months	30 months	36 months
Males	n	162	199	145	95	68	65
	m	96.2	144.0	196.6	259.6	312.6	364.3
	±	2.7	4.0	6.1	7.8	9.6	13.3
Females	n	200	220	165	11	92	89
	m	88.1	129.0	174.0	220.4	270.5	309.5
	±	2.2	3.5	5.5	7.4	9.0	9.2

n = number of animals studied; m = mean weight (kg)

Table 7.47 Growth and development compared between Gobra Zebra (fed *ad lib.*) born in 1968 and 1970 and sample animals born in 1965 to 1968 (maintained on Sahelian pasture)

		Birth			6 months			12 months		
		n	m	±	n	m	±	n	m	±
Males	control	227	25.0	0.5	162	126.2	2.7	199	144.0	4.0
	ad lib. 1968	14	21.3	1.6	15	126.3	12.2	14	248.7	18.1
	ad lib. 1970	9	26.0	2.6	7	130.8	21.5	3	283.6	8.0

		Ad lib.		Control	
		24 months	36 months	24 months	36 months
Males	n	14	10	95	65
	m	490.0	634.2	296.6	364.3
	±	24.2	25.5	7.8	13.3
Females	n	38	25	110	89
	m	387.8	422.6	220.4	309.5
	±	15.6	20.4	7.4	9.2

n = number of animals studied; m = mean weight (kg)

Genetic improvement

Genetic improvement of the Gobra Zebu is carried out at the Dahra Djoloff station. At the present time, only selection is practised. One crossing trial with Pakistani Zebus between 1960 and 1970 showed that the performance of the local breed was as good as that of the imported animals, and that crossing was of no economic advantage.

Kankrej

Origin and history

The Kankrej or Guzerat breed originates from a state to the north of Bombay called Gujerat to which it owes its name. This region, of about 2000 km², is situated under the Tropic of Cancer, latitude 21–24° north between longitudes 71° and 74° east. This is a low dry region with few trees, temporary water flows, sand dunes and black clay plains. The mean rainfall varies from 500–700 mm with a wet season from July to October (4 months).

The Kankrej breed seems to be very old.

Importance and distribution

This breed is known in the neighbouring regions under the breed names of Wadhiar, Wagad, Sanchore (Radjpoutana) and is very similar to the Malvi breed of Radjpoutana which only differs in the horns.

Numbers are of the order of 500 000 in Gujerat. The Kankrej breed has been used to improve other Indian breeds. It is known under the name of the Guzerat on the American continent, notably in Brazil where it was imported from 1914 to 1921 and there are now several million of this breed in the region.

It is one of the principle constituent elements of the American Brahman breed created in the United States (see page 339).

Description

The Kankrej breed (Plate 7.15) is one of the heaviest among the Indian breeds. Taking on national prestige, it has been bestowed with a standard by the Indian Council of Agricultural Research.

The coat varies from silver grey to iron grey or steel black. The new-born calves have a reddish brown chignon (tuft on top of the head) but this colouration disappears towards weaning age (6–10 months). The forequarters, the hump and the hindquarters are darker than the trunk, in particular in the males. The tail ends in a black tuft. The horns are strong, lyre or cup-shaped, with a cutaneous cover more developed than in the other breeds; this is very characteristic. The nose is narrow and the muzzle has the appearance of being turned up. The ears are very characteristic due to their size and because they droop. The limbs are well formed and well set. The feet are small, round and solid. The hump is well developed and 'conical hat' shaped in the male. Details of dimensions are given in Table 7.48.

Table 7.48 Dimensions of the Kankrej breed of cattle

	1 year old	2 year old	Adult
Females			
weight at birth (kg)	153	244	421
length from point of shoulder to point of hips (cm)	109	124	140
height of withers (cm)	108	120	131
height of chest (cm)	51	56	66
width of hips (cm)	31	37	51
thorax perimeter (cm)	130	150	178

	1 year old	2 year old	Adult bull	Adult bullock
Males				
weight at birth (kg)	180	250	615	554
length from point of shoulder to point of hips (cm)	114	119	159	161
height of withers (cm)	114	122	158	150
height of chest (cm)	54	55	77	81
width of hips (cm)	33	36	57	59
thorax perimeter (cm)	136	150	201	113

Figures recorded at Northcote Livestock Farm, Chharodi, Bombay State, India.

Rearing techniques and types of production

In its natural homeland, the Kankrej breed was exploited by herders (Rabari, Bharwads, Maldhari) who settled and became herder-cultivators. Part of the herd (dry cows and followers) continue to move to other grazing areas during the dry season. In India, these animals are only destined for draught use and milk production. In Brazil and the United States, they are used for meat production.

Utility

Numerous milk production records have been studied. For the results obtained in the Indian government farms, they stand at between 600 and 2500 kg per lactation (300–350 days) with a mean of about 1500 kg.

They are renowned in India for their draught capabilities – a pair of bullocks on a good road and yoked to a cart with pneumatic tyres can pull a load of 1800 kg and cover 40 km in 10 h, or on shorter journeys travel at 4.8 km/h.

In Brazil the growth rates shown in Table 7.49 have been observed.

Genetic improvement

In India, selection is carried out by traditional stockmen according to ancient criteria.

In Brazil, the local bloodstock has its own register of origin and selection, orientated towards the production of meat and calling more and more on modern methods.

Ongole or Nellore

Origin and history

This breed, like many others, takes its name from the region from which it originates, which is on the route taken by the Arya to invade India. This area is contained between longitudes 79° 2′ and 80° 2′ east, and latitudes 15° and 16° north. It is a flat land, bordered by the Gulf of Bengal and crossed by permanent flows of water whose banks support excellent herbage. Rainfall varies from 762 – 900 mm spread between May and September. In the driest parts, on alluvial soils, there are permanent pastures and elsewhere the fallow lands are grazed. In the rice producing areas, the animals are fed on vetches, lentils and rice straw and they exploit the wooded areas.

The numbers of Ongole Zebus in India are estimated at 1 500 000 head. The breed has been exported to Brazil, Sri Lanka, the United States, the Fiji islands, Vietnam, Indonesia and to Malaysia.

The numbers of breeding stock exported are not known. On the American

Table 7.49 Average weights (kg) of Kankrej Zebus

Age	Male	Female
Birth	29.1 ± 1.2 (20)	28.0 ± 1.0 (33)
At 3 months	79.5 ± 2.1 (38)	70.5 ± 2.4 (49)
At 6 months	137.5 ± 4.5 (36)	122.4 ± 2.0 (46)
At 9 months	200.9 ± 7.0 (29)	174.3 ± 5.2 (40)
At 12 months	249.4 ± 9.3 (21)	214.5 ± 7.0 (36)
At 15 months	281.8 ± 15.9 (13)	241.5 ± 7.8 (33)
At 18 months	363.2 ± 19.7 (9)	276.6 ± 7.8 (32)
At 21 months	412.4 ± 17.8 (7)	307.9 ± 9.8 (27)
At 24 months	456.3 ± 17.0 (6)	340.6 ± 8.0 (23)
Daily liveweight gain from birth (kg)	0.269	0.197

The figures in brackets indicate the number of animals observed. From figures furnished by the state livestock experimental station situated near to Uberaba.

Table 7.50 Average dimensions of Ongole Zebus

Dimensions	At birth	1 year old	2 year old	Adult
Females				
weight (kg)	27	226	279	400–450
length from point of shoulder to point of hips (cm)	68	117	117	133
height of withers (cm)	76	117	119	132
height of chest (cm)	–	58	58	–
width of hips (cm)	–	41	41	48
thorax perimeter (cm)	69	145	147	173
Males				
weight (kg)	30	218	349	540–610
length from point of shoulder to point of hips (cm)	77	117	135	159
height of withers (cm)	79	119	132	149
height of chest (cm)	–	58	71	–
width of hips (cm)	–	41	47	55
thorax perimeter (cm)	71	142	168	210

continent, the Nellore breed has brought to the American Brahman breed some of its most marked characteristics, notably the coat and horns. In Brazil and the United States, pure-bred herds have been conserved and the breed contributed to the constitution of the Indu Brazil breed.

Dimensions of the breed are given in Table 7.50.

Description

The Ongole breed, originally from the north of the state of Madras in India, is a breed of large stature but not very compact. It is white or light grey in colour. The horns are short and bulky, growing outwards and backwards. The forehead is bulging, the eyes elliptical, bordered by a circle of black skin. The ears are moderately long and slightly drooping. The dewlap is well developed as is the umbilical fold and the sheath, which is hanging. The limbs are long and well muscled. In the males, the hump is well developed and erect.

Rearing techniques and types of production

In its country of origin, the breed is exploited in different ways.

In the alluvial and rice growing areas, the herds are small (less than 10 head) and move to the hills in the rainy season from July to October. They are partly used for milking. The bull calves are better cared for than the heifer calves because they are destined for work and often exported to other regions for this job.

On the American continent, Nellore Zebus are only exploited on ranches for meat.

Utility

Milking ability has only been measured in India. It is moderate (1000–1500 kg per lactation) (Table 7.51).

Table 7.51 Milk production from Ongole cows

Years	Average production in one lactation (kg)	Average length of lactation (days)	Average length of dry period (days)
1936/37	13	31	14
1937/38	1434	303	129
1938/39	1220	306	128
1939/40	1514	329	265

The growth of Nellore Zebus has been studied in Brazil and the observations shown in Table 7.52 have been made.

Table 7.52 Weight of Ongole Zebus (kg)

Age	Males	Females
Birth	29.8 ± 0.6 (21)	24.8 ± 0.7 (30)
3 months	74.0 ± 1.5 (52)	66.1 ± 1.7 (57)
6 months	129.0 ± 2.0 (54)	118.2 ± 2.9 (54)
9 months	185.5 ± 4.2 (44)	173.0 ± 3.7 (54)
12 months	232.0 ± 5.1 (32)	195.8 ± 1.5 (50)
18 months	331.5 ± 9.5 (18)	254.5 ± 5.8 (42)
24 months	436.4 ± 22.3 (7)	312.5 ± 5.9 (35)
Daily liveweight gain from birth to 24 months	0.313	0.190

Figures communicated by the state livestock experimental station near Uberaba, Brazil. The figures in brackets indicate the number of stock observed.

Plate 7.17   Madagascan Zebu cow (Madagascar)

Plate 7.18   Madagascan Zebu bull (Madagascar)

Genetic improvement

Genetic improvement is principally carried out in Brazil.

The Madagascan Zebu

Origins and history

It is obvious that the Madagascan Zebu has been introduced by the immigrants coming from Indonesia via the Indies, Arabia and East Africa.

A breed without a hump (*Bos taurus*), perhaps still existing in the most

Plate 7.19   Sahiwal cow (Madagascar)

Plate 7.20   Sahiwal bull (Madagascar)

inaccessible regions of the island could have preceded this breed, and is known under the name of 'Baria cattle'. The word 'Madagascan', indicating the bullock, is of Bantu origin (Omby) and not Asiatic. Whatever the case may be, the breed presents a homogeneity of form and no sub-breed is recognised. It has been present in the island for about 1000 years.

Importance, distribution and numbers

The cattle population of Madagascar amounts to 10 million head, of which 1 per cent are the product of crossing of the Madagascan Zebu with other foreign breeds. The same breed is represented in the whole island. Since the beginning of the century, live animals have been exported to the nearby island of Reunion for meat purposes. The Madagascan Zebu has not been exported elsewhere.

Description

The Madagascan Zebu (Plates 7.17 and 7.18) is an animal of near average size.

All coat colours are encountered with a predominance of black pied, black and red pied. The horns are of average size, and cup- or lyre-shaped. The hump, which is very pronounced in the male, is erect, while in the female it is sometimes almost insignificant. The head is small with a straight profile and often concave. The ears are small. The dewlap is well developed and there is no umbilical or preputial fold. The conformation of animals in good condition is good. The dimensions shown in Table 7.53 were recorded by Serres *et al.* (1968).

Rearing techniques and types of production

Traditionally, milking is not practised in Madagascar. The cattle herds are reared for meat and work. The ancient tradition of cattle rustling has, for centuries, made night corralling a general practice. In all countries, the steers have been used for about 150 years for cartage, and more recently for yoked cultivation. Traditionally and still today in rice growing areas, herds are used for treading the rice fields, an exhausting operation practised at the beginning of the rainy season when the animals are unfortunately in a poor condition.

The types of production have evolved and continue to evolve. Traditionally, Madagascar produced grass-fed bullocks of 5–8 years of age for the home market and for export, and these had often benefited from a period on grassy pastureland for 6–8 months (Dabokandro). Some animals in the Tananarive region were very intensively grass-fattened in troughs to produce hyperfat carcasses (deep beef). The cultivation of the savannas of the lowlands, because of demographic development, causes these practices to increase.

Utility

The milking capacity of the Madagascan Zebu is very poor. The Madagascan cow has a bad temperament and only gives milk to its calf. Measurements over five lactations of Zebu cows established a mean of 6 litres in 12 days.

Since the nineteenth century, attempts at improvement of milk production have been carried out by crossing with European breeds (Bordelaise, Breton, Swiss Brown, Normandy and more recently the Friesian) and the result is a population around Tananarive called Rana.

The capacity for draught has been widely used and measured by Centre d'etudes d'Experimentation en Machinisime Agricóle Tropical (= Experimental Centre for studies of agricultural machinery) (CEEMAT).

Table 7.53 Dimensions and weights of adult Zebu cows

Stations (number of cows)	Kianjasoa 42	Miadana 52	Solila 25	Babaomby 12	Boanamary 9	Adranolava 9
Height at withers (cm)	116.0 ± 0.6	112.7 ± 0.5	115.8 ± 1.6	112.2 ± 3.1	116.5 ± 3.9	115.8 ± 5.4
Height at sacrum (cm)	125.3 ± 0.8	122.2 ± 0.6	122.6 ± 1.8	119.7 ± 3.4	123.8 ± 4.1	122.7 ± 4.9
Perimeter of thorax (cm)	157.5 ± 1.6	150.4 ± 1.2	143.6 ± 2.0	151.2 ± 3.7	144.5 ± 7.6	148.7 ± 4.9
Scapulo-ischial length (cm)	140.1 ± 1.2	137.9 ± 0.7	134.6 ± 2.0	137.0 ± 5.6	136.5 ± 9.6	137.4 ± 7.6
Length of pelvis (cm)	46.4 ± 0.4	43.6 ± 0.2	42.6 ± 0.9	44.0 ± 0.8	42.8 ± 2.4	43.9 ± 2.4
Width of pelvis (cm)	42.5 ± 0.4	40.9 ± 0.3	38.1 ± 0.8	40.0 ± 1.6	38.5 ± 1.8	38.8 ± 2.2
Weight (kg)	326.1 ± 6.4	279.4 ± 4.9	236.6 ±10.3	no weighing machine available	248.4 ±38.1	278.5 ± 6.1

Table 7.54 Pulling power over a long period

Pulling team	Weight (kg)	Age (years)	Average effort (kg)	Maximum effort (kg)	Speed (km/h)	Power (kgm/s)	Work time (h/d)	Duration of trials (d)
1 pair of Madagascan Zebus	650	4–5	80	150	2.5	56	4 h 45	3
2 pairs of Madagascan Zebus	1300	4–5	160	400	1.8	80	5 h 45	2
1 pair of Brahman bullocks	1060	6	147	310	2.4	97	4 h 40	11
1 pair of Renitelo	1110	5.5	150	360	2.9	120	3 h 40	–

(source: CEEMAT)

Table 7.55 Mean weights of Zebus in different parts of Madagascar

Commercial abattoirs in Madagascar	Number of animals	Av. weight (kg)
Diégo	11 549	313
Tuléar	14 854	334
Fianarantsoa	1 079	328
Tamatave	8 370	315
Tananarive	27 026	281
Tananarive municipal abattoir	40 193	401
Total	103 071	342.2

The true aptitude of the Madagascan Zebu is meat production. The Madagascan Zebu is penalised by its reduced stature as proven by the weights recorded by Serres *et al.* (1968) in commercial abattoirs in different parts of the country (Table 7.55).

The growth of the Madagascan Zebu at grass continues until an advanced age.

The maximum potential for growth in the Madagascan Zebu has been measured and is relatively limited (cf. the Renitelo breed, Tables 7.93 and 7.94).

Table 7.56 Butchering characteristics – comparison between Madagascan Zebus and Brahman crosses

Type of animal	Liveweight	Stomach (contents)	Carcass (weight)	Carcass (yield)	Wastage (per cent)
3/4 Brahman (average)	397.0	47.0	233.5	59.2	66.7
1/2 Brahman (average)	392.0	48.5	226.3	57.6	65.8
Madagascan Zebu (average)	357.5	42.9	198.6	55.5	63.1

Finally, the butchering yield has been compared with that of different Madagascan Zebu × Brahman crosses (Table 7.56) and with the Renitelo.

Genetic improvement

In the pure breed, selection of the Madagascan Zebu by progeny testing has been carried out at the Centre for Animal Research (CRZ) at Miadana (Majunga) since 1970.

Genetic improvement of the butchering capacity of the Madagascan Zebu has been carried out at CRZ Kianjasoa since 1925. Crossing with the Limousin, then the Africander, leads to the creation of the Renitelo breed, fixed since 1963 and in the course of being multiplied in state farms.

Improvement by crossing with the Braham has been a failure due to the excessive susceptibility of this breed to streptothricosis.

Improvement of milking capacity in the Madagascan Zebu is being carried out at CRZ Kianjasoa, and it has been attempted at CRZ Miadana by crossing with the Brune des Alpes, but this has not continued.

The Sahiwal

Origin and history

Sahiwal cattle are very close to the Zebus of Afghanistan and have a varying proportion of Gir blood. They are also called Montgomery from the name of a neighbouring region in Pakistan where they are numerous.

Importance, distribution and numbers

Numbers in the area which they originate from are not known. Reputed to be one of the best milking breeds in India, the Sahiwal has spread into the states of Punjab, Delhi, Uttar Pradesh, Bihar, Madya Pradesh, Bhopal and Bengal.

At the beginning of the twentieth century, Sahiwal cattle were exported to the British West Indies where they contributed to the formation of the Jamaica Hope breed.

Between the two World Wars, the breed was introduced into East Africa (Kenya, Tanzania) where a very productive milking blood line has been selected.

Sahiwal Zebus have also been imported into Tunisia and from there into Senegal.

From East Africa, the breed has been exported to Madagascar where a small herd has been studied at CRZ Miadana for several years.

Finally, the Sahiwal Zebu has been imported into Australia, where it contributes to the formation (currently) of the Australian Milking Zebu (AMZO) breed. From here it is spread by artificial insemination, notably to New Zealand for the production of Sahiwal × Friesian half-blood heifers destined for export to Thailand.

In the area from which it originates, the Sahiwal breed has been the object of crossing operations notably with the Friesian breed, with the purpose of improving milk production. These operations are sometimes very old, as was the case in the military farms between the two World Wars.

In 1974, the results, targets and objectives of the 'All India Coordinated

Table 7.57 Dimensions (comparative data recorded at CRZ Miadana in Madagascar)

Dimensions	Males			Females		
	Indian Sahiwal	Miadana Sahiwal	Miadana Madagascan Zebu	Indian Sahiwal	Miadana Sahiwal	Miadana Madagascan Zebu
Weight (kg)	544	461.2	425.1	408	356.9	279.4
HG (height to withers) (cm)	137.2	126.0	117.3	121.9	120.6	112.7
PT (perimeter of thorax) (cm)	203.2	173.1	164.5	168.9	159.5	150.4
LSI (scapulo-ischial length) (cm)	160	149.5	143.7	134.6	139.4	137.9
LC (length of hindquarters) (cm)		47.7	48		47.2	43.6
IC (width of hindquarters) (cm)		49.8	40.8		48.9	40.9
LT (length of head) (cm)		54.0	47.2		51	46.0
IT (width of head) (cm)		27.5	21.7		21.3	19.9
PT/HG	148.1	137.4	140.2	138.5	132.2	133.4
Index of length LSI/HG	116.6	118.6	122.5	110.4	115.5	122.3
Index of hindquarters IC/LC		104.4	85		103.6	93.8
Index of head IT/LT		50.9	45.9		41.7	43.2

Planning' on the rearing of milking cattle were published. These forecast the creation of a new more productive breed having 75 per cent blood from European breeds (Friesian, Brown Swiss and Jersey) and 25 per cent Sahiwal blood.

In 1980, the results obtained in the coastal region of Kenya by the alternate crossing of Sahiwal × Ayrshire practised since 1939 were analysed. This system seems to have enabled the combination of the Sahiwal adaptation to hot zones with the productivity of the Ayrshire breed.

Description

The Sahiwal breed is one of average stature with a broad elongated body, fairly close to the ground. The most common is wheat coloured, more or less dark and in rare cases speckled with white.

The forehead is large and bulky in the male but average in the female and the ears are of average size bordered by black hair. The horns are short, dense and often loose at the base in the females.

The hump is a conical hat shape in the male, dense and hanging down on the side, and barely visible in the female. The dewlap and the preputial crease are very developed and fleshy. The hocks are spread and never straight. The tail is very long, almost touching the ground and ends in a black tuft. The hooves are tender and wear out rapidly on hard ground.

Rearing techniques and types of production

In the area from which the breed originates, in days gone by the Sahiwal was exploited by herders, the Junglies, using available pasturelands. The region has been parcelled out, irrigation has enabled the extension of cultivation and livestock rearing has receded. Now, the cultivators each have several animals, the cows being used for milk production and the males for draught purposes.

The Sahiwal breed has been developed in military farms and intensive dairy farms.

In East Africa, the milking herds are maintained on artificial pastures with feed supplementation. The breed's principal use remains that of milk production.

Utility

The predominant feature, which is the basis of the breed's expansion, is its milking ability.

Table 7.58 Milk production of Sahiwal cows in India

Average of number of recorded stock in different years	Average production per lactation (kg)	Average duration of lactation (days)	Average duration of dry period (days)
127	1936	306	128
224	2306	308	193
112	2478	320	115
169	2314	306	142

The production shown in Tables 7.58 and 7.59 was recorded in India. In Madagascar, the production of Sahiwal cows has been compared with that of 3/4 Brahman × Madagascan Zebu cows at CRZ Miadana and observations were also made at Naivasha (Kenya) on Sahiwal females.

The milking ability of the Sahiwal, most certainly superior to that of numerous indigenous breeds of the tropics, remains in the same league as the production that is now obtained by crossing with specialised breeds such as the Friesian. The Sahiwal cow is often penalised by its temperament and the conformation of its udder, which is often voluminous.

As regards meat production, the growth rates below were recorded at CRZ Kianjasoa and Miadana (Madagascar) and compared with those of the local Madagascan Zebu (Table 7.60).

Genetic improvement

Genetic improvement of the Sahiwal breed for milk production is carried out according to rational methods in India and in Kenya. It is accelerated by crossing with the European milking breeds.

Table 7.59 Milk production of Sahiwal cows in Madagascar

	Percentage lactations not included	First lactation		Second lactation		Third lactation onwards		Overall	
		kg	days	kg	days	kg	days	kg	days
Sahiwal Miadana Naivasha	8.7 ?	1340 (798–1683) 1057	262 (184–305)	1301 (731–1885) 1770	270 (138–354)	1590 (486–2766) 1934	286 (170–387)	1487.4 ± 335 1529	278 ± 44
3/4 Braham Miadana	26.9	817 (384–1260)	179 (113–294)	959 (457–1486)	214 (102–273)	1062 (507–2117)	245 (169–335)	1008.7 ± 203	229.5 ± 35

Table 7.60 Growth of Sahiwal cattle in Madagasca: weight (kg)

	n	3 months	6 months	12 months	18 months	24 months	30 months	36 months	42 months
Males Sahiwal Kianjasoa	7	87 ± 12.4	134 ± 27.7	197 ± 32.0	252 ± 34.4	337 ± 28.7	376 ± 29.3	447 ± 35.5	478 ± 33.7
Males Sahiwal Miadana	14	60 ± 7.2	92 ± 14.3	160 ± 17.7	205 ± 17.2	250 ± 18.3	288 ± 16.4	322 ± 22.3	356 ± 18.6
Males Madagascan Zebu	86	70 ± 2.5	102 ± 3.2	140 ± 4.3	176 ± 4.9	218 ± 4.8	255 ± 5.4	282 ± 5.7	318 ± 4.6
Females Sahiwal Kianjasoa	8	71 ± 22.6	116 ± 27.2	176 ± 21.8	226 ± 16.4	254 ± 24.5	305 ± 17.5	350 ± 31.3	414 ± 21.2
Females Sahiwal Miadana	13	56 ± 8.8	90 ± 11.4	151 ± 12.3	186 ± 12.1	220 ± 9.5	248 ± 10.7	276 ± 15.9	294 ± 13.8
Females Madagascan Zebu	77	66 ± 2.2	95 ± 3.5	129 ± 5.5	161 ± 4.6	188 ± 4.7	215 ± 5.5	238 ± 4.3	262 ± 4.6

Table 7.61 Central Africa: numbers of humpless cattle tolerant to trypanosomiasis
(units in thousands)

Country	Breed	The tolerant herd			
		Pure	Cross	Total	Percentage
Cameroun	Namji	10		13	4.2
	N'Dama	3			
Central African Republic	Baoule	22		22	7.1
Gabon	N'Dama	1.5		3	0.9
	Lagunes + Baoule	1.5			
Congo	N'Dama	31		40	12.9
	Baoule crosses	8	1		
Zaire	N'Dama	231		231	74.7
	Baoule				
Overall total		308		309	100.0

Table 7.62 West and West-Central Africa: numbers of breed tolerant to trypanosomiasis
(units in thousands)

Country	Breed	The tolerant herd			
		Pure	Cross	Total	Percentage
Senegal	N'Dama & Métis	1 208		1 208	15.2
Gambia	N'Dama	219		219	2.8
	Baoule				
Mali	N'Dama	320	530	850	10.7
	Cross Méré & Bambara				
Burkina Faso	Méré, Lobi		850	850	10.7
Guinea Bissau	N'Dama	250		250	3.1
Guinea	N'Dama	2 000		2 000	25.2
Sierra Leone	N'Dama	234		234	2.9
	N'Dama	15		26	0.3
Liberia	Baoule	6		26	0.3
Ivory Coast	N'Dama & crosses		60	330	4.2
	Baoule & crosses		270		
Ghana	West A. Shorthorn,	547		608	7.6
	Sanga		61		
Togo	Lagunes,		190	190	2.4
	Lagunes, Borgou				
Benin	Somba,	82	450	532	6.7
	Lagunes, Borgou				
Nigeria	Muturu + N'Dama	650		650	8.2
	+ Ketuku				
Overall total				7 947	100.0

The humpless breeds (*Bos taurus*)

Baoule-Muturu

Origin and history

It seems to be established, notably by Epstein's studies, that these small cattle with short horns, which are found from Liberia to the south of Sudan (Nuba cattle) through Cameroun (Bakosi), Nigeria (Muturu), Benin (Somba) and the Ivory Coast (Baoule), belong to a blood stock introduced into Africa in very ancient times. This is confirmed by their incontestable tolerance to trypanosomiasis.

Bordering the Gulf of Benin, populations are found which are known under the general term of 'Beast of the lagoons', Dahomey, which originate from the Congolese animal and in part from that of Zaire and the Central African Republic.

In contrast to the N'Dama, the humpless cattle with short horns are never kept by populations with a pastoral tradition. Animals of settlement, they constitute an occasional addition to the revenues of cultivations in the economies of the villages.

Importance, distribution and numbers

Tables 7.61 and 7.62 list the estimated numbers in different countries of the Baoule and related breeds. It is estimated that they represent some 2.5 million head in total.

It is argued that, as regards the increase in numbers, there are two opposing trends.

1. On the one hand, in their area of origin, there is a tendency to absorption by various Zebu breeds which have the advantage of greater stature.
2. On the other hand, in the area of their adoption (essentially the Congo Basin), an expansion has continued since the first introductions at the beginning of the century.

Description

The West African Shorthorn includes numerous local types or breeds (Somba, Boule (Plates 7.21 and 7.22), Maturu, Bakosi) and a sub-type with a very reduced stature is often distinguished and known as Lagune (Plates 7.23 and 7.24). In a general way, the breed amounts to cattle without a hump (*Bos taurus*), of small or very small stature, with very reduced or even non-existent horns. There is a very large variety of coats, generally pied, particularly black pied but also red pied or three-coloured. Uniform coloured coats are also seen, mostly black but sometimes grey.

Plate 7.21   Baoule cow (West African Shorthorn) (Ivory Coast)

Plate 7.22   Baoule bull (West African Shorthorn) (Ivory Coast)

Generally speaking, these cattle are close to the ground and the conformation of the animals in good condition is better than most. Their dimensions are shown in Tables 7.63 and 7.64.

Table 7.63 Body dimensions of Baoule cattle. Adult animals

Females			Males		
Perimeter of thorax (cm)	Height to withers (cm)	Scapulo-ischial length (cm)	Perimeter of thorax (cm)	Height to withers (cm)	Scapulo-ischial length (cm)
140.4 ± 2.6	100.0 ± 1.7	121.2 ± 2.6	128.4 ± 1.6	95.7 ± 1.1	112.3 ± 1.7

Plate 7.23   Lagune cow (West African Shorthorn) (Ivory Coast)

Plate 7.24   Lagune bull (West African Shorthorn) (Benin)

Table 7.64 Body dimensions of West African Shorthorn cattle:
5-year-old animals

Breeds	Perimeter of thorax (cm)	Height to withers (cm)	Scapulo-ischial length (cm)
Lagune	136.3 ± 2.1	96.2 ± 1.1	119.7 ± 1.3
Somba	135.6 ± 1.4	97.1 ± 0.8	120.2 ± 1.4
Borgou	145.3 ± 1.4	106.0 ± 0.9	128.4 ± 1.4

Rearing techniques and types of production

In the area from which they originated, the shorthorn cattle live in and around the villages, feeding freely on the fallows. They are not milked unless they are looked after by a Peul herder. They are not used for cultivation. They are slaughtered for traditional ceremonies.

In the areas of their adoption, they are not used for traction but are sometimes used for cultivation and are often actively traded as steers for meat.

Utility

The milking capacity of the shorthorn cattle is generally not exploited and always limited. The figures shown in Table 7.65 are estimates: the productions indicated for the N'Dama and the Jersey × N'Dama crosses are given as a standard for comparison and were achieved under the same conditions.

Their capacity for draught, which is generally not used, is limited by their poor stature and has not been assessed.

Their principal use, linked to their tolerance to trypanosomiasis, is thus meat production in the humid tropics infested by tsetse.

Observed growth rates and butchering values are shown in Tables 7.66 and 7.67.

Well adapted to the humid tropical savannas, the shorthorn humpless cattle are renowned for high fecundity, which compensates for their poor stature in the trypanosomiasis infested zones.

Table 7.65 Milk production of some cattle from the tropics

Baoule	Lagune	Ghana Shorthorn	Méré	N'Dama	Jersey × N'Dama
150 kg† 3089 litres (in 4 months)	125 litres†	1.5 litres/day (over 185 days)	500–600 litres (in 5–6 months)†	588 ± 158 kg* (175–889) 400–600 kg†	1 277.3 ± 51.8 kg

* Semi-intensive or semi-extensive rearing
† Extensive rearing

Table 7.67 Butchering value of carcasses of Baoule and N'Dama cattle

Breeds	N'Dama	Baoule	Jersey × N'Dama
Ages	3 year 3 months	–	3 year 8 months
Live weight (kg)	389.0	269.0	389.5
Warm carcass weight (kg)	203.5	135.0	222.0
Commercial yield (%)	56.5	54.8	57.0
True yield (%)	63.1	60.3	64.3
Index of fat	4.5	0.5	5.8

Table 7.66 Growth rate of Baoule and N'Dama cattle: weight (kg)

Breeds	Birth	3 months	6 months	9 months	12 months	18 months	24 months	36 months	48 months
Baoule									
Males	12.5 ± 0.3	36.5 ± 1.3	61.2 ± 2.2	81.6 ± 2.8	92.8 ± 3.2	127.2 ± 4.3	162.0 ± 5.3	212.8 ± 10.0	—
Females	12.0 ± 0.2	36.7 ± 1.0	61.7 ± 1.9	84.7 ± 2.3	95.8 ± 2.7	123.6 ± 2.8	145.8 ± 3.4	166.0 ± 6.4	—
N'Dama									
Males	17.7	55.1	89.8	114.8	129.7	176.6	227.4	311.2	328.6
Females	16.7	51.4	84.3	109.4	120.7	154.2	190.9	259.8	268.7
Jersey × N'Dama									
Males	19.3	61.0	105.3	131.8	145.3	185.8	231.7	312.6	392.2
Females	17.6	56.5	99.0	122.3	137.1	184.0	214.6	297.0	326.4

Genetic improvement

This is only conducted in a systematic way in the Ivory Coast. Those who are interested in this subject are often not assisted as much by their own countries as by the international aid organisations which consider that this animal lacks genetic heterozygosity. It can be noted that in certain countries, meat production is based on the sheep which is smaller again than the Baoule-Muturu cattle.

Criollo

Origin and history

Found as related types in all the countries of America, these Criollo or 'Creole' cattle are animals descended from European cattle introduced into Central and South America and into the Caribbean by the first European immigrants. The origin of these animals is therefore essentially Iberian (Spain and Portugal) and the type varies according to country. In the course of the last three centuries, these populations have adapted to the natural conditions of their adopted countries and have acquired original production characteristics. Considered to be insufficiently productive, they are often crossed either with improved European breeds (Shorthorn, Hereford, Brown Swiss, Charolais, Holstein) or with Zebu breeds.

Concerning Zebus, studies of the ticks of Latin American cattle showed their African origin. The spread of *Caleotropis procera* from the disembarkation points of African cattle indicates that they were imported with the slave convoys in the sixteenth century and from India at the end of the nineteenth century and the beginning of the twentieth century. Imports of North American blood stock (American Brahman, Santa Gertrudis) were intensified, from the 1930s and 1940s, into the Caribbean as well as into Brazil, Venezuela, Colombia etc.

The Criollo cattle of Venezuela are still numerous in that country. The reference type is the Criollo Limonero, from the region of the rivers Guasare, Socuy and Limon.

It is an animal with a shiny mane, pigmented skin and fawn or grey coat which is often dark at the extremities and around the eyes, and sometimes white mottled under the abdomen. The head is large, the forehead concave, the horns fine and dark at the ends. The Criollo (Plate 7.16) is a humpless breed, of average stature and average conformation.

They are known in Venezuela under the name Criollo, in Central America under the names 'Chino' and 'Boroso', in Brazil 'Caracu' and 'Mocho National'. In Colombia they are called 'Sinu', 'Costeno', 'Con Cuernos', 'Harton des Valle' and 'Criollo de Cuba'.

The Criollo breed was the only one found in Venezuela up to the Second World War.

Criollo animals comprise several tens of millions of cattle of the 240 million in Latin America. The numbers have tended to fall compared with those of improved stock.

Rearing techniques and types of production

Criollo cattle are associated with two of the oldest types of stock rearing in Latin America. These amount to production systems relying on natural tropical pastures. It is generally free-range rearing. In the regions of small, densely populated poor farming communities, Criollo cattle are sometimes kept inside for milk production (Table 7.68) and draught purposes.

The dominant use is the production of meat which has been the object of numerous studies.

The recorded growth rates from birth to 18 months are shown in Table 7.69.

According to the same researchers, the live weights of cows are related to the number of calvings; the weights recorded are given in Table 7.70.

Table 7.68 Lactations of three types of Criollo Limonero breed cows

Type	Number of cows	Production (kg)	Variation (%)	Duration (days)	Duration (%)
A	61	1670 ± 47.9	22.4	264.7 ± 6.2	18.3
B	61	1849 ± 47.2	19.9	257.5 ± 6.1	18.5
C	146	1685 ± 34.8	24.9	259.9 ± 3.9	18.1
Total	268	1719 ± 24.7	23.5	260.4 ± 2.9	18.2

Table 7.69 Comparative growth rates of the offspring obtained by crossing Criollo Limonero and Criollo Llanero crosses with Criollo, Brahman and Santa Gertrudis bulls

Source of variation		Weight (kg)		Daily liveweight gain (g/d) up to:	
Bulls	Cows	Birth	Weaning	Weaning	18 months
Criollo Limonero	Criollo Limonero	25.5	*152.5*	*616.0*	*379.3*
Criollo Limonero	Brahman	30.9	*168.7*	*671.0*	*480.5*
Criollo Limonero	Santa Gertrudis	*31.0*	*174.6*	*698.0*	*478.4*
Criollo Llanero	Criollo Limonero	24.5	*143.3*	*599.0*	*385.2*
Criollo Llanero	Brahman	29.0	*172.4*	*699.0*	*462.2*
Brahman	Brahman	25.9	*160.2*	*655.0*	*423.3*

The means in the same column in italics are significantly different at the 1 per cent level

Table 7.70 Liveweight of Crillo and Brown Swiss cows according to number of calvings

Breed	1st calving		2nd calving		3rd calving		4th calving	
	n	m̄ kg	*n*	m̄ kg	*n*	m̄ kg	*n*	m̄ kg
Criollo	141	364.9	79	398.5	47	429.8	15	435.6
Brown Swiss	21	386.1	21	449.5	14	517.7	13	540.5

n = no. of cows; m kg = mean weight in kg

Kouri

Origins and history

According to the stockmen of the Lake Chad region, this breed is authentically original. It is considered that, like the N'Dama, it could be a direct descendant of the Hamitic long-horned animal, the first domesticated cattle known in Africa. A relationship can be seen between it and the bullocks of certain bas-reliefs of the Pharaonic era.

Basically, the Kouri is a stable breed whose area of origin is situated at Lake Chad in a region between latitudes 12° 20′ and 14° 20′ north, and longitudes 13° and 15° 30′ east.

This region includes the following areas:

1. areas of free water to the north-west and to the south;
2. an archipeligo made up of a multitude of islands strung out to the north-east;
3. marshes to the south-east and to the south.

The lake, whose area varies between 10 000 and 26 000 km², is shallow and sometimes dries out completely. The Kouri cattle are reared by Kouri and Boudouma herders on the islands, the marshes and on the edges of the lake which constitute a wet enclave in the middle of the Sahel. The rainfall varies between 250 and 500 mm per annum.

Importance, distribution and numbers

The cattle production of the region, where the Kouri are found, is estimated at 270 000 animals, of which 50 000 are pure-bred.

Expansion of the breed is not possible in the restricted geographical area of its homelands. Acclimatisation trials have been carried out in various regions of Chad, Niger, and Nigeria where the results have been variable but always limited. The breed is considered to be shrinking due to its absorption by various Zebu breeds of the region. Crossing with these breeds improves their stature and their butchering and milking characteristics.

Description

The Kouri (Plates 7.25 and 7.26) is an animal of large size, the biggest in West Africa, without a hump and characterised by very long horns.

The head is long and straight, the forehead large and hollowed by the implantation of the horns, which are the most notable characteristic of this breed. The horns, which are of circular cross-section, can reach 70–130 cm in length with a circumference of 35–55 cm at the base. They are shaped in a very broad curve and are sometimes bulbous, sometimes loose, sometimes absent. Their alveolal structure reduces their density.

Plate 7.25 Kouri cow (Chad)

Plate 7.26 Kouri bull (Chad)

The coat is most often white with pigmented mucous membranes, but there are individuals which are red, red pied or having grey coloured shoulders.

The limbs are long, powerful and thickset, with large strong joints, and are very straight. The hooves, which are light and flaky, are large, thick and very open. This breed shows a marked sexual dimorphism. The dimensions have been recorded (Table 7.71).

Utility

The uses of the Kouri have received little study. Milk production, considered high by the traditional herders, is estimated as being between 3 and 6 litres per day for a cow at the height of its lactation, or 600–800 kg per lactation.

Plate 7.27   N'Dama cow (Mali)

Plate 7.28   N'Dama bull (Mali)

The capacity for traction is unknown and the animals are only employed for carrying. Their mild and even sluggish temperament does not suggest a significant capacity for work.

The butchering capacity has been studied because of the presence of a commercial abattoir at N'Djamena, Chad. The carcass yields shown in Table 7.72 have been recorded.

Genetic improvement

The Kouri breed has only been the object of a modest selection programme. It is considered to be in danger of extinction, which is regrettable considering its exceptional aptitudes *vis-à-vis* other cattle in its area of origin.

Table 7.71 Dimensions of the Kouri breed of cattle

Nature of measurements	Malbrant et al.			Joshi et al. (1950)		Kone (1958)
	Bulls	Cows	Bullocks	Bulls	Cows	
Weight (kg)	650.0	400.0	550.0	500.0	360.0	480.0
Height of hindquarters (cm)	154.6	145.4	156.6	–	–	158.0
Height of withers (cm)	146.0	136.0	151.0	152.0	140.0	149.0
Height of belly (cm)	77.1	69.0	78.1	–	–	–
Width of haunches (cm)	49.2	46.0	50.2	48.0	45.0	34.0
Scapulo-ischial length (cm)	122.3	116.3	124.0	152.0	144.0	165.0
Perimeter of thorax (cm)	195.0	184.0	211.0	193.0	172.0	183.0
Length of head (cm)	65.9	59.3	68.0	–	–	61.0
Width of head (cm)	32.1	24.6	27.5	–	–	–

Table 7.72 Statistics from the Fort-Lamy abattoirs concerning the slaughter of neutered (males and females) Kouri cattle

Sex	Nature of statistic	4 years	5 years	6 years	7 years	8 years	9 years and over	Total
Castrates	Number	209	232	107	134	54	18	754
	Total weight (kg)	36 390	42 880	21 383	29 629	11 382	4 217	145 881
	Average weight (kg)	174.1	184.8	299.5	221.1	210.7	234.3	193.4
Males	Number	162	94	43	58	17	1	375
	Total weight (kg)	26 217	16 818	8 288	11 786	3 680	180	66 969
	Average weight (kg)	161.8	178.8	192.7	203.2	216.4	180	178.3
Females	Number	2	4	4	3	10	12	35
	Total weight (kg)	288	575	545	511	1 691	1 928	5 578
	Average weight (kg)	144	143.7	146.2	170.3	169.1	160.6	159.3

N'Dama

Origin and history

The N'Dama is well recognised as having had a very ancient presence in Africa. In the region from which the breed originates, Fouta Djallon in Guinea, it has been reared by a settled Peul population for several centuries. It is considered, in fact, that the first introduction of Peul herders to Fouta Djallon was in 1534 by Koli Galadjo. The N'Dama cattle and their owners are the descendants of the ancient inhabitants of the Sahara.

Importance, distribution and numbers

In its Guinean homeland, the N'Dama is the only cattle breed represented. The official statistics put the number of cattle in Guinea in 1981 as 1 250 000 head. It is highly likely that the N'Dama population of Fouta Djallon is more than 1.5 million animals. The breed can also be found in Senegal and in the south west of Mali. Since the 1930s nucleus stocks have been created in Zaire (Van Lancker), where numbers are estimated at 40 000 head, then later they were created in Congo (Niari Valley) where N'Dama numbers could be 20 000, in Central African Republic, in the north of the Ivory Coast and in Nigeria. Since the Second World War, the breed has been in increasing demand in the Guinean zone because of its tolerance to trypanosomiasis.

A long time ago, the N'Dama breed was exported to the West Indies (Virgin Islands) and South America and it contributed to the creation of new breeds, in which it has lost its identity.

Plate 7.29   N'Dama bull (southern Ivory Coast)

Plate 7.30   Herd of young N'Dama (Aboukamekro ranch, southern Ivory Coast)

Description

The N'Dama (Plates 7.27 and 7.30) is a humpless animal, of small to average stature. The coat is most frequently fawn, uniform and white under the belly. The extremities (head, extremities of the limbs and tail) are often darkened and sometimes almost black.

There is a small percentage (less than 20 per cent) of pied coats, the white spots frequently being flecked with brown. Exceptionally, black pied colouration is found in herds of animals.

The horns of the N'Dama are substantial, well developed, most often lyre-or cup-shaped, but animals are also encountered with atrophied horns or even having loose or completely discarded horns, and it was these which were

Plate 7.31 Afrikander bull (South Africa)

Plate 7.32 Ankole cows (Rwanda)

originally noted by the authors who described the breed.

The conformation of the N'Dama in its homeland is generally mediocre, but since the conditions of rearing have improved, the breed tends to show that it has good potential for conformation. Although the head most often manifests a rather excessive volume, the body is thick-set, rather short, and the muscular parts well developed. The limbs are fine and the hooves small and hard. The animal is generally fairly 'spirited', the young often being slim. The temperament is alert and the animals quickly adapt to good as well as to bad treatment. In their homeland, they are very quiet and easy to handle whereas on ranches they often prove to be indisciplined and even aggressive.

The average values of the main dimensions are shown in Table 7.73 and are compared with different breeds in Table 7.74.

Rearing techniques and types of production

In its homeland of Fouta Djallon, Guinea, the N'Dama breed is exploited in small herds of 5–100 head which are settled or undertake small migrations in the dry season to the lower coastal regions and those that are better irrigated. The cows are partially milked, the milk being consumed by the owners and part of it being sold either fresh or curdled. The excess males and cast cows are sold for meat.

About half a century ago, animal-drawn cultivation was introduced into Guinea and relied on the use of N'Dama bullocks whose docility and hardiness are indispensable to the rural development of the humid savanna zones.

In the Congo basin, Nigeria and the Ivory Coast, the N'Dama herds are exploited solely for meat (generally by ranching) and the females are not milked. As a result there is a better growth rate in the young and an improvement in stature, but also a reduction in docility which is aggravated by the fear which the ranch employees have of animals belonging to a species foreign to the region.

Utility

Although the N'Dama might be used for milk production in its homeland, its aptitudes in this sphere are mediocre. From 1952 to 1958, the lactations of N'Dama cows at National Centre for Animal Research CRZ at Sotuba (Mali) were measured. The production observed is given in Table 7.75.

In the first year the animals were maintained on a typical Soudanian pasture. In the course of the following years, the plane of feeding was augmented during the dry season, with 1–1.5 forage units of concentrated feed per day. In 1976, the lactations of 11 N'Dama females at CRZ Minankro-Bouake (Ivory Coast) were recorded: for a period of 206 ± 29 days, the production was 588 ± 158 kg.

The aptitude of N'Dama bullocks for traction, which is exploited in their homeland, has not been evaluated.

Table 7.73 Dimensions of the N'Dama breed

	Males	Females
Weight (kg)	328.6 ± 20 (20)	286.7 ± 8.3 (34)
Height at withers (cm)	116.4 ± 1.6 (15)	113.6 ± 0.8 (30)
Perimeter of thorax (cm)	164.1 ± 5.6 (15)	156.2 ± 1.8 (30)
Scapulo-ischial length (cm)	145.3 ± 4.6 (15)	141.0 ± 2.2 (29)
Length of head (cm)	46.4 ± 1.1 (15)	44.8 ± 0.8 (30)
Width of head (cm)	26.7 ± 1.1 (15)	23.8 ± 0.4 (30)
Length of hindquarters (cm)	47.5 ± 1.6 (15)	46.3 ± 0.5 (30)
Width of hips (cm)	40.5 ± 2.1 (15)	40.9 ± 0.8 (30)
Height of brisket (cm)	56.4 ± 1.6 (15)	56.7 ± 0.6 (30)

Numbers in brackets represent numbers of animals examined

Table 7.74 Comparative dimensions of different humpless breeds

Relationship	N'Dama	Baoule	Charolais	Limousin
Males				
LSI/PT	0.89	0.86	0.74	0.73
PT/HG	1.41	1.40	1.70	1.69
LSI/HG	1.25	1.21	1.26	1.23
LH/LC	0.85	0.81	1.10	1.10
Females				
LSI/PT	0.90	0.87	0.81	0.82
PT/HG	1.38	1.35	1.53	1.47
LSI/HG	1.24	1.18	1.23	1.21
LH/LC	0.88	0.82	1.07	1.02

LSI = Scapulo-ischial length; PT = perimeter of thorax; HG = height of withers; LH = width of hips; LC = length of the hindquarters.

Table 7.75 Milk production from N'Dama cows

Year	Production (kg)	Duration (days)	Numbers
1953	421.67	0.300	40
1954	488.6	–	–
1955	481.1 ± 11.87	–	47
1957	686	–	–
1958	658.73	–	–

The well recognised vocation of this breed is meat production in the preforest savanna zones infested with tsetse, where its tolerance to trypanosomiasis confers an exceptional advantage upon it.

The growth of the N'Dama, despite its limited adult stature, can be good as proven by the results shown in Tables 7.76 and 7.77 which were recorded at Minankro-Bouake. The butchering characteristics are also shown in the table.

Table 7.76 Increase in weight of N'Dama cattle: males

Age	Weight (kg)	Average daily liveweight gain (g)	Age	Weight (kg)	Average daily liveweight gain (g)	Age	Weight (kg)	Average daily liveweight gain (g)
Birth	17.7	629	4 months	66.2	333	17 months	165	387
1 week	22.1	500	4.5 months	71.2	407	18 months	176.6	397
2 weeks	25.6	429	5 months	77.3	427	19 months	187.9	237
3 weeks	28.6	386	5.5 months	83.7	381	20 months	195.0	319
4 weeks	31.3	343	6 months	89.8	413	21 months	204.9	257
5 weeks	33.7	414	7 months	102.2	210	22 months	212.6	235
6 weeks	36.6	357	8 months	108.7	203	23 months	219.9	250
7 weeks	39.1	386	9 months	114.8	132	24 months	227.4	208
8 weeks	41.8	371	10 months	118.9	193	27 months	246.4	254
9 weeks	44.4	386	11 months	124.7	161	30 months	269.5	281
10 weeks	47.1	357	12 months	129.7	97	33 months	295.1	177
11 weeks	49.6	429	13 months	132.6	226	36 months	211.2	138
12 weeks	52.6	357	14 months	139.6	203	39 months	323.8	52
3 months	55.1	340	15 months	145.7	383	42 months	328.5	78
3.5 months	60.2	400	16 months	157.2	252	45 months	335.6	

Table 7.77 Increase in weight of N'Dama cattle: females

Age	Weight (kg)	Average daily liveweight gain (g)	Age	Weight (kg)	Average daily liveweight gain (g)	Age	Weight (kg)	Average daily liveweight gain (g)
Birth	16.7		4 months	61.8	360	17 months	146.7	250
1 week	20.3	514	4.5 months	67.2	380	18 months	154.2	223
2 weeks	23.6	471	5 months	72.9	360	19 months	161.1	267
3 weeks	26.2	371	5.5 months	78.3	375	20 months	169.1	206
4 weeks	28.8	371	6 months	84.3	397	21 months	175.5	213
5 weeks	31.2	343	7 months	96.2	226	22 months	181.9	158
6 weeks	33.8	371	8 months	103.2	207	23 months	186.8	137
7 weeks	36.3	357	9 months	109.4	148	24 months	190.9	160
8 weeks	39.1	400	10 months	114.0	103	27 months	205.5	238
9 weeks	41.3	314	11 months	117.1	116	30 months	227.1	241
10 weeks	43.7	386	12 months	120.7	27	33 months	249.1	116
11 weeks	46.2	357	13 months	121.5	116	36 months	259.8	25
12 weeks	48.8	371	14 months	125.1	203	39 months	262.1	77
3 months	51.4	340	15 months	132.0	223	42 months	269.2	141
3.5 months	56.5	353	16 months	138.7	258	45 months	282.0	

Table 7.78 Butchering characteristics of N'Dama cattle

	Males (per cent)	Females (per cent)
Yield	50.7	44.4
Net yield*	65.2	58.4
Meat, carcass	76.1	73.7
or which:		
roasting meat	35.3	35.6
braising and boiling meat	40.7	38.2
Bone	17.8	19.4
Tallow	5.9	6.1
Waste	0.3	0.7

* Stomach and intestine contents deduced

Finally, as with the other tropical and temperate humpless cattle, the N'Dama has a fecundity very much higher than Zebus. It has been shown in the Ivory Coast that the annual number of births in relation to the number of cows served was, over 14 years, 88.5 ± 3.2 per cent, and for 378 observations the mean interval between calvings was 420.8 ± 9 days.

This fecundity, which persists even in the zones infested with bovine trypanosomiasis, constitutes a considerable asset for the development of the N'Dama breed.

Genetic improvement

Improvement is effected either by selection of local breeds by reproduction of the animals with the best qualities, or by crossing and introducing breeding stock from imported breeds with high performances.

As an example, such improvement was made the object of considerable attention by the responsible livestock research agencies of the following countries: Ivory Coast, Mali, Senegal, Niger, Madagascar and Kenya.

At Casamance in Senegal, in a zone infested with *Glossina palpalis* and *G. morsitans*, the Kolda ranch of 1400 ha was created for selecting N'Dama stock and small ruminants tolerant to trypanosomiasis.

In Mali, the works conducted at the National Centre for Animal Research, Sotuba, involve a complex breeding programme based on crossings with imported breeds.

In the Ivory Coast, with the creation of the Korhoga Livestock Rearing Centre (1934), a nucleus of N'Dama has been constituted with the object of selecting male breeding stock for distribution in the rural areas.

In 1943, the actual site of the Minankro-Bouake Research Centre was surveyed and in 1952 N'Dama cattle from the Odienne region were introduced into the framework of a well defined animal improvement programme.

In 1956, The Minankro-Bouake Centre for Animal Research was orientated towards selection of the N'Dama breed and the programme has been carried out since 1962.

In 1965, a Baoule humpless group was constituted for the genetic study of this breed and further, in 1965, the study of N'Dama crossing with the Jersey was undertaken.

Intermediate breeds (composites)

Afrikander

Origin and history

The Afrikaner breed is known as the Afrikander or Africander to foreigners and it originates from South Africa.

The distant origin of these cattle has been made the object of very elaborate studies, notably by Thornton, Curson and Epstein.

It is indisputable that it constitutes a breed resulting from very ancient crosses between Zebus and humpless cattle, with a dominance of Zebu blood introduced into Southern Africa at the time of the Hottentot migrations late in the fourteenth century.

This breed was adopted by the Dutch immigrants when they founded their first settlements in 1652. These farmers moulded the cattle to their needs, which were essentially for draught purposes.

At the time of the 'Great Trek' (1836–42), the 'Voortrekkers' took their Afrikander animals northwards with them. The survival of this breed was compromised by the 1896 and 1899 epidemics of rinderpest, then by the Boer War (1899–1902).

The Afrikander Breeders' Society was created in 1912 to contribute to the restoration and development of the breed.

Importance, distribution and numbers

The Afrikander breed is the most widespread of the beef breeds in Southern Africa and Namibia. It has the status of a national breed with 13 000 000 animals and with about 4 million cattle just in South Africa. In the most favourable regions of the country, notably when the latitude (Cape Province) or the altitude temper the excesses of the tropical climate, it gives way to other specialised British or continental European breeds.

There are significant Afrikander populations in Zimbabwe, Mozambique, Zaire (Shaba) and Zambia.

Outside of the African continent, it is considered that the Afrikander might have been imported into the United States of America from the beginning of the nineteenth century and contributed to the formation of the famous Texas Longhorn which disappeared before 1900. Afrikander cattle were exported to America again in 1931 and to Australia in 1956.

In 1946, a herd imported into Madagascar became the contributor to the creation of the Renitelo breed.

Some Afrikanders exported to the Philippines in 1937 disappeared during the Second World War.

Description

The Afrikander (Plate 7.31) is an animal of large stature. The standard of the breed prescribes that the animals should give a general impression of a deep oval form.

The bull should have a masculine aspect, vigourous, robust with well developed horns and a powerful neck provided with a much-folded dewlap. The cervicothoracic hump should be well marked, erect and firm. The cow has a feminine aspect in balance with its surroundings.

The coat includes all the shades of red, and white spots are tolerated on the underside. The skin and mucous membranes are amber coloured.

The head is large with sweeping arching below the eye sockets giving an oval shape to the eye socket which is slightly inclined towards the bottom.

The horn is a characteristic of the breed and is long and spreads laterally. The cross-section of the horns is a flattened oval shape. The horns spread towards the base, in the extension of the crown, then towards the rear and then rises again towards the front, upwards and to the rear again. Their colour is ivory white with amber coloured extremities. In the male, the horns are heavier and shorter than in the female.

The hooves, which are of a dark colour, should be robust.

The dimensions for 4-year-old animals are shown in Table 7.79, (see also Table 7.80).

Table 7.79 Dimensions of Afrikander cattle: 4-year-old

Dimension	Mean (cm)
Length of head	51.30
Width of head	22.50
Height of withers	123.58
Length of body	136.00
Depth of chest	58.00
Thoracic perimeter	152.88
Abdominal perimeter	177.43
Weight (kg)	301.98

The adult bulls and bullocks generally attain 1000 kg liveweight and the young intensively fattened animals reach 500 kg at 18 months old.

Rearing techniques and type of production

In South Africa, the Afrikander breed is essentially used for ranching. It is well known for its ability to make use of the natural pastures of semi-arid and

Table 7.80 Liveweight and average dimensions of Afrikander cattle at the
Mara Research Station

Sex	Age	Weight (kg)	Length of body (cm)	Height at withers (cm)	Height at hips (cm)	Perimeter of thorax (cm)	Depth of chest (cm)
Females	1 year	218	115	113	108	136	46
Females	2 year	353	140	130	126	164	61
Females	adult	540	154	134	132	187	68
Males	adult	900	175	142	146	224	76

(Source: Bonsma et al., 1953, in Joshi, 1957.)

Table 7.81 Reproduction performance of Afrikander cows as a function of
their feeding regime

Reproduction preformance	Rate of distribution of ration including 60% forage			
	High	Average	Low	Very low
Weight at 8 months (kg)	160	157	158	155
% increase compared with previous weight				
first winter	31	31	7	− 15
second winter	24	9	2	− 15
% of calves in first calving season	80	73	87	40
% of calves in second calving season	73	82	100	100
Weight in third summer	287	293	293	298

subhumid zones. The historical capacity of the Afrikander for walking long distances and its resistance to heat is clearly a great advantage in these rearing conditions.

In the regions sufficiently wet for the cultivation of cereals, the herds feed on the stubble of maize and sorghum after the harvest.

The type of production is the 3−4-year-old bullock.

Utility

The Afrikander breed is not used for milk production.

Historically, the main aptitude sought was that of draught. The docility of the animals and their physical resistance have been selected with this in mind.

Nowadays the most appreciated aptitude is the animals' capacity for meat production from grass in the tropics. The resistance to various tropical parasites and notably to ticks, its hardiness and the ability to exploit the veldt (feed natural pasture) are the principle characteristics.

Penzhorn 1975, quoted by Osterhoff (1975), demonstrated an exceptional capacity for recuperation of Afrikander females after periods of scarcity of feed, and this is illustrated in Table 7.81 for heifers from 8 months of age on different feeding levels.

Furthermore, research comparing the mortality rates of calves before weaning for different breeds, found that the lowest rate was for the Bonsmara breed (0 per cent) and the Afrikander (8 per cent) with a maximum of 25 per cent for the Aberdeen Angus.

The Afrikander cows are reputed for their mothering ability and longevity.

Genetic improvement

The Afrikander breeders society actively pursues the genetic improvement of the breed in South Africa.

Ankole

Origin and history

This is without doubt the longhorn Hamitic animal with traces of Zebu crossing.

Importance, distribution and numbers

The spread of Ankole cattle covers an area between longitudes 27° and 32° east, and latitudes 3° and 5° north corresponding to the following regions:

- Uganda: the districts of Tori, Kigezi and Ankole;
- Tanzania: the districts of Bokula, Kibondo, Kasulu and Ofipa;
- Republic of Burundi;
- Republic of Ruanda (numbers estimated at 683 000 head);
- Zaire: the territories of Bunia, Irumu, the districts of Bukavu (Kivu); the territories of Rutshuru, Uvira Fisi and Ouvenga.

In Zaire, the numbers are estimated at about 435 000 head.

Description

The Ankole cattle (Plates 7.32 and 7.33) are animals of average to superior stature, with a straight back, a rounded hump which is nevertheless hardly noticeable in the female. The horns are long and fine but there are varieties without horns or with short horns and others with very developed horns (sacred Inyambo cows). Uniform coloured coats are most frequent, mostly being dark red brown or dark red and sometimes red pied.

The following body dimensions shown in Tables 7.82, 7.83 and 7.84 have been recorded.

Table 7.82 Dimensions of the Ankole breed: males (adjusted values)

| Age (months) | Horizontal length of body | Different heights | | | | Perimeter of metacarpus |
		to the withers	to the back	to the hips	from sternum to the ground	
1	72.5	80.7	79.2	89.7	49.9	13.2
2	77.3	84.8	83.3	93.1	51.5	13.6
4	87.9	93.6	92.1	100.3	54.8	14.6
6	100.0	103.3	101.8	108.0	58.4	15.6
Bulls						
18	118.1	119.8	118.0	123.5	65.1	17.8
24	124.5	123.8	121.7	130.4	66.2	18.6
30	131.3	127.9	125.5	134.5	67.2	19.4
36	138.5	132.1	129.4	138.7	68.3	20.3
Bullocks						
18	110.4	110	111.2	118.8	61.8	17.1
24	115.8	115.4	114.7	122.6	63.1	17.8
30	121.4	119.3	118.3	126.5	64.5	18.5
36	127.3	123.4	122.1	120.5	65.8	19.2

Values in cm

Table 7.83 Dimensions of the Ankole breed: females (adjusted values)

| Age (months) | Horizontal length of body | Different heights | | | | Perimeter of metacarpus |
		to the withers	to the back	to the hips	from sternum to the ground	
1	70.6	79.0	78.4	85.2	49.5	12.5
2	75.4	83.1	82.2	89.3	50.9	12.9
4	85.8	91.8	90.5	98.1	53.7	13.8
6	97.7	101.5	99.6	107.7	56.8	14.7
12	102.8	107.7	104.4	111.8	60.1	15.8
18	107.9	110.8	108.0	115.5	61.2	16.2
24	113.4	114.0	111.8	119.3	62.3	16.7
30	119.1	117.3	115.7	123.2	63.4	17.1
36	125.1	120.7	119.7	127.2	64.5	17.6

Values in cm

Rearing techniques and types of production

The breed lives at high altitudes near to the Equator, which are free from trypanosomiasis. Very generally, the herds are settled or make short migrations to the flood valleys at the end of the dry season. Milking is regularly practised. The animals are little used for draught.

Utility

The comparative lactations of Ankole cows and Ankole × Sahiwal crosses are shown in Tables 7.85 and 7.86.

Table 7.84 Dimensions of the Ankole breed of cattle

Age (months)	Dimensions of chest				Dimensions of pelvis				Weight (kg)
	width (cm)	depth (cm)	Perimeter of thorax (cm)	width of back (cm)	width at hips (cm)	width at coxo-femoral joints (cm)	point of buttock (cm)	Av. length of pelvis (cm)	
1	17.2	30.5	96.2	14.5	18.4	20.5	12.9	24.5	49
2	18.1	32.8	103.0	15.5	20.0	21.7	13.5	26.1	58
4	20.2	37.8	116.5	17.8	23.6	24.5	14.9	30.0	86
6	22.5	43.6	131.6	20.4	27.9	27.6	16.4	34.4	127
12	24.0	46.0	137.9	22.7	30.4	29.6	16.8	34.9	150
18	25.6	48.6	144.5	24.3	32.4	30.9	17.8	37.0	176
24	27.2	51.4	151.5	26.0	34.6	32.4	18.8	39.1	226
30	29.0	54.3	158.7	27.8	37.0	33.8	20.0	41.5	268
36	30.9	57.4	166.4	29.8	39.6	35.4	21.2	43.9	310

Table 7.85 Comparison of first lactations of Anokole cattle

Lactations	Ankole			F_1 Ankole × Sahiwal		
	No.	Average	CV	No.	Average	CV
Age at first calving (months)	23	40.17	13.5	18	38.4	17.1
duration of lactation (days)	30	255	11.4	18	246.2	24.8
Daily production (kg)	30	3.69	–	18	4.16	–
Total production (kg)	30	943.4	16.9	18	1025.5	38.7

CV = coefficient of variation

Table 7.86 Comparison of milk production (all lactations of Ankole cattle)

Lactations	Ankole			F_1 Ankole × Sahiwal			F_2 F_3 to F_4 Ankole × Sahiwal		
	No.	Average	CV	No.	Average	CV	No.	Average	CV
Interval between calvings (days)	44	491.2	21.6	34	396.8	18.1	43	390.0	19.4
Duration of lactation (days)	33	239.1	22.3	16	234.9	13.5	31	246.8	14.9
Daily milk production (kg)	33	3.43	–	16	4.50	–	31	5.25	–
Total milk production (kg)	33	821.0	19.0	16	1059.2	16.4	31	1295.8	22.5

CV = coefficient of variation

Plate 7.33   Ankole bull (Rwanda)

Plate 7.34   Droughtmaster bull (Queensland, Australia)

Droughtmaster

Origin and history

The Droughtmaster is a new tropical cattle breed originating from Queensland, Australia. The area from which it originated lies between latitudes 11° and 20° south, in a region with a very contrasting tropical climate where, since the beginning of the twentieth century, the *Boophilus microplus* tick is widespread.

The Droughtmaster is a composite breed including about 50 per cent Zebu (Brahman) blood and 50 per cent European blood (Shorthorn, Devon, Red

Plate 7.35   Renitelo cow (Madagascar)

Plate 7.36   Renitelo bull (Madagascar)

Poll). There could equally have been infusions of Afrikander and Santa Gertrudis blood.

The principle importations of Zebus took place in 1933, then from 1950 to 1954.

Importance, distribution and numbers

By 1975, there were 36 500 Droughtmasters registered in the herd book. In Australia, the breed in its entirety amounted to several hundreds of thousands of individuals, principally in Queensland, the north of New South Wales and in the Northern Territories.

The breed has been exported to Indonesia, Malaysia, Brazil, the Solomon Islands, Nigeria, Ghana, Pakistan, New Guinea, Taiwan and China.

Description

The Droughtmaster (Plate 7.34) is an animal of average to superior size, with a long body and having a pronounced cervicothoracic hump in the male but a hump of reduced size in the female.

The coat should be uniform, light wheat coloured to dark wheat coloured.

The head is large with short horns. The animals are often dehorned. The ears are large but straight. The dewlap and umbilical fold should not be too prominent.

The conformation is that of an excellent butchering animal. Weight increases are shown in Table 7.87.

Table 7.87 Typical weights of Droughtmaster cattle

Age in weeks	13	26	52	104
Males (kg)	175	258	466	740
Females (kg)	115	184	325	620

Rearing techniques and types of production

The Droughtmaster is a tropical free-ranging animal. It is the result of selection from the extensive rearing enterprises in Queensland where the main criteria are reproduction and growth from pasture as well as resistance to ticks and the diseases transmitted by ticks.

The type of production is the 2–3-year-old grass-fed bullock, which at 400–500 kg liveweigh will give a carcass of 200–250 kg for the local market and for export. Intensive grazing of steers and young bulls is little practised in Australia and range grazing enables economic production of the type of carcasses demanded by the market.

The females are selected on their reproductive capacity and the rules of the herd book make provision for the exclusion of all heifers which have not calved within 3 years or of all cows which have not produced two calves in 3 years.

Utility

The main attribute of the Droughtmaster is its meat producing ability (Table 7.88). Nevertheless, there are reports from Pakistan that females of the Droughtmaster breed compared favourably, as regards their milking ability, with the Bhagnari, Tharpakar and Sahiwal breeds and their crosses. The cows sucked their calves for 210 days and were milked as well. The Droughtmaster heifers produced an average of 26 litres of milk per day compared with 15 litres for the Bhagnari, on the same level of feeding.

The milking ability of the Droughtmaster, although not exploited in Australia, is thus relatively high, which explains the growth rates of calves during their first year of life.

Table 7.88 Growth rates for different breeds of cattle in India

	Droughtmaster	Bhagnari	Tharpakar	Sahiwal
Average birth weight (kg)	32	23	20	20.4
Daily liveweight gain from 0 to 12 months	0.64	0.41	0.37	0.38

Despite the stress of the voyage, Droughtmaster heifers imported into Pakistan had their first calf at an average of 918 days or 200 days earlier than the Bhagnari, and their second calf was born after an interval of 447 days or 98 days less than that of the Bhagnari.

For private livestock rearing in Queensland, Francis showed that, over 8 years, the mean calving interval was 11.47 months and that only 1.83 per cent of 764 calves died at birth or during the first 3 days after calving; this statistic was only 1.6 per cent up to the age of 6 months.

The growth rate of the Droughtmaster is high up to the age of 2 years at least. In Brisbane in 1967, growth rates were noted for male and female animals between the ages of 6 months and 2 years (Table 7.89).

Table 7.89 Comparative growth rates for different breeds in Queensland

	Hereford	Shorthorn	Brahman	Droughtmaster	Santa Gertrudis	Bradford
Kg/day	1.03	0.940	0.830	1.020	0.990	1.07
Total no. of animals	209	78	52	20	20	17

Adult bulls reach 750–1,000 kg and cows reach 450 – 600 kg
(J. Francis 1967)

Genetic improvement

Selection of the Droughtmaster is actively pursued by commercial breeders and members of the Droughtmaster Breeders Society. A herd is maintained at the Faculty of Veterinary Science of the University of Queensland, at Saint Lucia near Brisbane.

Renitelo

Origin and history

The Renitelo breed originates from the J.B. Randriambeloma* Animal Research Centre (CRZ) at Kianjasoa. It is the result of phenotypic and

* The first Madagascan veterinary surgeon and first director of CRZ

genotypic selection carried out on a population of cattle which were the issue of crossing between Madagascan Zebus, Limousin humpless cattle and Afrikanders. In the Madagascan language, the word 'Renitelo' means 'three mothers'.

From 1923 to 1927, Limousin breeding stock imported from France were used for crossing with the Madagascan Zebu but many of their descendants disappeared during the Second World War, the victims of tropical diseases. In 1946, crossing of the survivors with the Afrikander breed enabled the establishment of a population which was approximately 50 per cent Afrikander, 25 per cent Zebu and 25 per cent Limousin, which was subjected to progeny selection from 1963 to 1972. The breed is today stabilised and a state organisation, the State Farms, ensures multiplication by absorption crossing of the Madagascan Zebu.

The Renitelo breed is established in middle west Madagascar and the government has created herds for suitability studies in the south and west of the country.

The Renitelo breed is a recent example of a new breed created in the tropics by crossing and re-crossing of Zebus and humpless breeds, and of tropical and European stock.

Importance, distribution and numbers

At CRZ Kianjasoa, the Renitelo nucleus herd has 500 animals. On the farms of Omby State, there are about 3000 cattle of varying blood mix.

Description

The Renitelo breed has been created by the crossing of the Madagascan Zebu, the Limousin and the Afrikander, and by the *inter se* crossing of the offspring for a period of 40 years (Table 7.90).

Table 7.90 Comparison of weights of Zebu type cattle (kg)

Male animals	6 months	12 months	18 months	24 months	30 months	36 months
Zebu	117	170	212	220	302	336
Afrikander–Zebu	130	200	257	302	360	407
Limousin–Zebu	112	191	250	320	371	432
Renitelo	158	205	273	323	392	423

The Renitelo (Plates 7.35 and 7.36) are larger than average sized animals with a uniform red coat, from fawn to dark auburn red. The horns are of various types, but are generally large and cup- or lyre-shaped. The males have a small, but nevertheless marked, cervicothoracic hump which is imperceptible in the females. The ears are small, the forehead straight or convex. The dewlap is well developed and there is no umbilical or preputial fold. The body is long and the conformation developed towards the hindquarters (as a result of Limousin influence) by a rump which in well finished animals is very well rounded.

Dimensions recorded are given in Table 7.91.

Rearing techniques and types of production

The Renitelo is a tropical free ranging-animal suited to ranching.

The type of production is the 3–5-year-old bullock for the local or export market.

Utility

The milking abilities of the Renitelo have not been measured directly, nevertheless they have been estimated as a function of calf growth and are between 600–900 kg per lactation.

The aptitude of the Renitelo has been studied by CEEMAT and compared with that of the Madagascan Zeb (see p. 373). Renitelo draught oxen are very much sought after by Madagascan farmers.

The principal value of the Renitelo is meat production. This is confirmed from data collected by Serres et al. (1968) and other research workers (Tables 7.92, 7.93 and 7.94).

Genetic improvement

Genetic improvement of the Renitelo breed is carried out at CRZ Kianjasoa by progeny testing.

Table 7.91 Average dimensions of Renitelo and Zebu: adult females

Dimensions	Renitelo (n = 26)	Zebu (n = 51)	Gain in format or weight	% gain
Height at withers (cm)	130.69 ± 1.08	116.17 ± 1.44	14.52 ± 2.52	12.4
Height at sacrum (cm)	136 ± 1.26	123.48 ± 1.78	12.78 ± 3.04	10.3
Perimeter of thorax (cm)	179 ± 2.38	149.41 ± 2.82	29.66 ± 5.20	19.8
Scapulo-ischial length (cm)	159 ± 3.97	137.86 ± 2.06	21.98 ± 6.03	15.9
Pelvic length (cm)	49.13 ± 0.72	44.07 ± 0.92	5.06 ± 1.64	11.4
Pelvic width (cm)	49.42 ± 1.48	38.92 ± 0.90	10.50 ± 2.38	26.9
Length of head (cm)	54.23 ± 0.62	46.54 ± 0.88	7.69 ± 1.50	16.3
Width of head (cm)	24.00 ± 0.40	19.39 ± 0.48	4.61 ± 0.88	23.7
Weight (kg)	429.96 ± 11.76	269.94 ± 8.60	160.02 ± 20.36	59.2

Table 7.92 Maximum growth potential compared between Renitelo and Madagascan Zebus

Animals		Starting weight	Age at start of Experiment (days)	3 months	6 months	9 months	12 months
	m	169.125	291.625	91.875	139.625	166.000	185
Renitelo	n	8	8	8	8	8	8
	SD	10.1320	10.4947	4.4136	5.753	8.787	9.6598
	m	98.70	325.0000				103.900
Zebu I	n	10	10				10
	SD	4.7353	12.9649				4.0206
	m	188.4	451.500	83.100	126.700	164.800	163.000
Zebu II	n	10	10	19	10	10	10
	SD	5.7430	5.9651	2.6053	4.3768	5.1006	7 1180

15 months	18 months	21 months	24 months	27 months	30 months	33 months	36 months
230.8750	299.625	342.375	407.875	438.7500	500.375	526.3750	564.6000
8	8	8	8	8	8	8	5
10.0203	12.5583	11.2582	11.6625	11.8181	16.5399	16.1255	10.2645
122.200	172.0000	201.4000	263.3000	279.6000	326.6000	343.1000	362.4285
10	10	10	10	10	10	10	7
5.7522	5.7522	5.8275	4.7282	7 2021	8.6502	10.6733	12.8338
181.600	223.200	259.5000					
10	10	10					
6.8608	5.9885	8.0488					

m = mean weight (kg); n = number of animals studied; SD = Standard deviation

Table 7.93 Growth of Renitelo cattle at CRZ Kianjasoa: weights (kg)

Year	Sex	3 months	6 months	12 months	18 months	24 months	3 years	4 years	5 years
1974	M	104	162	227	306	356	470	555	620
	F	98	153	176	220	250	328	356	382
1975	M	105	161	198	263	332			
	F	99	141	184	264	287			
1976	M	113	180	199	268	301	424		
	F	108	164	190	273	305	404		
1977	M	100	166	215	240	307	461	579	663
	F	112	172	199	267	308	372	453	455
1978	M	87	163	215	267	310	474	563	652
	F	91	171	200	253	293	374	486	474
1979	M	112	159	218	302	347	480	597	684
	F	99	151	199	300	330	402	427	498

Santa Gertrudis

Origins and history

The Santa Gertrudis breed of cattle is the oldest of the modern 'composites'. It was created at King Ranch, a livestock rearing establishment covering 400 000 hectares in Texas in the United States.

Table 7.94 Comparative growth of Renitelo cattle at pasture

Animals*		3 months	6 months	9 months	12 months	18 months	24 months	30 months
Renitelo castrates *ad. lib.*	m	91.875	139.625	166.000	185.2500	299.6250	407.8750	500.3750
	n	8	8	8	8	8	8	8
	SD	4.4136	5.7536	8.7871	9.6598	12.5583	11.6625	16.5399
	CI	10.4381	13.6072	20.7814	22.8454	29.7003	27.5818	39.1168
Renitelo entire Extensive	m	98.11	152.88	189.58	201.70	292.29	344.88	406.93
	n	17	17	17	17	17	17	15
	SD	2.7438	5.4972	6.7246	6.4144	8.3418	7.5808	7.3172
	CI	5.8168	11.6540	14.2561	13.5985	17.6846	16.0712	12.5124
Significance		no significant difference	no significant difference	no significant difference	no significant difference	no significant difference	significantly different	significantly different

* All these animals had the same rearing up to an average age of 10 months (292 days)
m = mean weight (kg); n = number of animals studied; SD = Standard deviation; CI = Confidence Interval

Table 7.95 Comparative butchering characteristics 'produced' in Renitelo cattle and Zebus by rational feeding

	Departure liveweight (kg)	Arrival liveweight (kg)	Warm carcass (kg)	Dry carcass (kg)	True yield (percentage)	Index of muscle
Renitelo	733.6	666.5	411.5	399	63.8	18.79
Zebu I	489.5	451.7	267			19
Zebu II	505.7	459	285.4	282	65.3	18.1

Plate 7.37   Santa Gertrudis cow (Texas, USA)

Plate 7.38   Santa Gertrudis bull (Texas, USA)

In 1910, Robert J. Kleberg undertook to cross Brahman Zebus and Shorthorn cows which were on the ranch and this was with the objective of combining the resistance of the Brahman with the productivity of the Shorthorn.

In 1920, this crossing produced an exceptional male, the bull 'Monkey' which had approximately 3/8 Brahman blood and 5/8 Shorthorn blood, was docile, had remarkable conformation and a cherry-red coat. At 1 year old, the animal weighed 500 kg. It was used on the female crosses and employed intensively.

In 1940, the United States Department of Agriculture, recognised this type of

Plate 7.39   Normandy cow (northern France)

Plate 7.40   Charolais bull (Australia)

cattle, which had become the basis of the Texan herds, as being a pure breed and called it the Santa Gertrudis, the name of the land upon which the King Ranch was established.

Importance, distribution and numbers

The Santa Gertrudis breed is found in all the countries of the American continent. It has been exported to Africa, (Union of South Africa, Nigeria), and to Asia, to Europe (USSR), and to Oceania (Australia, Fiji, New Caledonia). In most of the adopting countries, a National Herd Book is established.

Plate 7.41   Friesian cow (Madagascar)

Plate 7.42   Jersey cow (Channel Islands)

Plate 7.43   Pie-rouge de l'Est cow (French type of Simmental)

Plate 7.44   Hereford bull

Description

The Santa Gertrudis (Plates 7.37 and 7.38) is a large animal, symmetrical and muscular. It should have a fine glossy coat and fairly developed ears. The coat is dull red. The temperament should be docile. There are types without horns. In normal grazing conditions, an adult bull should weigh about 900 kg and a female should weigh about 550 kg. The Santa Gertrudis calves are small (30 kg at birth) but have a rapid growth which enables them to reach higher than average weaning weights.

Plate 7.45   Jersey × N'Dama half-blood bullock on *Stylosanthes guianensis* pasture (Bouake, Ivory Coast)

Plate 7.46   Jersey × N'Dama half-blood cow (Bingerville, southern Ivory Coast)

Rearing techniques and types of production

Originally the Santa Gertrudis was created to meet the needs of extensive rearing enterprises in the tropical areas of the United States (States bordering the Gulf of Mexico).

The countries to which the breed has been exported use the breed for rearing on grass, to take advantage of its resistance to tropical climatic and pathogenic factors and for its ability to produce from an extensive rearing system.

Plate 7.47   Milking shed Jersey × N'Dama half-blood cows (Bouake, Ivory Coast)

Plate 7.48   Montbeliarde × Peul Zebu quarter-blood cross (Mali)

In the developed countries of the tropics, it is frequent for the young animals weaned on grass to be subject to intensive grazing before slaughter.

It has proven to be true that the Santa Gertrudis breed is well suited to this type of intensive rearing, with however a propensity, inherited from the Shorthorn, for rapid and significant deposition of sub-cutaneous fat.

The types of production are thus the 2–4-year-old bullock from grass and 14 to 24-month-old young bulls and steers from intensive grazing systems.

Utility

The milking ability of Santa Gertrudis cows is not exploited. The observations recorded at the University of Texas showed that, with a mean of 5.9 kg per day, the Santa Gertrudis cow was the best milking animal of the American beef breeds. This explains why despite the low weight at birth, the Santa Gertrudis calves have high weights at weaning.

The results shown in Table 7.96 were observed at the Sanbra Charlim selection farm in South Africa, for animals reared on pasture at 2 hectares per adult animal of 'sour veldt'.

The main value of the Santa Gertrudis breed is the production of meat from grass. These cattle are characterised in particular by the rarity of calving problems, their excellent growth during the suckling stage, their docile temperament and their resistance to tropical parasites.

It is frequent for there to be liveweight gains of 1.65 kg per day in intensively grazed steers. In South Africa there has been recorded a group with a liveweight gain of 2.16 kg per day.

In certain countries, the cows which have not calved at 45 months of age, have not had a calf for two consecutive years or have not produced two calves in 3 years are removed from the herd book.

Genetic improvement

In several countries (Australia, Argentina, South Africa), local Santa Gertrudis breeders' societies have been created. They organise and control selection in the same way as the mother society in the United States of America.

Table 7.96 Average growth of Santa Gertudis cattle and two other breeds for comparison: male and female calves

	Brahman	Charolais	Santa Gertrudis
Bull-calves			
Number	7	8	14
Age at weaning (days)	228.0	245.25	233.6
Weight at weaning (kg)	232.14	247.62	247.14
Daily liveweight gain before weaning (kg)	0.88	0.86	0.95
Growth in 114 days (kg)	16.43	58.63	36.07
Daily liveweight gain after weaning (kg)	0.14	0.52	0.32
Heifer calves			
Number	8	10	23
Age at weaning (days)	236.37	250.0	247.52
Weight at weaning (kg)	214.38	241.2	247.26
Daily liveweight gain before weaning (kg)	0.77	0.83	0.86
Weight gain in 114 days (kg)	20.6	48.3	42.52
Daily liveweight gain after weaning (kg)	0.18	0.43	0.37

Some sheep and goat breeds of the tropics

Sheep

In 1981, the numbers of sheep in the tropics were estimated at 228.9 million or 20 per cent of the world total and are broken down as follows: Africa 110.1 million (9.7 per cent), America 48.5 million (4.2 per cent) Asia and Oceania 70.3 million (6.2 per cent). The numbers in developed countries are 528.5 million (46.7 per cent).

These are the sheep and goats which have resulted from the many transfers of breeds, many of which took place before recorded history. Their aptitude for travelling long distances, their resistance to drought and their prolificacy have been the determining factors.

There are cultural factors involved: the flocks can be protected by the children and numerous religious rites are accompanied by sacrifice of young animals or animals prepared for this purpose. Finally, the carcass of a sheep or goat is not so big that it cannot be consumed by one or two families.

As for cattle, only a few typical tropical breeds will be described.

The Macina wool sheep

Origin and history

Comparison between the wool sheep which live on the edges of the Niger, above and below Tombouctou, and those of the south of the Maghreb, tends to indicate a common origin. Historically, the exchanges between Morocco and Mali were very significant. Furthermore, Saharan cave drawings, from before the time of cattle, in which wool sheep figure, testify to an extremely ancient presence of peoples and of a ram culture.

Importance, distribution and numbers

The Macina wool sheep are found on the edges of the Niger, on each side of the river. The greatest concentrations of the breed are seen around Macina, Mopta, Goundam and Tombouctou, with flocks being found up to Gao and Tillabery.

They are reared practically in the flood zone of the Niger between latitudes 14° and 17° north and are not adapted to the regions where there is more than 600 mm of rainfall per annum. The numbers of these sheep are estimated at 2 million head.

Plate 7.49   Macina wool sheep

Plate 7.50   Djallonké ram

Description

These animals (Plate 7.49) are of average size, 70–80 cm to the withers. The rams are 30–35 kg in weight and the ewes from 28–35 kg. With intensive feeding they can reach 90 kg in 2 years.

The facial profile is slightly aquiline, the drooping ears are large and slender and pendants are fairly frequent. The rams have very well-developed horns which are prismatic and turn towards the rear. At the lower end they make one and a half turns perpendicularly to the plane of symmetry of the body. When the females have horns, which is a less frequent occurrence, these are of

Plate 7.51 Djallonké ewes

Plate 7.52 Peul short-wool sheep (Niger)

reduced size. The carcass is light, the neck flat and short, with withers non-existent, the back straight and sharp, the hindquarters sagging and with little muscle, the rump flat and the tail long.

The first lambing takes place around 18 months of age and twin births are frequent.

Rearing techniques

The herds are of smallish size and seldom include more than 100 head. They are maintained on extensive grazing and collected each evening into enclosures surrounded by thorn branches.

Mating is free and the ram lambs are often castrated and sold as 'house sheep' which live near to the houses and receive by-products from the preparation of food, rice bran and particularly millet bran. Well nourished, they reach weights of more than 70–80 kg and are sacrificed on the occasion of the Feast of the Sheep (Aid el-Kebir).

Utility

These sheep are raised for their wool. The wool covers the body up to the head but the belly is bare, the fleece is usually white and when it is two-coloured the spots are brown or black and this is limited to the head. The fleece is dry, open, bulging and unfortunately encumbered with soil and trash picked up from the ground or from rubbing against vegetation (cram cram – *Aristida*). At one year, it weighs up to 1200 g but more generally between 600 and 700 g. The wool fibres are 15–20 cm long and in exceptional circumstances 30 cm long. Their average diameter is 45 μm with extremes of 20 and 90 μm.

The dry, rough wool is easily spun by hand and used for the making up of coarse fabric and above all of the cloth called 'Mopti', which is found all over West Africa. Their characteristic patterns are inspired by Moroccan art; the fleece is dyed maroon or black in shades of the leaves and roots of plants (sorghum, andropogens, karite etc.).

The carcasses have little muscle, the fat cover is practically non-existent, except in overfed cases, and the kidney fat is quite plentiful; carcass yield is rarely more than 40 per cent.

The ewe gives 200–400 g of milk per day at the beginning of the lactation.

Genetic improvement

In the 1920s and 1930s, it was hoped to create a livestock industry based on fine woolled sheep, whose production would be exported. With this end in view, Merinos d'Arles and Cape Merinos were imported into the El-Oualadji sheep station. Despite some encouraging results, the trials were abandoned, not through fickleness but because of the argument that the improved wool would never find profitable outlets among the fine wool (tonnages too small, quality very average) and above all that the wool obtained would be less easy to spin and weave by traditional methods.

The trials carried out in the 1940s in the United States at Fort Wingate in New Mexico, in which the improvement of Navajo sheep fleeces was tried by crossing with rams of fine woolled breeds such as Rambouillet, Coriedale etc., drew the same conclusions.

Djallonké sheep

These sheep are raised south of 14° north in Guinea, Mali, Niger, Benin, Nigeria, Ghana and in Republic of Central Africa.

They are mainly characterised by their small size and their adaptation to fairly humid climates. Their profile is rectilinear, the forehead is flat, the nose slightly bulging in the rams, the head large, the face of average length and the muscle thick (Plate 7.50 and 7.51).

The horns of the ram, which are of average length, are prismatic, turned forwards, and before a spiral is completed the point comes round to touch the cheek. In the ewe the horns are usually absent. The elliptical socket has slightly pronounced protrusions, the ears are short, thin and half drooping. The neck is of average length and sometimes has pendants. The body is round, the withers are sunk in the ewe and the buttock is round.

Sexual dimorphism is very clear-cut, the coat is white with black spots more or less all over the head and neck; in extreme cases they cover all the forequarters.

The coat is close cropped and shining on the body, in the ewe as well as in the ram. In the latter, there is a mane and a ruff which reaches the withers and is similar to that of the Mouflon.

The size varies between 0.40 and 0.60 m, and in general, animals from the southern region are lower on the legs.

The weight varies between 20 and 30 kg. The yield of meat is from 46–48 per cent and is of good quality.

Genetic improvement

Crossing trials with Merinos have given fleeces reaching 400–500 g. The trials have not been continued.

Short coated Peul sheep

Origin and history

These are the sheep which are most often represented in the cave drawings at Aïr, Niger.

If the term 'Peul sheep' is used in the plural, it is these sheep which are found in the whole of the Sahelian and north-Soudanian zones of West and Central Africa and which are raised by the Peul herders. According to the region, one observes minor modifications which concern secondary characteristics, distribution of bands of colour more particularly. Geographic isolation and the choice of certain peculiarities by groups of herders are responsible for these.

They are called Peul-peul in Senegal, Toronke and Warbe in Mali, Bali-bali in Niger, Waili in Chad, Ouda in Niger and Chad.

Description

Animals of large size, from 0.65 to 0.75 m to the withers, they have well built bodies and their adult weight varies from 30 to 50 kg (Plates 7.52, 7.53 and

7.54). In very well nourished condition, they weigh up to 80–90 kg at 3 years of age (house sheep).

Their profile is convex, the horns are well developed in the rams and carried horizontally with the ends turned outwards. When the ewes have horns, they are fine and long. The ears are narrow, thin and drooping. The nape of the neck has a bulge in the ram and the lamb. The neck is muscular with neither main nor ruff, the withers are prominent, the back slightly dipping, the inclined rump is round. In animals in good condition, the fine tail reaches the hocks. The limbs are strong and muscular.

The fleece is short and the colour varies according to the sub-breed, being black pied in Peul-peul, pied with small black spots in the Warbes, uniform

Plate 7.53   Peul short-wool sheep (Niger)

Plate 7.54   Peul Peul sheep (Senegal)

white in the Bali-bali, and two-coloured in the Oudas, the front being dark brown or black and the rear white.

Utility

The Peul sheep are one of the best meat sheep, having yields of 48–50 per cent. They easily lay down sub-cutaneous or kidney fat, which is firm and white. The meat, which is of good colour, does not have the odour of grease. The size of the cutlet corresponds to the demand from restaurants (two cutlets per portion).

Plate 7.55   Moroccan long-wool sheep

Plate 7.56   Black head Persian ram (Ethiopia)

When dry, the fleeces weigh 0.6–0.8 kg. Of good size and tanned with acacia pods, they give quality 'sheep-skins' which are used by artisans locally (buckets, bags, shoes).

Long haired Moorish sheep

These animals are found in Mauritania, Mali and Chad where they are known as 'Arab sheep'.

These are animals of average size, convex-shaped and long (Plate 7.55). They are close, in regard to conformation, to the short-haired Sahelian sheep but they are more scrawny. The fleece is uniform black with white spots on the rump fairly often and is formed of long black straight fibres with a slight down.

This is a mediocre meat animal; the fleece is used for the construction of tents and ropes. The skins of the young animals, which are tanned complete with the fleece, are used to make blankets.

Genetic improvement

Crossing between the black long haired sheep and Karakul rams, to produce astrakan linings, have been studied in Mali and Chad. Continued crossing has enabled the production of saleable 4–8-day-old lambs at the 15/16 and 31/32 generations. General adoption is restricted by problems of adaptation by the stockmen to the techniques particularly of retrieval and preparation of the skins.

These livestock enterprises had the merit of demonstrating pathological problems such as parasitism of the digestive system and cobalt deficiency in the forage; the latter had originally been attributed to parasitic or infectious causes.

Fat-tailed sheep

Known by the name Barbarin, these sheep are found in Tunisia, Turkey and the Middle East, and it can be considered that those found in tropical East Africa and Madagascar are of the same origin.

According to the region, one can distinguish the breeds Abyssinian (Ethiopia), Masai (Tanzania, Kenya and Uganda), the Long-tailed Tanganyika (Tanzania) and the Madagascan (Madagascar).

The only notable differences concern the form of the tail, which, always voluminous, is more or less short. In certain breeds, fat covers the hindquarters (Somali Persian Black Head, East Africa), (Plates 7.56 to 7.59).

Description

In general the characteristics are not typical of those found in the Middle East.

Plate 7.57   Abyssinian fat-tail ram

Plate 7.58   Carcass of Macina wool sheep

These are animals of large size when reared in favourable conditions, the rams measuring 70–80 cm at the withers and weighing 40–60 kg. The females are smaller and weigh 30–50 kg.

The head is strong and the horns, which are well developed in the male, are spiral. The long ears are drooping.

The fleece has long locks of wool and is of average openness.

The coarse wool is white or beige, with chestnut and sometimes black spots. The coloured spots tend to be more frequent on the head, ears and neck. In the Persian Black Head breed, only the head is black.

The fat tail can reach 5–6 kg, it is in a more or less globular shape and often

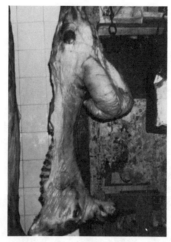

Plate 7.59   Carcass of fat-tail sheep

Plate 7.60   Sahel goat

it is split in two by a central parting. In well nourished animals, fat deposition tends to be concentrated on the rump. It is even considered in certain regions to be an ethnic characteristic.

Utility

These are meat producing sheep whose yield of meat is more than 60 per cent due to the weight of the tail.

The meat has a stronger odour than that of the fine tailed sheep.

The coarse wool is used to make cloth and tents.

Goats

General

In 1981, the number of goats in the tropics was estimated at 243.49 million, or 59 per cent of the world goat population which is distributed as follows: Africa 129.7 million (27.6 per cent), America 15.5 million (3.3 per cent), Asia and Oceania 98.3 million (20.9 per cent), the number in developed countries being 25.0 million (5.3 per cent).

Being raised in freedom, either in large flocks in the dry regions or in

Plate 7.61   Humid zone dwarf goat

Plate 7.62   Sub-humid zone goat

sedentary flocks, without any deliberate selection on the part of the stockmen, geographic isolation and environmental conditions have been the only determinant factors of their evolution. Thus the characteristics of Sahelian goats are practically the same in Senegal, Niger, Soudan, Egypt, Ethiopia and Kenya and thus they are clearly opposite to those characteristics of goats from the humid zones of the regions near to the Atlantic (Plates 7.60 to 7.62).

The relationship between the goats of Egypt and those of the Sahel is certainly due to the fact that goats subsist better than sheep in the very dry zones and make better use of the coarse shrub and thorny grazing.

Whichever tropical region they are reared in, it is argued that animals which perform poorly under confinement can live with an average parasitic

Plate 7.63   Male of the Maradi breed (Niger)

Plate 7.64   Red Maradi goat (Niger)

infestation, but are very sensitive to viruses (small ruminant plague) and mycoplasmosis.

Dry-zone goats

Description

These are animals of large size, long bodied, 80–95 cm to the withers in the male and 70–75 cm in the female, and the weight varies from 25 to 30 kg (Plate 7.60).

The head is small and triangular with a flat forehead and the nose is straight.

The rather long horns in the male are thickset, flattened, ringed and spiral, turned towards the rear and speading outwards, while those of the female are finer.

The ears are short and either horizontal or drooping. Beards and pendants are frequent.

The neck is flat, thin and long, the chest sloping downwards, narrow and long, and the belly drawn in.

The hindquarters are short and inclined, and the tail short and raised.

The udder is pendulous and the teats easy to milk.

The coat varies with variety and region with two or three colours – black, white and red in the Tuaregs, grey in the Moors and mixed in Ethiopia.

The coat is fine and short and the male has a mane which extends to the hindquarters.

Utility

Very prolific; they often produce twins.

Milk production is about 70 kg for lactations lasting 120 days.

The meat has no odour except in old entire males. The yield is from 40 to 45 per cent.

Humid-zone goats

Often known as the 'Fouta-Djallon goat', they are well distributed over the mountains of Guinea but not limited to this area. They are found in Africa in all the zones reached by rainfall of more than 1000 mm and, reared in freedom, they are very independent.

Description

Humid-zone goats weigh 18–20 kg, are of small size, about 35–50 cm high and, the higher the atmospheric humidity, the more the size is reduced (Plate 7.61).

Their very short legs give them an extremely characteristic appearance.

The head is strong with a straight profile which is slightly concave, the forehead has bony pegs, the ears are long and often held horizontally or even erect. The neck is short and broad at the base. The body is round, the withers sunk and the chest large. The limbs are very short and the sub-sternal space is very small being 20–25 cm according to size of the animal.

Utility

These animals are very hardy and survive perfectly in areas infested with tsetse. The castrated males fatten easily and the yield of meat reaches 55 or even 60 per cent.

The Red Maradi goat

Distribution

This variety of goat, which is of average size, has gained an international reputation for the qualities of its skins which, because of the quantities traded, is esteemed in London and Paris.

The greatest populations are found on either side of the Niger/Nigeria border, in Maradi, Zinder and Zaria and Sokoto.

Description

This is a goat of average size. The height to the withers in males is about 65 cm, that of the female is scarcely less and sexual dimorphism is negligible.

The head is fine, the horns, which are of average development, are triangular, flattened and face backwards. The ears are long and drooping or horizontal (Plates 7.63 and 7.64).

The neck is slender and in the male it is short. The body is full, although the length of the limbs makes it appear greyhound-like.

The coat is a chestnut colour with uniform mahogany coloured tints and is short and thick.

Utility

Very prolific; twin births are common and three- or four- kid births are not unusual.

Milk production is largely sufficient to feed the young and varies from 0.2 kg to 0.5 kg over 80–100 days in the dry season, and from 0.5 kg to 1.5 kg over 100–200 days in the rainy season.

It is a good butchering animal, the yield of meat is from 45 to 50 per cent on average and in castrated males reaches 55 per cent.

The skins, which are very much appreciated for their light texture, are used for the quality Moroccan trade and for suede garments.

Genetic improvement

Genetic improvement began at the beginning of the 1940s in Niger by mass selection programmes, elimination of mottled males by castration, and by diffusion of selected fertile males. The distribution of the red goat is extensive and exports to other countries of West Africa have been carried out with success.

PART III

ANIMAL PRODUCTION SYSTEMS

8
Types of animal production

Types of rearing according to the objectives of production

Livestock enterprises are usually distinguished as being nomadic, transhumant, settled, traditional, modern or industrial types. Each of them is in fact an explanation of the agricultural background perceived, dealt with and exploited differently according to the nature of the social organisation, the cultural and technical heritage, and the objectives sought by the human group involved.

It seems to us that the classification of production systems which allows the most coherent generalisation consists of taking account of the final objectives of production:

1. subsistence rearing,
2. rearing solely to build up capital,
3. rearing for profit,
4. rearing and/or using animals for power.

Subsistence rearing

This is the sole activity of the herder and his family. The surpluses are exchanged in order to procure grain, salt, cloth, cooking utensils, jewellery etc. and the use of money is reduced to the minimum. The animals have a social role: the loan of animals, passing them on as an inheritance, endowment, gifts etc. weave a web of obligations of dependent relationships, of subordination, which assures the cohesion of families and social groups and form the hierarchies between different groups.

The choice of milking beast whether it be camel, cow, goat or more rarely sheep, and rearing techniques is dependent on the nature of the forage resources but also due to cultural factors. Thus in the same ecological niche, in Niger for example, the Peul herders raise large Bororo cattle and big Bali-bali sheep while the Tuareg herders have Arab Azawak cattle and Targui sheep whose ethnic characteristics are very different.

In such types of rearing, there is no external contribution at the production stage and the exchange of produce is reduced to the minimum and based on barter. Capital growth only comes about because of excess herd growth which remains to ensure the subsistence of the stockman and his family after sales or exchanges have been made.

Rearing solely to build up capital

The concern for capital growth is not absent from subsistence rearing, but it is not of prime importance. This second category of rearing is carried out particularly by farmers, artisans and people working in the tertiary sector (traders, persons receiving salaries from the public or private sector) who invest their savings in herds. The protection of their herds is entrusted to stockmen from the previous group when the investors are related to them, or more generally to salaried or migrant share-herders from pastoral ethnic groups who have left their original group: formerly these might have been individuals ostracised by their own groups and more recently might be members of the dependent classes, liberated by the improvement in their civil rights.

As for subsistence livestock rearing, the choice of animals is dictated by availability of funds (here monetary) but also by cultural factors.

Rearing for profit

In this category is included all livestock enterprises whose ultimate aim is monetary gain, and in which the techniques aim to obtain, at the best cost or

Plate 8.1   Peul toys: Zebus modelled in clay by children

Plate 8.2   Judgement of a cattle thief – Tutankhamun's treasure (Cairo Museum)

Plate 8.3   Peasant milking Azawak cow, Filingue (Niger)

least effort, animal products which are saleable at the best price. The animal is an agent of conversion of available forage resources, some being used where they stand in the pastoral area and others coming directly from the agricultural sector, basically: grains, forage crops, surpluses and by-products from harvests and finally the by-products from the industrial sector or from processing: meal from meat or fish, cattle cake etc.

The stockman is a true entrepreneur with all that entails: an ability for forecasting and management beyond just knowledge of the techniques of husbandry.

This sector, except for poultry and pig keeping, is relatively recent.

Rearing for profit can be the sole activity of the entrepreneur or can be associated with another enterprise such as joint exploitation of agriculture and livestock rearing, finishing livestock for slaughter or fattening at pasture in association with, for example, an agro-industrial complex or an agricultural operation.

Rearing and/or use of animals for power

In this category, the maintenance of the animal aim is to use them for power rather than for production.

All the large domesticated animals are used (camels, horses, mules, donkeys, cattle, buffalo) and the type of work dictates the choice of animal. Thus to lift water, cattle and buffalo are used more than horses, donkeys and camels.

The camel, despite the construction of roads in desert areas, remains an exceptional pack animal. Cattle and donkeys are above all used for carrying, and the development of their use for pulling carts and for mechanised cultivation is made after breaking (training) them to work between the shafts of carts and cultivation equipment, and in certain regions by a complete technological change in the ways of doing things.

The horse has a place on its own and was the means of penetrating the continents. The cave drawings of the Sahara, the descriptions of Herodote and the chronicles of Tarik el-Sudan show that it was more a vehicle of war than an instrument of farmers. From a cultural point of view, Islam spread the attraction of the horse and, up to the recent past, it was not found in the south in the trypanosomiasis zones where it was unable to survive. In Niger, the exact point is known where the horsemen stopped at the River Niger to the north of Benin.

Rearing systems

Whether one considers the animal or the herd as the elementary unit of production, the factors which condition their maintenance and production cannot be isolated:

1. water and forage resources which depend above all on rainfall (Table 8.1);
2. availability of man power which depends upon the size of the family or pastoral group.

Except for occasional difficulties, there ought to be a harmonious relationship between these factors and stock numbers. Also one needs to consider the association that is formed by the animals and the territory in which the stockman exploits the resources for rearing them.

Table 8.1 Types of livestock rearing as function of rainfall

Rainfall index	Type of production	Animals reared
less than 50 mm	Occasional oasis	Camels and goats
50–200 mm	Nomadism over large distances	Camels and goats
200–400 mm	Transhumance	Cattle, goats and sheep
600–1000 mm	Transhumance tendency to settlement – occupation of the non-agricultural areas – fallows	Cattle, sheep, goats and poultry
more than 1000 mm	Settled rearing or with some short distance transhumance generally upland	Cattle, sheep, goats and poultry

If, on the territory under consideration, the forage is abundant and the water easily accessible right throughout the year, the animals could be maintained on small areas of land and the livestock enterprise will be settled.

If, for some reason such as the water or forage resources diminishing in the course of the year to a level below the minimum required by the livestock, the enterprise could only remain settled if the stockman built up stocks during the period of abundance, or intensified the production of forage from the area of land at his disposal by agricultural techniques, or finally, if he brought into his land, forage or water, which was available from elsewhere. The latter in fact has the effect of increasing the effective size of his land.

In the opposite case, it is the animals which have to be moved to exploit water and forage at favourable times. This wandering is a true reaping process in the second degree, carried out by the animal for the profit of man. It is not peculiar to livestock rearing as is seen in the agricultural field where 'cut and burn' systems come from identical motivations to that of nomadic pastoralism and movement aims to counteract the insufficiencies of agricultural yields. The cycle continues until the activity of the biomass has restored the fertility of the arable ground. For livestock rearing, the cycle is generally shorter.

While nomadic stock-rearing has instigated more studies than other systems, it is because each type has made an original response to the ecological problems that it had to resolve. To summarise, the question is:

- how to feed herds throughout the year when the forage and water resources of an area vary within such limits that it is not possible, from one month to the next and from one year to the next, to make small forecasts of the food resources and the availability of water and that, in addition, the size and distribution of rainfalls prohibit forage cultivations?

The number of replies to this question is a sign of the complexity of the situations. It is also necessary to look for the origin of the advantages which came to them, considering the fact that these livestock enterprises are subsistence. The symbiosis between man and his herd is such that the sociocultural factors, which hold considerable weight in the conduct of herding, are more fascinating by their oddness than the purely technical and economic factors which prevail in the other types of livestock enterprise and which, themselves, have a universal value.

If it were necessary to establish a hierarchy of factors of production, one could say that the more the rearing is sedentarised, the more technical and economic factors respectively take precedent over the cultural and sociological structures.

Whereas, up to the recent past, rearing and agriculture were practised by different ethnic groups, each occupying neighbouring ecosystems, convergent evolution is now being assisted (pastoralists becoming farmers and farmers partially turning to stock-rearing). The agriculture/stock-rearing association is tending, when the rains are sufficient, to become the rule in a new ecosystem, in which the animals' food not only comes from simple foraging exploitation of the uncultivated land (fallows and communal lands) and by-products of cultivation, but from forage crops (legumes, grasses and weeded out plants).

The exploitation of resources is carried out by an intimate association of agriculture and stock rearing. The unit of production becomes farming and stock rearing is one of the elements. It participates directly in the creation of revenue by the sale of its products, but indirectly by increasing the work potential of the agricultural sector and by maintaining fertility.

At the limit, agriculture can be conceived as furnishing the primary materials for stock rearing; the forage crops, the additional crops, become principle crops and can benefit from very modern techniques such as mechanisation and chemical fertilisers. Stock rearing is intensive, concentration of herds becomes the rule and factory farming 'without the soil' or 'zero-grazing', is the most sophisticated form (fattening yards for cattle and housed rearing for pigs and poultry).

Nomadic and transhumant livestock-rearing

Causes of nomadism and transhumance

When the area exploited by a herd cannot continue to ensure its maintenance and the stockman cannot do anything about this deterioration, the animals should be moved.

Insufficiency of available forage and water resources are the most frequent causes, but there are others:

1. temporary occupation of the land by crops and rivers;
2. swarming of insects and parasites: tsetse fly, the vector of trypanosomiasis, for example.

The details of the quest for water and forage are numerous and authors have included all the rearing systems which involve moving, and that which might involve the details of movements, under the term 'nomadism'.

The word 'pastoralism' has been proposed to define, in short, a method of agricultural exploitation based upon extensive herding and this term includes all the systems in which the movements of the herds and men are major components.

Presentation of the different definitions relating to pastoral nomadism enables understanding of what pastoralism is.

For the research worker, the movements of herds are the major factor because, from knowledge of them, one can gain an understanding of the choice of livestock rearing techniques which might be modernised to give improved performance. We have proposed the following definitions.

1. *Transhumance*: cyclical seasonal movement of herds in synchrony with the rainfall regime, in order to exploit the forage and temporary water resources in an agrarian area whose stockmen have the technical mastery by custom certain rights.
2. *Nomadism*: non-cyclical movements of herds and encampments made at risk of upset and destruction of the vegetation which follows them in vast territories whose use is regulated by custom or by force.
3. *Migration*: movement in totality, with no intention of returning, by a part of the ethnic group outside the limits of its traditional area of grazing.
4. *Sedentarism*: the group remains in the same place all year round in an area around a centre of habitation or a conglomeration with, however, daily movements of certain animal units out to a certain distance from the centre.

Numbers and composition of herds

Numbers

All graziers dislike revealing the numbers in their herds. Even the figures obtained by those who have their complete confidence are only indicative, because the herd, such as it is seen with the stockman, can be only a part of his wealth, the rest being dispersed in other herds, or even being only partly in his ownership.

The detailed account effected during health prophylaxis operations can enable sufficiently exact estimations of the overall composition of the herds, of the pastoral groups, but not of the numbers of individual herds.

In subsistence rearing, one can however have an idea of the lower limit of the numbers by bringing together the nutritional requirements of the family and the production of the herd, the lower limit being 'the quantity of stock necessary to ensure feeding of the group'. An estimation of the upper limit is arrived at by bringing together the animal numbers with the manpower resources of the family and it is then the greatest number that the stockmen could possess and which it could control, guard, water and feed.

Brown, in Kenya, defined the *minimum pastoral number for subsistence per family* starting from the nutritional needs, which allows availability each day of a sufficient maintenance ration with a small surplus in good years.

A family of 6.5 adult equivalents, which has a requirement of 15 000 kcal per day, will consume 21 litres of milk per day, or 16 litres plus 2.41 kg of meat, or 10.5 litres and 4.82 kg, a very likely average being about 3/4 milk plus 1/4 meat, or 5606 litres of milk and 704 kg of meat per annum. This volume of milk corresponds to 7 cows* (10 tropical cattle units) or 4 camels in lactation, or a herd of 14 to 15 milking cows and (with the bulls and young males and heifers) a herd of 35 to 40 head of which half are milking cows.

From data observed in West Africa and using the Tropical Livestock Unit, the weight of which (250 kg) corresponds to that of the beast of the region, we have found that in order to obtain 5600 litres of milk and 700 kg of meat per year, a herd of 24 Azawak Arab Zebu cows in lactation would be necessary, or a total of 74 head (60 Tropical Livestock Units). With a herd of humpless cattle of the N'Dama breed, the corresponding figures will be 26 cows in lactation or a total of 61 head (45 Tropical Livestock Units).

These differences are due to conformation of the breeds but also to conditions of maintenance. In effect, the figures above are valid for herds maintained in extensive rearing conditions in the indigenous areas of the two breeds i.e. Sahelian for the Zebus and Soudano-Guinean for the humpless cattle.

If the herds receive complementary feeding during the periods when the grazing is of poorer quality. The overall numbers required to obtain the same results will be no more than 48 (16 cows in milk) for the Azawak Zebus and 38 (14 cows in milk) for the N'Dama.

Table 8.2 has been drawn up from a bibliographical publication by Th. Monod from observations of research by IEMVT and the author.

The figures shown have an indicative value. The recent drought has shown, at least for the Sahelian zone, that they had a certain value and the families which could reach the end of the drought with a minimum head of stock had survived and kept themselves together.

Composition of the herds

Dupire (1970) shows the desired composition of the herd in subsistence rearing situations.

The herd ought to include numbers of cows in milk assuring daily food and revenue, one or two bulls, and then the greatest number of beef stock possible to constitute a 'reserve store which can be put to use in certain circumstances, some bull calves as a source of ceremonial sacrifices, heifers and heifer calves'.

Tables 8.3 and 8.4 give some examples of herd compositions from the analysis of surveys conducted in several regions of Africa.

Drahon, having counted 75 000 cattle on their return from transhumance when the herds cross an arm of the Niger to enter into the wetlands, found 70.6 per cent were females of which 65 per cent were cows of more than

---

* In these estimations, Brown uses as reference the Standard Stock Unit animal of 450 kg, or two cattle of 225 kg, 10 goats, 1 camel. We use 1 Tropical Livestock Unit i.e. the animal of 250 kg.

Table 8.2 Appropriate numbers of livestock maintained by pastoralists

Geographical areas and population	Way of life	Sheep/ goats*	Cattle*	Camels*
Saharan and Sahelian Africa				
1) Nomadic (North Saharan) to summer steppe	nomadic	25		1.3
2) Semi nomadic North Saharan	semi-sedentary	6−15		
3) Saharan				
Hoggar		15		10
Hoggar	nomadic	35−40		
Sahara septentrional		20−30		3− 5
Tibeaté		5−36		4−15
Regueibat L. Gouacem		20−30		5−15
4) Sahel				
Tuaregs (W. Africa)				
Warior religious	nomadic	50−100	44	
Imrad	nomadic	180	20−30	
Kal Antessar	nomadic	60	9.3	
Tuaregs nigerian	transhumants	200	40	10
Tuaregs Gourma (Mali)	transhumants	100	100	1
Moors	transhumants	30−50	−	5−10
Peuls of Mali Central	transhumants			
Peuls Bororo Niger	transhumants			
Sudanian Africa				
Peuls Delta Central Mali	semi-sedentary		200−400	
Peuls of Cameroun	″			
Bambara	sedentary			
Guinean Africa				
Peuls Fouta Djallon	sedentary			
Bouake	sedentary			
East Africa				
Masai (Kenya)	transhumants semi-sedentary		180−200	
Tutsi (Rwanda)			−	
Ethiopia			−	
Outside Africa				
Baseri zagros			100	
Kurds anatolian			120−130	
Afghanistan				
Humid upland Africa in %				
Cameroun			30−75 60−70	
M Bororo and Foulbé			> 75 20−30	
Adamaoua			> 200 5.	

* Average number of animals within the herd for one tent or family

Table 8.3 Composition of transhumant herds (per cent head of cattle)

| | Senegal Ferlo (1) | Senegal (2) | Mali (region of Mopti) 1972 (3) | | | Burkina Faso Sideradougou (5) | Niger | | Chad Transhumants (Batha) (7) |
			Peul (Delta)	Peul (Seno)	Tuareg		Peul Transhumants (6)	Tuareg Transhumants (6)	
Males									
Bull calves	11.0	15.6	9.7	10.0	12.0	11.6*	12.5*	13.5*	9.1
Young bulls	8.6	5.8	13.2	17.5	17.5	5.7	5.3	5.6	14.3
Bulls	9.3	3.5	15.2	8.7	8.7	5.6	6.1	5.5	11.4
Total males	28.9	24.9	38.1	37.3	38.2	22.9	23.9	25.0	34.8
Females									
Heifer calves	11.0	20.9	11.1	10.1	11.5	14.6*	17.9*	18.2*	9.3
Heifers	12.7	10.3	15.5	16.3	17.5	19.2	14.4	13.9	18.8
Cows	47.4	43.9	35.3	36.3	32.7	43.3	43.9	42.9	37.1
Total females	71.1	75.1	61.9	62.7	61.7	77.1	76.2	75.0	65.2
Total	100.0	100.0	100.0	100.0	100.0	100.0	100.0	100.0	100.0

1. Fayolle et al. (1974) Valuation of the cattle population of the sylvo-pastoral zone of the Republic of Senegal. IEMVT–GRST, Senegal.
2. Denis J.P. and Demus P. (1977) The development of rearing inconsistency in experimental units. ISRA–GERD training centre, Bambury.
3. Coulomb J. (1972) Livestock rearing development project in the Mopti region (Republic of Mali). Study of the herd. IEMVT.

Table 8.4 Composition of sedentary or semi-sedentary herds (per cent head of cattle)

	Mali		Niger	Burkina Faso	Chad	Guinea	Ivory Coast	Cameroun	Rwanda
	Region of Mopti (3)	Southern Region (4)	Sedentary (6)	Sahel (5)	Southern Farmers (7)	Guinea Bissau	N'Dama Herders	Adamaoua	
Males									
Bull calves	8.5	7.6	11.2*	11.2*	5.0	27	9	7.5	9
Young bulls	14.7	11.2	5.4	9.8	22.4	15	12	18.0	12.0
Bulls	19.1	16.5	4.3	10.56	34.4	2	4	8.1	0.8
Total males	42.3	35.3	20.8	31.5	61.8	44	25	33.6	21.8
Females									
Heifer calves	8.8	8.7	15.6*	14.4*	4.5	16	10	7.5	10.1
Heifers	17.3	14.4	15.1	14.0	11.0		20	10.4	22.0
Cows	31.7	41.6	48.4	40.1	22.7	40	45	38.5	46.1
Total females	57.8	64.7	79.1	68.5	38.2	56	75	66.4	78.2
Total	100.0	100.0	100.0	100.0	100.0	100.0			

* Animals aged from 0 to 10 months (animals having milk teeth).
3. Coulomb J. (1972) *Livestock rearing development project in the Mopti region (Republic of Mali). Study of the herd.* IEMVT.
4. SEDES, 1975) *Livestock rearing development project in the sedentary rearing zone of Mali. Study of the herd.* SEDES.
5. Dumas R. *et al.* (1978) *Pastoral zone of Sideradougou (Upper Volta).* IEMVT.
6. Coulomb J. (1971) *Pastoral modernisation zone of Niger. Economics of the herd.* IEMVT.
7. Goffings J. P. *et al.* (1976) Qualitative inventory of the Chadian herds. SEDES.

Table 8.5 Composition of transhumant herds (Central Mali)

	Animals observed	Percentage of herd	Percentage of group by sex
Breeding bulls	1.530	1	6.7
Bulls 1 to 4 years	7 619	9.9	33.8
Bull calves of 1 yr or more	5 519	7.2	24.5
Working bullocks	670	0.9	3.0
Bullocks for slaughter	7 221	9.4	32
Total males	22 559	29.4	100
Cows of more than 3 yrs	35 322	43.9	65.0
Heifers of 1 to 3 years	12 427	16.2	22.9
Heifer calves of 1 yr or more	6 552	8.5	12.1
Total females	54 301	70.6	100
Total (general)	76 860	100	

3 years of age, and 29.4 per cent were males of which 32 per cent were bullocks for butchering and 7 per cent were bulls for breeding purposes (Table 8.5).

In other works conducted in the transhumant areas, the results are comparable. The number of females is between 61 per cent and 77 per cent and of these there are 53–66 per cent cows. The number of males is between 23.9 per cent and 38.2 per cent and of these there are from 14 per cent to 41 per cent bulls.

Among the sedentary rearing situations (Table 8.5), the number of females in relation to the number of males varies within wider limits than among the transhumant ones. In Chad, the number of cows in the agricultural herds is in the region of 38 per cent and in the sedentary herds in Niger it is 79 per cent.

There appear to be two very different speculations. In the south of Chad, the relatively high number of males is due to draught and carrying animals. In the sedentary zone of Niger, the farmers have a tradition of rearing and milk production with the aim of exchanging the increased number of milking stock, the strong demand for butchering stock reducing the number of bulls (4.2 per cent) and bull calves (5.4 per cent) to the minimum.

In the same countries, the rather high number of males in relation to females in the sedentary situations is very clear: at Mopti in Mali, 37.8 per cent in transhumant herds, 42.3 per cent in sedentary herds, and in the south of Mali only 34.3 per cent.

At Adamaoua in Cameroun, where two neighbouring ethnic groups, the Foulbés, who transhume from a sedentary base, and the more mobile M'bororos, cohabit, it has been observed that the bull and heifer calves are more numerous in the M'bororo herds with a higher number of males in the M'bororo herds than the Foulbé ones and vice versa for females.

Transhumant livestock rearing – the transhumant calendar

In transhumance, movements are cyclical. They affect, according to ethnic group, either the whole of the population, men and animals, who move their residence, or only the guards who accompany the herds.

The rhythm is regulated by the seasons and five periods in the year have been identified:

- the rainy season;
- the period following the rains, when cereals are harvested;
- the cool dry season;
- the warm dry season;
- the period in anticipation of the rains.

Each of these periods corresponds to characteristic features of the vegetation and to possibilities for drinking.

For the part of the *rainy season* favourable to the growth of forage, fresh grass is abundant and although, at the beginning, its nutritive value is lower due to its high water content, the animals consume it just as willingly. In the period which immediately follows the rainy season, the herbaceous vegetation wilts and hardens very quickly and in the course of the *cool and warm dry seasons*, the process of thinning out of the herbaceous cover is accelerated. The *period when the rains are awaited* is the most trying for the animal and its duration depends upon the amount of the vegetation biomass produced during the previous rainy season and on the stocking level carried on the land.

The possibilities for drinking follow a cyclical form: in the rainy season the pools are numerous; all low-lying clay land and all sandstone or basaltic hollows are drinkable. The drying out of temporary pools obliges the stockmen to dig water-holes and wells in order to stay on the pastures or to move to permanent water sites (lakes, rivers, boreholes).

Variations in available forage and drinking facilities enables categorisation of herd movements in the course of the transhumant cycle.

1. First phase: from the first rains, disperal of herds which abandon the permanent watering places in order to drink at the pools and puddles formed by the first rains and to graze the areas situated beyond the limits of the dry season, but nevertheless not too far away.
2. Second phase: when the rainy season has set in, when the rains are falling in the dryest areas and pools are formed there: movement in the direction of the saline lands or the pastures which are unusable in the dry season because of lack of water.
3. Third phase: towards the end of the rainy season, return to the saline lands using pastures temporarily open because of small pools.
4. Fourth phase: if it is possible, the latter lands continue to be used because of waterholes dug by the stockmen.
5. Fifth phase: progressive regrouping around the most significant water points (wells, water courses) and this happens up to the next rains.

Transhumance to pasture exposed after flooding is unfortunately only possible on the edges of the big rivers (Niger, Senegal, Nile) and lakes (Chad, Debo, Albert, etc.) enables reduction of the period of shortages at the end of the dry season. They can support up to 1500 kg of liveweight per hectare for 4–5 months.

Each year this cycle starts again. The effectiveness of the system rests on the abundance and regularity of the rains which control the abundance of the forage resources. In fact, apart from very rare exceptions, the animals always find drinking at the permanent watering sites but it is there that the pastures become depleted the most.

This shortage can have climatic origins such as rainfall deficit which occurred in the Sahel in 1960s. The origins can be in the irrational exploitation of the grazing lands by overstocking, which might be due to an over rapid drying out of small pools from the rainy season or due to the easy access to water sources with large supply capabilities (boreholes).

Besides working against shortages, transhumance plays a prophylactic role. Abandonment of the grazing land for a part of the year breaks the cycle of internal (helminths) and external (ticks) parasites and enables biological and physical agents to destroy microbes and viruses. Finally, animals which have the opportunity to graze forage of different compositions have less chance of suffering phosphate deficiencies or trace element (cobalt, magnesium, zinc, etc.) deficiencies. Some examples will permit a better grasp of the value of techniques for the exploitation of agrarian areas used by transhumant graziers and their significance in the elaboration of sociopolitical structures.

Transhumant livestock rearing in the Central Niger Delta of Mali

The choice of the Central Niger Delta in Mali is justified by the size of the populations concerned (900 000 inhabitants which is one-twentieth of the population of the country) and the importance of the role of their livestock enterprise in the economy (1 500 000 cattle, 2 400 000 sheep and goats which is one quarter of the national livestock population) and above all is justified by the high degree of organisation in the exploitation of the agrarian area.

The behaviour of the Malian Peul stockmen cannot be understood in the absence of an historical perspective. Nomads, who are said to have arrived in the region around the fifteenth century, built a true state (Dina) which was at its climax in the nineteenth century. Organisation established pastoral traditions and the rules of Islam. Cheikou Ahmadou was the most noted Peul sovereign of this state and to him is attributed the establishment of most of the code of conduct for herds, which the graziers did not dispense with until the recent past. When the political powers tried to modify them, this was a failure and the actual development plans reinstated the essentials.

This traditional organisation had, as a means of exploiting the pastoral area by stock-rearing associated with typically agricultural activities (food crops) and fishing, meeting points for transhumant graziers who have to leave the river banks at flood time and who make their herds graze one part or the other of the Niger up to the Mauritanian Sahel to the north and to the borders of Burkina Faso in the south and west. The result is the sedentarisation of part of the population in permanent villages.

All exploitation is centred on the wet lands (the bourgoutiers), vast low-lying areas which are submerged by the flood of the Niger and watered, from the rains, by the blind arms of the Delta. The pastures of the wet lands, which are mostly composed of *Echinochloa colona* (syn. *Panicum burgu*), *Vetiveria* spp., *Paspalum* spp. and *Cynodon* spp., have such a forage value that they can support up to 10 Tropical Livestock Units per hectare during the periods when they are accessible from November/December to June (Plate 8.8).

When the wet lands are inaccessible, the herds transhume; their cycle of behaviour is perfectly established for herd movements and their stopping places.

At the beginning of the transhumance, the animals are gathered together in herds according to their age, sex, production etc. – the *gartis*, the *bentis* and the *doumtis*.

The *gartis* are the transhumant herds which travel long distances. They are made up of bullocks and reserve bulls, dry cows, in-calf cows, bull calves, some breeding bulls and a small number of cows with calf at foot, whose milk will provide food for the herders.

The *bentis* are the herds which are kept close to the villages on pasture areas which are reserved for them. They are composed of cows with a suckling calf which are kept for milk production, as well as some breeding bulls. They do not transhume as far as the *gartis*.

The *doumtis* only include some milking cows which are kept permanently in the villages.

From the end of June, when the herders find out that there is water in the Sahel (the rains will disperse the ticks), the *bentis* herds abandon the wet lands where the grass has become sparse and transhumance commences.

The *bentis*, composed of animals which are less able to travel long distances, leave later than the *gartis* and do not travel as far. The signal of their departure is given by the swarming of the biting flies (Simuliidae, Tabaniidae, *Stomoxys*), at the same time as the total submergence of the banks of the Niger.

In leaving the wet lands, the herds are organised into groups for the transhumance.

According to the rules of *Dina*, established in the last century, the groups (*Diadd'e*) should be composed of seven herds (*sefre*; plural: *tiefes*), each including 300 head under the responsibility of three herders and the group being commanded by a head herdsman (*amirou diadd'e*).

At the time of the 1942–43 transhumance, Drahon identified 13 trans-humant groups among some 70 000 cattle on their return from transhumance (Table 8.6). Except for two groups which were one or two herds, the rest were composed of 8–44 herds, the majority having between 12 and 16 herds.

Among the herds, the number of cattle varied from 200 to 514 (one only), the most frequent number being around 330 which is close to the theoretical figure of 300 established by Dina. One group, namely that of Hore Nay Gallo

Table 8.6 Composition of herds. Census by group and transhumance on return to the Sahel in November–December 1943

Names of transhuman groups	Number of herds	Breeding bulls	Cows + 3 years	Young bulls 1–4 years	Heifers 1–3 years	Bull-calves 0–1 year	Heifer-calves 0–1 year	Working bullocks	Total number by group	Average herd size
Diatarabé-Peul and Diatarabé-Bosos	16	85	3 198	480	1 082	612	706	217	6 380	398
Séogonkodji (Sogonari and Diagana)	12	87	2 536	402	829	448	416	101	4 819	401
Tioubikofji (Djippoulé)	15	91	2 724	578	877	388	410	35	5 093	340
Tianguédji (Djippoulé)	12	85	2 262	480	812	324	362	22	4 347	362
Tionadji (Sougoulbé)	12	113	2 676	662	953	382	548	34	5 368	447
Komongalloukodji (Djippoulé)	44	314	5 777	1 555	2 169	1 026	1 236	72	12 149	276
Koumbé-Kodji (Goumbé-Nyasso)	21	230	3 876	1 028	1 510	495	813	52	7 977	380
Tioki-Nyasso (Goumbé-Nyasso)	19	101	1 972	478	672	276	295	18	3 812	200
Horé Nay Gallo (Djippoulé)	8	50	1 223	250	472	113	185	14	2 307	288
Ouro N'Dia (Ouro N'Dia)	49	271	5 636	1 089	1 804	969	1 049	55	10 873	221
Nay Hadi Hadji (Djippoulé)	1	10	260	55	89	36	58	6	514	514
Independent herds (Djippoulé)	2	12	332	58	129	62	65	13	671	335
Dioura (Dioura)	23	108	2 850	504	1 029	388	409	31	5 319	231
Totals	234	1 530	35 322	7 619	12 427	5 519	6 552	670	69 629	

The names in brackets are those areas of Diaka to which the transhumant groups are linked.

(Djippoule), was very close to this norm being eight herds with average numbers of 288 head.

More recently, Gallais (1975) found similar figures.

During the travels which are similarly established as a code of conduct, exploitation of grazing lands by the *gartis* is made around the stopping places which are perfectly spaced out in a north–south line and generally on denuded high ground with one or more enclosures made from thorny branches (*zeribas*) to protect the herds from predators (lions, hyenas, wild dogs).

The traditional droving routes and stopping places of the *gartis* and *bentis*

Plate 8.4   Bullock transport in the Sahel

Plate 8.5   River crossing on return from transhumance – the herd classed as the best has the honour of crossing first

Plate 8.6   Return from transhumance: the herd is waiting for the signal to cross the river

were modified in the 1940s by the flooding of the Markala dam and the establishment of vast irrigated areas. The tradition of co-operation between the heads of the transhumant groups enabled the establishment of a true pastoral code at a conference convened in 1952.

Grazing on the Sahelian pastures stops in October with the coming of the warm winds which dry out the pools and also reduce the size of the biting insect populations close to the rivers.

When the *gartis* enter the grazing areas of the *bentis*, the cows of the latter join their original herd again in the transhumant groups. These, clearly individual, groups occupy positions on the north bank of the Diaka which are located by the prominence (Toghés) attributed to them by tradition and they establish themselves there on a day fixed by the group heads.

The return into this zone is the only time of the year when all the animals are assembled together and when one can see the complete herds in their entirety. They wait for the signs to enter into the wet lands and these come at the end of November – beginning of December when the Niger and the Diaka are far from the low water mark, the herd cross by swimming with the herders, and the calves are ferried across in canoes (Plates 8.5 to 8.7).

Up until the 1960s, the wet lands were divided into zones attributed to each transhumant group and the allocation was made by the traditional chiefs. Thus there was a geographic separation of the herds and their entry into the wet lands could be organised in such a way as to avoid conflict.

The return of the herds and their herders is a time of festivity which lasts several days. The best herders, judged by the condition of the animals, receive reward from the owners and official payment. The women and young girls bring out their festive costume and display their jewels (photograph page 455). Animals are sacrificed to confirm engagements or to honour hosts.

The festivities finish and life resumes its normal course. Some days after entry into the wet areas, the owners take out almost all the cows with a suckling calf from the herd in order to make up *bendis*, milk producers in the villages, either for feeding their families or for exchanging for rice. This exchange can be made following the loan of cows with calves at foot to Rimaibe cultivators who give rice in exchange for milk.

Plate 8.7 Return from transhumance – taking the calves across the river by canoe

Plate 8.8 The wetlands in November

Plate 8.9   The wetlands in March

The reconstituted *gartis* exploit the wet lands from December to June as the retreating waters render them accessible. They move further away from the village where the main part of the group is settled. The guards of the herd live with their family in straw huts built on the sand banks of tributaries of the Niger and the Diaka.

As to the *doumtis*, they do not transhume at all. Composed of milking cows, they remain in the villages to provide milk mainly for the children, many of whom are born at the beginning or during the rainy season. These cows are chosen from among the oldest ones because the period in the zone which is wet for 2–3 months, when the blood sucking insects and ticks are swarming, is very bad for them and this is so despite the precautions taken by the herders such as night pasturing and putting the most sickly animals in shelters. After observations made in the Central Niger Delta, it has been estimated that the daily removal of blood by blood sucking insects was of the order of 150–300 g per day for an ox (lost by sucking and also bleeding through the wounds). It is not surprising, therefore, that many of the cows from the *doumtis* die and that others might be sterile for one or several years.

In this type of transhumance, where one part of the human group is sedentary, the authority of the chiefs has to be unquestioned and the devotion of the herders indispensable, for it is these who have the formidable responsibility of keeping watch on the herd. To one herder who asked for a mosquito net, an *amirou* did not reply, but in refusing it to him said 'he who is covered by the mosquito net, cannot act in time to chase the lion!' and one Peul speaker commented: 'to the fat herder a lean herd, to the lean herder, a fat herd.'

In certain ethnic groups, where the herds are exclusively held by the family, all the family moves with its animals.

Alongside the technical code of conduct relating to the movements of herds, Cheikou Ahmadou foresaw a fundamental organisation in which the right of

Peul women in festive costume on the day of the return from transhumance (Mali)

use of the wet lands was attributed collectively to sociohistoric groups, its administration was entrusted to a *dioro diom hudo* who assured the recognition of a right of pasture (*tolo*) and of rights of passage to certain fords on the rivers Niger and Diaka.

While it conserved the principles of Cheikou Ahmadou, the pastoral code of Dina evolved with time. The most remarkable modification has been the concentration, into the hands of several families, of the fundamental ownership of taxes, a phenomenon due to mixing between groups, those who leave losing their right to fundamental ownership and those who are accepted into the area only having a right of usage.

Family appropriation was again accrued by the extension of fundamental allocations to the traditional chiefs that Cheikou Ahmadou had introduced and which was used by the colonial administration to recompense for services rendered.

This concentration was accompanied by an increase in the dues from grazing. At the time of Dina they represented, for a herd of 50 head, the value of 10 kg of paddy and in 1958, one bull-calf worth 3000 CFA* francs or the value of 150 kg of paddy.

If the Peul had reserved the use of the wetlands for their own herds, they would certainly have entered into conflict with the other graziers of the region, the Tuareg and the Moors. The perception of a right of grazing was a way of bringing about a recognition of their fundamental ownership and their 'generosity'. The latter was in fact limited, considering the fact that the outsiders were only freely admitted into the wetlands in March–April after their exploitation by the Peul, when the grass there has become scarce and of poor quality (Plate 8.9). This subordination of the Tuareg and Moorish graziers to the authority of the Peul was rather badly accepted and bloodshed occurred in 1931. This antagonism was not limited to Mali, as seen at the beginning of the 1940s, when confrontations resulting in deaths took place in the central zone of Niger.

With independence, nationalisation of the land, the suppression of all traditional land rights and of the responsibilities of the traditional chiefs, a new situation was created. The annual conferences of the wetlands which took on the ideas of 1952, had the objective of establishing a new code of conduct for the exploitation of the grazing areas, which each year are being taken over by the development of rice fields and more recently by industrial cultivation of sugar cane.

The principles of exploitation were specified in the late sixties:

1. the right of exploitation without discrimination implies the suppression of traditional dues in all their forms;
2. the precedence of certain herds according to tradition with a reduction of the watiting time for the others;
3. the respect and the restoration of the traditional herding routes and stopping places;
4. the fixing of the date of entry into, the wetlands by the Conference according to the rainfall pattern.

After 10 years, a *modus vivendi* has been established. Transhumant itineraries have been re-established, the precedence for entry into the wetlands has partly been respected, but the most obvious phenomenon is the liberation

---

* CFA = Communauté Financière Africaine (= African Financial Community)

of the pastures from exploitation by the non-Peul graziers, which was for them a means of survival from the drought of the Sahel.

These wetlands have, for a century, provided the large majority of the livestock for export and have been a source of wealth for Mali. Actually, one can almost say that they are victims of their own success and they resemble a promised land, but the effects of over-grazing are apparent in several areas. The reduced density of homogenous populations of *Echinochloa* is the most disquieting symptom of this.

The animal populations which exploit the delta now belong as much to the Peul as to the Tuareg and to the Moors. Gallais estimates that the overall level of stocking for a surface area of 1 250 000 ha is 1 200 000 Tropical Livestock Units. For 7–8 months, or from November to June, the available area is reduced to 1 ha per Tropical Livestock Unit.

Highland transhumance in Cameroun

Whereas transhumance is carried out in the rainy season in the Soudano-Sahelian zone, it is carried out in the dry season in Adamoua, a plateau situated between latitudes 6° and 8° north at an altitude varying between 1000 m and 1200 m. It is motivated by the search for new pastures and above all by the concern which the stockmen have to avoid contact between their livestock and the tsetse fly, the vector of trypanosomiasis.

The tsetse can only live and reproduce if the ambient temperature is 24–28° C and the humidity high, 85–95 per cent. All are conditions which are fulfilled during the rainy season in the valleys and the low ground, whereas the infestation is less on the plateau because the temperature is lower. In Adamoua, there are several species of tsetse.

1. There are those of restricted habitat, which hardly leave the cover of the forest canopy. In the rainy season, the whole of the forest is infested while in the dry season the tsetse abandon the heads of the water courses and move to the confluents of the main rivers, where they can only infest the livestock when they come close to the tree canopy or when they come to drink at the water courses which border them.
2. The others have a dispersed habitat in the savannas, which they occupy completely in the rainy season. During the dry season, the populations of surviving insects concentrate themselves in the wooded areas and so the livestock can be infested at pasture even in the dry season. However this is not the case if the vegetation is of the steppe type, when the flies cannot find wooded shelter.

At the beginning of the dry season, the herds gather on the meadows which border the rivers on the lower edges of the plateatu, a sign that the dry season is coming (the tsetse are disappearing from the forest canopy), and the herds descend into the valleys up to the limit of the lush zone (the tsetse are less numerous in the savanna zones).

When the natural pastures are exploited, the herds move in to the fallow fields and the stubbles in the lower altitude agricultural areas while, in the savannas, fires destroy the large grasses whose regrowths will be grazed. A sign that the rainy season is approaching is that the showers increase, the more significant regrowths enable the animals to disperse, the humidity becomes sufficient to enable swarming of the insects and, although the forage might be abundant, the graziers lead their herds to the plateau, whose resources they exploit as sedentary stockmen.

The general scheme of things, which corresponds to a changing of altitude, is adapted by the different ethnic groups and thus the Foulbé, whose herds are generally tended by employees or family members, make the transhumance in the same way as the M'bororo with the difference that, in the case of the latter, it is the whole family which moves and the distances covered are larger.

This description of transhumant herding in the Mali and Cameroun shows that the apparent anarchy of pastoral nomadism is in fact the materialisation of a coherent system of exploitation of limited but renewable natural resources. All the research carried out with regard to Niger, Chad, Cameroun, Nigeria and Kenya by several authors arrive at the same conclusion.

Sedentary rearing

In the tropics, where domestic and wild animals have to move in order to reduce the incidence of seasonal fluctuations of forage resources, livestock rearing is only sedentary if it is associated with crop production enterprises. The only exception is ranching which involves a sedentary system of exclusively animal production.

The plant cropping/livestock association exists in extremely diverse forms. It happens more often when the rainfall is higher and thus favours speculations in crop production more. In the arid or semi-arid zones, only animal production enables man to maintain himself and this has to be by practising itinerant herding.

Scavenging

Sedentary rearing coexists with cropping but with nothing complementary between the two activities. The animals only benefit from a small amount of attention which is most often limited to protection against wild animals. Wandering by the large and small animal is the rule and they are not fed. They are neither exploited for work nor for milk production and they are not often systematically exploited for meat production but are instead sacrificed on the occasion of traditional feasts. The manure is only used a little. The enterprise is limited to the ownership of the animals and to a more or less superficial control of them. This system of rearing, which is without doubt close to the first efforts at domestication, is about 10 000 years old and is found in Africa in the forest zones involving large and small ruminants. The practice is also found in Oceania in connection with pigs.

One can thus consider that this primitive system is frequent in the equatorial and humid tropics. The regions involved are those where traditional agriculture is essentially carried on with food crops, particularly starch crops (cassava, cocoyam and yam) associated with hunting and gathering.

For half a century, the humid tropics have enabled the development of export crops such as coffee, cocoa, rubber and oil palm which require no animal traction and have no effect on the evolution of the rearing systems. Economic development linked with these enterprises however favours the growth of meat consumption and there is an increase in the exploitation of animal numbers for meat.

The animal breeds which have evolved in such conditions often do not lend themselves to modern rearing techniques, notably to management in large herds and to herding in meadows of tall grasses because the food resources available to them over the centuries was limited and sparse on the edge of the humid forests and at the limit of the living area cleared by man.

Rearing associated with land cultivation

At a higher level of association, sedentary rearing combined with rice cultivation is found. There are different degrees of the dependence of animal enterprises and cropping enterprises.

At the least developed stage, traditional Madagascan rearing is found, such as still exists, in certain areas of the island. The animals are kept on the land that is unusable for rice cultivation. Their only intervention in the agricultural cycle is seen in the churning up of rice fields by treading. This operation is carried out at the beginning of the rainy season before the planting out of the rice plants. At this time the animals are already in poor condition as a result of suffering in the dry season and because the rice fields under cultivation generally occupy the only good ground capable of producing forage in the off-season. In the areas where treading is practised, there are neither ploughs nor any other drawn cultivation equipment. Generally, there are no carts either and manure is not used. Furthermore, in Madagascar, the cows are traditionally not milked. Treading, which lasts 3 weeks to a month, constitutes a considerable physiological test for the cattle, from which each year a certain number of them do not recover.

In Madagascar even, this method of involving animals in agricultural operations is tending to disappear with the growing use of various ploughing equipment designed for animal drawn cultivation.

In South-east Asia, the buffalo has been used for thousands of years as a means of animal traction in rice cultivation. The swing plough was the first tool which enabled the use of the power of buffalo, but today the range of equipment available to the peasants is very wide.

In dry-land farming, the equivalent of the ancient use of cattle and buffalo for rice cultivation is found and this is particularly so in India. In tropical Africa, animal drawn cultivation in sedentary livestock rearing is usually fairly recent and has been introduced in the course of the last half century. An exception is observed in the oases of the Sahara and in the Upper Nile Valley, where the use of camels as a power source is an age old tradition.

The spread of animal traction has been one of the most notable achievements of the development authorities in Africa. Varying results have accompanied these efforts.

In Madagascar, transport by Zebu drawn carts has been developed since the fifteenth century after the first Europeans, invited by the Royal Family, had taught the artisans how to construct carts and maintain them (Plate 8.10). The model still used over the whole island, today, dates from this period. In Southeast Asia, until recently, cattle drawn transport assured the essential trade required for economic activity.

Unknown in West Africa before the arrival of the Europeans, because the nomadic herders only used their bullocks (Plate 8.4) and camels for carrying, cattle traction could henceforth be considered to be definitely established in Senegal, Guinea and in the neighbouring regions (Plates 8.11 and 8.12). It only began to be accepted in the countries of the Gulf of Benin after the Second World War.

As regards the introduction into central Africa (Central African Republic and Chad), it only dates from the last quarter of the century. For this reason, the uses have diversified little and the plough is far from usual. Cattle drawn vehicular transport could not develop along with the automobile.

In intertropical America, the historic peopling by Spanish and Portuguese stock favoured the adoption of techniques practised in Europe for four centuries and for which there was a large use of cattle drawn traction.

Plate 8.10   Carts in Madagascar: the wheels have iron rims

Plate 8.11   Animal drawn cultivation: N'Dama cattle

Plate 8.12   Equipment for animal drawn cultivation: on an African market

Total integration of livestock rearing and agriculture

The ultimate stage, in which sedentary livestock rearing is combined with cropping plants, corresponds to that where the manure is used to increase the yields of the crops and where the cows are milked.

With regard to the exploitation of lactating females for milk production, in sedentary livestock rearing, this is fairly infrequent in the tropics and can only be considered firmly established in certain regions of South America. Another place where it is found is the sub-continent of India, where in fact very often the sedentary herders who milk their cows are descended from old nomadic or transhumant herders who have become sedentary fairly recently and where religious factors have brought about the development of rearing for milk production. The same applies in Soudanian Africa of trypanosomiosis-tolerant sedentary herds that are milked because they are kept by Peul herders. The milking of sedentary herds is however traditional in the Fouta Djallon in Guinea.

The use of manure or of soil with animal dropping from livestock holding areas to fertilise cropping land is still little practised in the tropics, although significant extension work is devoted to it.

A reason for this, at least for the Indian sub-continent, is that the shortage of combustible materials leads to the dung being strenuously gathered and dried for use as domestic fuel.

This applies equally to sedentary livestock keeping in the desert zones. In Guinea, an ancestral practice called 'tapade' can be considered as constituting the use of manure for the purpose of maintaining the fertility of the soil. In fact, one sees this in Foutah Djallon, a highland area (1500 m) inhabited for more than four centuries by sedentary Peul people who raise N'Dama cattle that are exploited mainly for milk and increasingly for meat. The villages of the cultivator-stockmen are ringed by fairly large enclosures (0.25–1 ha) which are successively utilised over the years for night-time penning of the livestock during the cropping season and then used for the most demanding crops (maize, tobacco, okra and particularly fonio (or hungary rice, *Digitaria exilis*)).

It is due to this practice that the Foulahs of Foutah Djallon should have avoided too great a degradation of the fertility of their lands which are already intensely eroded because of their slope.

The collection and use of manure and loose topsoil with droppings from cattle pens has been and continues to be a very important point stressed in extension programmes in the humid and sub-humid tropics. The adoption of the technique by farmers is rather slow.

Industrial livestock rearing

Finally, the economic development of the last decades has favoured the establishment of sedentary livestock enterprises of an industrial type (intensive beef lots for example), in areas close to centres of consumption and close to access and means of communication which allow dispatch of necessary primary materials. However this no longer amounts to real tropical systems of production but to a transfer of techniques largely used elsewhere.

Ranching

Definition

Numerous definitions have been given for this method of livestock rearing. It seems to us that it is best characterised by the following peculiarities: ranching is a method of open air livestock rearing, relying on the exclusive exploitation of pastures, which are usually natural, in a system calling upon the minimum use of manpower.

This method of stocking was born in the New World at a time when land was available on an immense scale and when it was underpopulated. It has persisted, in a general way, in the countries and regions with low population density and where the cost of basic living is very low.

Ranching occurs under extremely varied forms. It is probable that the Northern Territory of Australia is the area of the world where it is practised on the most extensive scale. It is here that there are large stock rearing properties belonging most often now to multinational companies (notably King Ranch). In this region, with its extreme climate and floods alternating with catastrophic droughts, the livestock stations can cover thousands of square kilometres.

Farm structures are reduced to the absolute minimum, such as stock marshalling enclosures and watering points. Often, gathering of the herds is carried out with the aid of helicopters and aeroplanes. The personnel, who are highly qualified, are very small in number.

The herds, whose movements are not limited by any enclosure, exploit the natural pasture and are only subjected to the minimum of operations (marking, castration, selection of animals for butchering). The stocking rates per hectare of pasture are extremely low (1 animal per 20–100 ha).

The opposite is the case in the humid or sub-humid tropics of Oceania and the Americas, where very intensive forms of livestock grazing are found. Here pastures, which are artificially fertilised and fenced off into small units, support stocking rates of up to 2.5 animals per hectare. Here also, the numbers of personnel are reduced to a minimum and again the systems amount to open air grass-fed rearing. In certain cases, the enterprises are economically viable even when they only cover a small area (50–300 ha). The establishments can no longer justify being called ranches when the animals are confined in enclosures and receive concentrated food, especially if it is no longer exclusively forage harvested from their meadows.

Ranching thus appears to be one of the pioneer methods of fundamental exploitation when, for a variety of reasons (climate, demography, etc.) the population is low for a sufficiently long time.

Very often, ranching has given way to more intensive methods of agricultural exploitation when the population increases in density, in particular by the opening of communications and wherever the soils and climate allowed enterprises other than pastoral and forestry ones.

Ranching persists for a long time in areas of unfavourable climate and particularly in arid and semi-arid zones.

The method of livestock rearing of the young countries, ranching distinguishes itself from the traditional nomadic or transhumant methods of stock-keeping of the peoples of Africa and Asia, firstly because of the small number of humans in relation to the livestock numbers and secondly because of the sedentarism, which is relative in the case of exploitation over such a large area.

In Africa for a quarter of a century, the two systems have coexisted with reasonable success.

The organisation of ranching

The personnel

In the majority of cases, the enterprise manager takes up the main functions himself. He installs and maintains the infrastructure and pastures, oversees and handles the herd and manages the grazing usage.

In the countries of the New World, in Australia and on the modern ranches now installed in Africa, the different functions are assumed by specialised personnel.

The infrastructures

With manual work being reduced to the minimum, guarding of the herd is replaced by the use of enclosures. The animals remain at pasture day and night throughout the year.

The manual work of 'stockmanship' involves inspecting the animals (counting them at various intervals), moving them in order to assure a rational use of the pastures, carrying out prophylactic operations (vaccinations, dipping) and performing physical tasks (sorting, weaning, marking, castration). The ranch therefore has a certain amount of indispensable infrastructure that facilitates the work of the personnel and improves their work output (Plates 8.13 to 8.18).

ENCLOSURES. The most important equipment is the stockpen or corral (America), square (New Caledonia), or stockyard (Australia). This amounts to an enclosure of varied area (100 m^2 minimum), often subdivided into smaller enclosures connected by passageways or gates and having walls or fences

Plate 8.13   Collecting yards (Goudali-Bororo cattle) Faro Ranch SODEPA Cameroun (photo: B. Gattolin)

Plate 8.14   Collecting yards: separation passage. Faro Ranche SODEPA Cameroun
(photo: B. Gattolin)

Plate 8.15   Sheltered corral (Brazil) with Gir cattle

constructed of very durable materials. Economy and longevity are the principal
characteristics of these materials which can vary a great deal according to the
region or country. Stock pens can be found made from growing branches
(Pacific islands), treated wood or old railway sleepers, metal tubing, old
railway lines, concrete or from dry earth . . . (Plates 8.13, 8.14 and 8.15).

The design of the stock pen is particularly important and account should
particularly be taken of the following.

1. Numbers and temperament of the stock are a major consideration – docile
    cattle are easier to manage and demand less resistant materials.

2. Pasture sites – the stock pens should be accessible from all parts of the ranch and preferably be situated within at least one day's walking from the furthermost part of the property.
3. Routine operations – if this only amounts to checking the stock, then the pen can be just a simple enclosure. Most often, however, the gathered animals have to be vaccinated, deloused, dipped, castrated, de-horned, weighed and marked. It is for these purposes that the stock pens most often include many adjacent small enclosures linked by passageways. The models shown in the literature are numerous. It is the practical details of daily experience which give the layout their value.

The stock pens should be built on well-drained land, in a well ventilated and if possible shaded area. If the herds have to be constrained for any length of time, a watering point, fixed or mobile, should be included in the scheme.

The dimensions of the gates and passageways should be adapted to the make-up of the herd. Sharp angles should be avoided. The animal should be able to see several metres in front of itself when moving.

Plate 8.16 Cattle weigh crush, serving a dual purpose for 'working' on the animal (photo: Maréchal)

Plate 8.17 Housing for a pit bullock, Madagascar (photo: Serres)

Plate 8.18   Drinking trough equipped for the distribution of mineral supplements in the water (USA)

THE DIP. In most parts of the tropics, it is necessary to dip the stock in order to remove external parasites, which are usually ticks. In the regions of Africa infested with tsetse, these treatments effectively contribute to the elimination of the fly and to the reduction of Diptera populations harmful to livestock (e.g. *Stomoxys*).

Dipping methods are treated in detail in Chapter 6, 'Animal production and disease', but we will recall them briefly.

The oldest form of this practice is total immersion in a solution of insecticide with the aid of an installation called a dipping tank (Plate 6.3). There are numerous models corresponding to the different types of animal. The volume of the tank should take account of the size of the animals and the number of times it is drained. This volume varies from 15 m^3 to 25 m^3. The tank is completed by an access passageway with ribbed flooring and by a dripping area at the exit. An animal of 400 kg removes an average of 2.5–3 litres of solution.

In countries where the cattle have close contact with man and where the latter takes the cattle to the place where they are 'pushed in', the bath should include a walking place submerged in a few centimetres of liquid to enable the drover to walk ahead of the herd and lead the cattle into the bath.

The principal advantage of the bath is the absence of any form of mechanism, and the insignificant variation in concentration in relation to the quantity of liquid involved.

Acaricide treatment can be carried out using spraying equipment. In this case, the animals are passed through a spray race – a passageway provided with hoops carrying spraying nozzles which ensure fine dispersion and penetration of the insecticide solution. The excess solution is recycled after having been drained into a reservoir of 2–3 m³ volume. A high pressure pump is the main element of the equipment.

This system is suitable for numbers of no more than 400–500 animals, for beyond this level, the variations in solution concentration (exhaustion of the insecticide) are such that it is preferable to use a dip. The inconvenience of the spray race is the existence of mechanical parts (pump) with the constraints of the equipment for power. The advantage is that it is the least wasteful of active product by leakage from the tank.

Finally, for small herds of fewer than 100 animals, the insecticide treatment can be carried out with the aid of hand pumps.

For ease of maintenance of the infrastructure and in order to rationalise the use of stock pens and passageways, a circular crush is often included in the stock pen or an annex of it.

THE CATTLE CRUSH. The physical and veterinary operations make a means of confinement of the animal necessary. There are a large number of models of crush in existence. Most frequently, they involve part of the passageway being designed as a head bail which allows immobilisation of the animal's head and limiting its forward and backwards movement. Some sophisticated models allow complete immobilisation by lateral compression of the animal. In order to handle calves, the crush can be tipped over on the ground, enabling access to any part of the cradled animal (calf cradle). Using the appropriate equipment, manpower reaches very high levels of output for the routine husbandry operations that have to be carried out – castration, marking, vaccination, dipping (several hundreds of animals per man per day).

THE WEIGH SCALE. Still insufficiently widespread, this piece of equipment cost often appears to be indispensible to the good management of stock (Plate 8.16). In fact, only weighing enables objective appreciation of weight gains, buying-in weight and weight at sale, and the comparison of growth rates. There are simple tough hydraulic models available cheaply and very largely usable even when the supply of spare parts is difficult.

FENCES. If there is one subject which the stockmen of ranching countries are capable of discussing for days on end, it is that of fences. There are as many types as there are particular situations.

The principal factors to note are listed below.

1. The temperament and size of the stock which they must contain are major considerations. If the beast is aggressive and powerful, the enclosure should be designed accordingly in the knowledge that no barrier can resist a bull from a large breed who is determined to carry out his duties with females exposed to his view.

2. The availability and cost of materials should also be taken into account.
3. The severity of the climate and environment can also be very important. In the regions where termites are rife, non-treated wood has a very short life. Where there are bush fires, not only the wood but metal also suffers.

DRINKING POINTS. The water requirements of livestock are discussed in Chapter 3, 'Animal production and climate' and water resources were the object of particular attention.

In ranching, watering must be assured in the most economic and the most reliable manner (Plate 8.18).

Each time there are permanent watering points, the laying out of the enclosures should facilitate access from the greatest possible number of plots.

In the arid and semi-arid zones, the installation of artificial watering points constitutes the most significant part of the costs of setting up ranches.

The means of extraction, see Chapter 3, takes account of the technical, economic and social context.

In the tropics, pastoral water supply has been a forerunner in the use of 'natural' or 'renewable' energy, notably wind power.

PASTURES. Exclusive reliance on grazing is the principal characteristic of ranching. Tropical pastures have been made the object of detailed treatment in Chapter 5 'Animal production and food resources'. Nevertheless, with ranching being an improved form of grass-fed livestock production, certain practices merit a more detailed analysis.

THE ROTATION OF PASTURES. The exploitation of natural pasture in all regions, and particularly in the tropics, is improved in the first stage by the practice of pasture rotation. This technique consists of limiting the time spent by the herd on a given plot and then using that plot again after a rest period during which other plots have been grazed consecutively.

The primary justification for rotation is the necessity to allow the nutritious and palatable species, sought by the animals, to recover and to reconstitute their reserves. Their exhaustion and disappearance is therefore avoided which would otherwise benefit the other less productive and less appetising or even completely useless or harmful species.

Rotation is practised within an annual period, but should equally be designed against the background of several years (3–5) in such a way as to avoid a situation where the time of grazing does not always fall at the same time of the vegetative cycle for a given forage species.

A secondary advantage of pasture rotation is the control of parasites because periodic removal of the herd for a greater or lesser length of time (generally 6 weeks to 6 months) interrupts infestation of the ground by parasites and allows decontamination of the pasture.

THE MAINTENANCE OF PASTURES. Under most climates, the maintenance of grassland constitutes a delicate state of equilibrium between two opposing types of evolution: degradation by nutrient loss and disappearance of the biomass (defoliation) as opposed to overgrowth then afforestation. According to the climate, overgrazing favours one or the other type of evolution. In the arid and semi-arid zones, overgrazing causes degradation of the vegetation. Conversely, in the sub-humid or humid zones, it favours progressive evolution towards overgrowth.

The stockman in ranching should be aware of maintaining this unstable equilibrium. According to the socio-economic context, it relies on different techniques.

The most economic method is fire, used in order to eliminate trash, to fight against overgrowth of pastures and to provoke a regrowth of grass.

Fire is most definitely the least costly tool, but without doubt the most difficult to use. Numerous studies have shown the advantages of off-season firing, practised 1 year in 3 or 4, as a means of increasing the productivity of pasture.

Rotation, in conjunction with the practise of off-season burning, enables doubling of the stocking rate per hectare in the humid zone in Madagascar.

Off-season fires are those which are lit in the rainy season, when half or the two periods of annual rain have already fallen.

In the developed regions of the tropics, mechanical means are more and more often used for the maintenance of pastures. They involve machines with a horizontal rotating knife (gyro-slashers) which destroy the trash and poor grasses and enable good plants to re-establish themselves from undamaged growing points below the cutting height. Favouring the accumultion of organic matter which burning would not have allowed, these machines enable soil improvement but their use is expensive.

It is often sufficient to pass with these machines once every 3–5 years in order to obtain the required result.

THE IMPROVEMENT OF NATURAL PASTURES. As in the temperate zone, the intensification of animal production has been linked to the development of legumes and more particularly of clover. The Leguminosae family of plants enables the increase of pasture productivity to be pursued at a low cost. *Stylosanthes* have been greatly used in Africa, in Madagascar, in South America and in Australia, to improve the forage value of natural grasslands. This involves annual species (*S. humulis*) in the arid and sub-arid zones and perennial species (*S. guianensis*, *S. hamata*) in the humid and sub-humid zones. The contribution of legumes to the intensification of production from natural tropical pastures is still far from having reached its limits.

Generally, the legumes have a later vegetative cycle than the grasses and extend the growing period of the forage as a result of this fact. They improve the grasses by fixing atmospheric nitrogen in the soil into a nitrogen source available for uptake by grass roots. They are less palatable in the rainy season and more palatable in the dry season, so contributing to ensuring a better balance of proteins and energy in the ration.

THE BUILDING UP OF FORAGE RESERVES. At the most extensive level, ranching excludes the building up of forage reserves other than reserve grass. In this case, the rotation of pastures will include parcels of land which will only be exploited during the poor season (dry season). If burning is practised in the off-season, it is these parcels which are treated in a way which benefits from the fire shifting the overall vegetative cycle.

More and more, particularly in the most developed regions of the tropics (America, Australia), the surplus forage from the rainy season is conserved to feed the livestock in the dry season. The advent of 'big bale'-making equipment has enabled the use of this method. Since the Second World War silage, often made in simple clamps in the middle of the parcel of land, has been the most popular method of conservation. The methods of conservation should, as in ranching, always make the minimum call upon man power just as much during the storing process as during the feeding process. Reliance on mechanisation is thus imperative with all the technicalities and economic considerations which accompany it.

FERTILISATION OF PASTURES. In the whole area of the tropics, the soils are generally deficient in one or more different elements and most particularly in phosphorus. The most developed regions (Australia, America) are those where, when the price of meat allows it, they apply at least phosphate and sometimes phosphomolybdenum fertiliser to the pastures. The use of these concentrated fertilisers enables aerial distribution (aeroplane and helicopter), which is fast and less costly per hectare than spreading by traditional methods. On well managed and legume enriched natural pastures, the application of phosphate fertiliser often proves to be an effective factor in increasing productivity.

Deficiencies can however only be corrected at the level of the animal by distribution of salt lick blocks or addition of the minerals to the drinking water.

The end-product of ranching

Most often, extensive livestock rearing is carried out to breed and produce weaned animals. The fluctuations associated with the reproductive cycle enable adjustment of the stocking rate to the capacity of the pasture according to the season of the year. The young weaned animals are destined for a more intensive system of rearing which allows them to use their genetic potential to the utmost.

In the regions far from the agricultural areas suitable for fattening (see next section), ranching can continue to be applied to the weaned stock up to an age of 2–4 years. This is the case of Oceania where, in favourable areas, animals from 2 years of age provide 'grass-fed' carcasses of 200–240 kg which represent the basic quality for export.

The creation of fattening ranches has been recommended in Africa to be situated at the boundary between the pastoral and agricultural zones, and to

Table 8.7 Theoretical yield of the herd according to the age at removal of the animals for butchering

Parameters:

Fertility	66 per cent
Mortality	10 per cent at 0–1 year
	5 per cent at 1–2 years
	3 per cent at > 2 years
First calving	3–4 years
Average life expectancy	13 years
Eqivalent to 1 TLU	= 1 animal of > 2 years
Animal of 1–2 years	= 0.66 TLU
0–1 year	= 0.33 TLU

First case: sale at 4 years   Constraint 100 TLU

Category	Numbers	Equiv. TLU	
Females of > 3 years	36	36	
Rearing 3–4 years	20	20	
Rearing 2–3 years	21	21	traditional
Rearing 1–2 years	22	14.3	tropical
Calves (bull and heifer) 0–1 year	24	8	extensive
	123	99.3 = 100	

Available: 20 of which four cast cows replaced by the same reared from 4 years + reared males and females (supernumerary).
Total available: 20, or 16.26 per cent.

Second case: same parameters but sale of animals for butchering at between 2 and 3 years.

Category	Numbers	Equiv. TLU	
Cows > 3 years	58	58	
Heifers 2–3 years	6	6	improved
Rearing 1–2 years	35	22.6	tropical
Calves (bull and heifer) 0–1 year	38	12.6	extensive
	137	99.2 = 100	

Available: 35 animals of which six cast cows. Rate of removal 25.54 per cent.

Third case: same parameters but sale for fattening between 1 and 2 years.

Category	Numbers	Equiv. TLU	
Cows > 3 years	71	71	
Heifers 2–3 years	8	8	intensive
Heifers 1–2 years	9	6	fattening
Calves (bull and heifer) 0–1 year	45	15	required
	133	100	

Available: 45 animals of which seven cast cows. Rate of removal 33.83 per cent.

TLU = tropical livestock unit

offer improved conditions to the animals coming from the traditional extensive system. This would accelerate their growth and regularise their performances.

The creation of ranches, whatever the end-product from livestock might be, sometimes finally appears to be a means of getting value out of fundamental reserves which are really destined for parcelling up and more intensive exploitation at a later date.

Fattening

General

One may refer to the definition 'fattening is the preparation of animals for butchering, whichever method may be used' (Plates 8.19 and 8.20).

Increase in yield from the technique can be obtained by improvement of the genetic qualities of the animals (cf. Chapter 7 'Animal production and genetics'), by improvement of the environmental conditions which include the fight against pathological factors and, above all, by improvement of feeding.

The latter, a swift measure, enables remarkable results to be obtained with local stock and with forage and agro-industrial by-products available locally.

It has been seen, that in extensive stock rearing, the animals experience alternating shortages and abundances which are prejudicial to good growth and to satisfactory production per hectare and per animal. However, if the tropical animal were fed correctly all year round, its production of meat could be doubled.

While fattening has been practised for centuries and in all the latitudes, its techniques have largely evolved in the last 30 years, particularly in the tropics.

These techniques have enabled:

1. achievement of the potential of tropical cattle breeds often suppressed by natural conditions;
2. the finishing of animals coming from extensive rearing situations;
3. the putting to profitable use of agro-industrial by-products (molassses, bagasse, middlings from cereals, cotton seed, new forage crops);
4. the initiation of herd restructuring with the shortening of production cycles, so contributing to an increase in the rate of exploitation and therefore overall productivity.

The theoretical calculations given in Table 8.7 allow comparison of the production obtained according to when the animals are sold for butchering:

1. at 4 years (traditional tropical extensive rearing);
2. at 2–3 years (improved tropical extensive rearing with short-term fattening before slaughter);
3. at 1–2 years (intensive fattening).

In the first case, the availability of stock for release for butchering is 16.2 per cent of the herd number, in the second it is 25.5 per cent and in the last case it is 38.8 per cent.

Fattening therefore appears to be a feeding method of particular interest and justifying an examination of its most frequent methods.

While the end-product of fattening is the preparation of animals for butchering, there are however particular situations to be considered.

The requirements of the market

At the present time in most of the tropical countries, the local markets accept a

Plate 8.19   Animal before entering a fattening lot (Bambilor Fattening Centre, Senegal, created by M. le General Chevance-Bertin)

Plate 8.20   Animal at the end of fattening and now ready for slaughter

variety of animal types. It is not the same for export purposes and it is foreseen that urbanisation and the evolution of distribution systems will tend to lead to a standardisation of carcass characteristics in the future.

If one takes, as a benchmark, the actual standards demanded on the various export markets, the demand corresponds to carcasses of 180–240 kg, well muscled and without excess fat cover (Plates 8.21 and 8.22).

In the tropics, this definition is applied more and more to meat for consumption in the urban centres. According to the most usual methods of butchering, this type of carcass provides cuts with detail corresponding to typical individual portions.

Taking account of the conformation of the tropical breeds and notably of

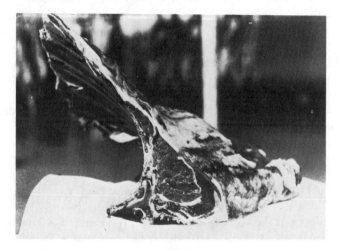

Plate 8.21 Side of beef from 'control' animal – not fattened

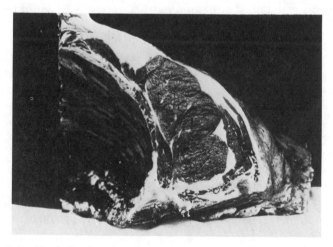

Plate 8.22 Side of beef after fattening

their smaller size than that of breeds from temperate zones, fattening is a means of attaining these technical objectives starting from available animal material. On the other hand, there is a tendency of graziers, in a number of regions, to trade their animals at an increasingly younger age. This runs the risk, given the same herd numbers, of a resultant overall fall in tonnage for which only fattening can compensate.

Rationalisation of production

Tropical climates are characterised by the alternation of dry and humid seasons which affects the feeding value of the forage. Two major phenomena result from this.

1. There is a tendency by the stockmen to trade the animals in preference at the end of the season of good grass growth (the rainy season) or at the beginning of the dry season, which often results in an over-supply to the needs of the market, and a drop in price.
2. The state of the animals gets progressively worse as the dry season progresses up until the return of the rains, and the quality of the carcasses coming on the market falls along with their number.

During the dry season of 1971 in Cameroun five lots of growing bullocks were managed in the following way:

1. Lot I (bullocks of the Foulbé breed) and lot II (Brahman × Foulbé crosses), loose-housed, received 5 kg of cattle cake containing 18 per cent crude protein + 20 kg of grass silage + 4 kg of hay per day;
2. Lot III, maintained at natural pasture, received 3.3 kg of molasses/urea/mineral mix per day;
3. Lot IV, was maintained at natural pasture, received 2.2 kg of cotton seed per day;
4. Lot V (control) was maintained exclusively on natural pasture.

Figure 8.1 indicates the adjusted weight changes (in percentage of the original weight).

Table 8.8 sums up the overall weight changes over the dry season.

Other observations, in Mali, Kenya and Senegal, and summarised below, show all the benefit of the improvement of feeding techniques to increase the productivity of tropical livestock.

In Mali comparisons were made between 3 to 4-year-old Moor and Peul Zebus raised on natural pasture (lot I) with, in addition, a supplement in the dry season (lot II), with supplementation all year round (lot III) and young Zebus of 1.7 years age initially reared at pasture with supplementation all year round (Tables 8.9 to 8.12).

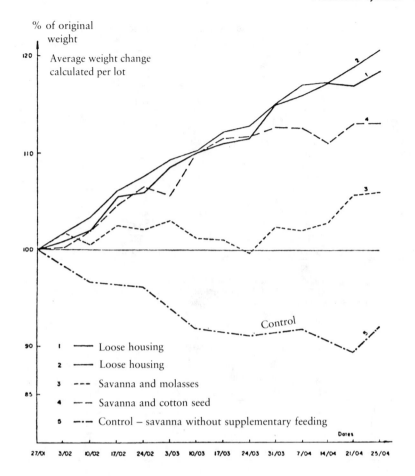

% of original weight

Average weight change calculated per lot

1 —— Loose housing

2 —— Loose housing

3 --- Savanna and molasses

4 — — Savanna and cotton seed

5 —·— Control – savanna without supplementary feeding

Control

Dates

27/01 3/02 10/02 17/02 24/02 3/03 10/03 17/03 24/03 31/03 7/04 14/04 21/04 25/04

Figure 8.1 Weight change curves

Table 8.8 Results of production trial with Foulbé bullocks: weight during dry season

Numbers	Lot I (13 head)	Lot II (13 head)	Lot III (10 head)	Lot IV (5 head)	Lot V (8 head)
Initial weight (kg)	346.3 ± 17.8	337.2 ± 20.2	343.1 ± 42.5	363.6 ± 105	345.3 ± 53
Final weight (kg)	410.5 ± 15.2	407.5 ± 5.7	363.7 ± 41.1	411.5 ± 106	317.7 ± 45
Variation – overall (kg)	64.2 ± 7.2	70.4 ± 10.9	20.6 ± 9.5	47.9 ± 14.4	− 27.6 ± 10.6
Variation – av. daily (g/d)	729.1 ± 83	799.8 ± 125.5	231.3 ± 107	537.6 ± 164	− 310 ± 120
Range (maximum) (kg)	972	1 080	483	685	− 551
(minimum) (kg)	517	(324)* 601	− 11	393	− 129

* A sick animal, indicated above in Lot II, showed a poor growth of 324 g per day.

Table 8.9 Killing out results of Zebus from production trial

| | Control | Slaughter (March) loose housing I and II | End of trial April | | | |
| | | | 3 to 4-year-old | | | 1–7-year-old |
			Lot I	Lot II	Lot III	Lot IV
Numbers considered	5	4	12	12	5	2
Live weight (kg)						
before fasting	348.1	401.5	414.4	412	410.3	425.7
after fasting	330.2	377.3	397.5	393.2	385.6	394.5
Carcass weight (kg)						
warm	181.7	214	229.4	25.9	216.8	235
dry	178.9	211	227.4	223	214.2	231
Rough yield (%)						
LW before fasting	52.2	53.3	55.4	54.9	52.8	55.2
LW after fasting	55.0	56.7	57.7	57.5	56.2	59.6
True yield*	60.8	63.4	63.3	63.6	62	63.5
Judgement of fattening	Poor	Average	Very good	Very good	Average	Average/good

LW = Liveweight
* The observations relating to the contents of the gut, fifth quarter and true yield, have only been carried out in lots I, II and III on part of the number killed (respectively 3, 3 and 2 head). For the three other groups, these observations have been made on all the bullocks killed.

Table 8.10 Composition of lots in production trials

Lot	Numbers (total)	Zebu cattle Moor	Peul	Average age (years)	Average weight (kg)
I	42	21	21	3.5	227
II	55	28	27	3.6	226
III	58	28	30	3.5	232
IV	43	35	8	1.7	176

Table 8.11 Weight gain in 9 months of animals in Zebu production trial

Weight gain	Lot I	Lot II	Lot III	Lot IV
Starting weight (kg)	229	227	233	178
Final weight (kg)	251	314	343	304
Weight gain (kg)	22	87	110	126
	± 6.74	± 8.10	± 8.65	± 10.25

Table 8.12 Killing out results of animals in Zebu production trial

Characteristics	Lot I	Lot II	Lot III	Lot IV
Number of animals	2	3	3	3
Live weight after 24 h fasting (kg)	282.5	292	327	298
Warm carcass yield (kg)	129.5	154	182	158
Carcass yield (%)	45.2	52.3	54.6	52.9

Only supplementation allows one to get near to the carcass weights sought but the young animals have a higher potential for growth.

This has also been confirmed in studies with Gobra Zebus (Table 8.13).

In good feeding conditions, these animals can produce 200 kg carcasses in 18 months, which is not possible from traditionally reared stock and aged 3.5 or 7.9 years, except after 4 months' intensive fattening.

In Kenya, four breed types were compared, traditional Boran, improved Boran, large size cross (Charolais or Friesian) (Plates 7.40 and 7.41) and small size cross (Angus or Hereford) (Plate 7.44), for two periods of fattening (68 and 111 days) with two types of regime (67 per cent concentrate/33 per cent forage and 33 per cent concentrate/67 per cent forage) (Table 8.14).

A period of 68 days is, even with a 67 per cent forage ration, sufficient to reach carcass weights of more than 180 kg with all the breeds.

The animals coming from the crossing of large or small sized European breeds make better use of the regimes that are rich in concentrate, the improved Boran having the most constant and high results with the two regimes.

Numbers of experiments have shown, in the same way, the necessity of fattening in the tropics to avoid weight losses in the dry season, and to regularise the weight and fleshing conditions of the carcasses at slaughter.

Fattening, then, is a means of allowing regular slaughtering and regular carcass quality by acting as the 'insert' between extensive rearing and the market consumer.

The insufficiency of communications networks means that very often butchering animals are transported by foot from the rearing grounds to the centres of consumption. While a number of studies have indicated that this practice is economically well founded, the stated weight losses corresponding to a lower cost than the cost of transport, it does not matter any the less that, whatever their condition might have been on departure, the animals often arrive at their destination emaciated. It is often necessary to make them put on weight again before slaughter, which is why fattening yards close to the slaughter sites are an advantage.

The prime motivation of fattening has been, and remains so most often, that of speculation. The owners of a fatteners enterprise are frequently people with the technical and financial means which allow them to buy the run-down animal when prices are low and to keep them to re-sell when prices have improved. It is frequent that purely speculative operations become real fattening exercises as a natural consequence.

Finally, the supply of finished animals can be justified by custom or by religious obligation, for example Mardi Gras gatherings, processions in Europe and pit bullocks in Madagascar (Plate 8.17).

Fattening methods

The different techniques can be classed according to their duration. In a general way, fattening relies on a minimum time of the order of 3 months up to

Table 8.13 Growth potential in Gobra Zebus

| | Young bulls | | | | | Control | | | | |
| | | | | | | Before fattening | | After fattening (4 months) | | |
	12 months	18 months	29 months	39 months	54 months	Young bulls 3–5 years	Bullocks 7–9 years	Young bulls 3–5 years	Bullocks 7–9 years
Weight before fasting (kg)	266.0	372.3	528.3	614.6	629.5	265.0	–	385.0	426.8
Weight after fasting (kg)	245.6	342.0	517.3	579.0	605.5	254.0	314.4	358.0	405.2
Loss in fasting (%)	7.6	8.1	2.1	5.7	3.8	4.0	–	7.0	4.6
Warm carcass weight (kg)	134.4	209.7	315.0	345.0	381.0	131.2	161.4	200.2	224.0
Cold carcass weight (kg)	131.1	206.0	312.3	339.0	373.0	128.7	157.9	197.1	221.0
Loss on drying (%)	2.4	1.7	0.8	1.8	2.1	1.91	2.2	1.6	1.3
Yield (kg)	54.7	61.3	60.8	59.6	62.9	51.9	51.4	5.9	55.2

Table 8.14 Influence of breed, fattening period and feed regime on fattening of cattle

| | Concentrate/forage in ration | | | | | | | |
| | 67/33% | | | | 33/67% | | | |
	Traditional Boran	Improved Boran	Large-sized Friesian/ Charolais	Small-sized cross Hereford/ Angus	Traditional Boran	Improved Boran	Large-sized Friesian/ Charolais	Small-sized Hereford/ Angus
Short fattening (68 days)								
Numbers	44	45	44	46	48	44	48	48
Final weight (kg)	380	392	426	401	382	375	414	384
Carcass weight (kg)	195	202	216	202	190	188	201	190
Daily liveweight gain (g)	1 015	1 360	1 470	1 370	1 045	1 130	1 265	1 115
Adjusted liveweight gain (g)	1 045	1 420	1 420	1 290	890	1 020	965	940
Long fattening (111 days)								
Numbers	46	44	47	48	48	48	48	48
Final weight (kg)	414	435	467	448	416	426	459	436
Carcass weight (kg)	220	233	248	237	216	223	235	224
Daily liveweight gain (g)	925	1 210	1 245	1 260	945	1 135	1 190	1 150
Adjusted liveweight gain (g)	1 075	1 400	1 410	1 405	1 005	1 230	1 205	1 175

a maximum of about 18 months to 2 years. The length of the period depends upon the characteristics of the animals used and the food resources available.

In the same country, Madagascar, the same animal, 5–8-year-old Madagascan Zebu, can be fattened at grass over 6–18 months (Dabokandro) or in an intensive way with concentrate food in 3–4 months (pit beef). It seems preferable to us then to operate the classification according to the feeding regimes and the nature of the main products used.

Grass fattening

This is the type which is still the most widely practised. It consists of reserving the best pastures for the animals destined for slaughter and giving them the most attentive care during the space of time necessary to reach the live-weight required. Feeding is basically forage with, sometimes, a small supplement of mineral or concentrate. The animals are maintained permanently at pasture.

In the best conditions, with animals having the most favourable genetic potential (often crosses between Zebu and European breeds) kept on fertilised artificial paddocks, daily live-weight gains of the order of 1 kg are observed and the final result, an animal of 400 kg live-weight furnishing a carcass of 200–240 kg, can be attained at the age of 24–30 months (Oceania, South America).

There are traditional methods of grass fattening in the tropics notably the Dabokandro in Madagascar. In this case, 3–7-year-old Madagascan Zebus are maintained for 6–18 months in an area which provides good natural pastures in both the dry and the wet seasons, and average live-weight gains of about 300 g per day are obtained.

In the Ivory Coast, on *Stylosanthes* pasture, with N'Dama humpless cattle, live-weight gains of 392 g per day have been obtained.

In Ethiopia, the farmers fatten the young bullocks at the edge of the fields with the lower leaves taken from the stems of the sorghum.

Grass fattening is a technique which is economical in material and human resources, but which generally implies a certain loss of energy by the animals when they move from one place to another to change pasture. On the other hand, selective grazing only allows the exploitation of a fraction of the available grass. Furthermore daily live-weight gains are often low, which takes on some significance when the forage products have true economic cost and, in particular, when they are cultivated. Finally, this technique is subject to seasonal fluctuations of forage production and retains a certain extensive character for this reason.

Intensive fattening

More and more, one sees forms of intensive fattening where the animals are confined in feedlots or pens and receive, in the trough, a completely balanced ration of forage, concentrate feed or diverse agro-industrual by-products.

The growth rates in the dry season of five lots of Foulbé Zebus, maintained according to the regimes in Table 8.15, were compared.

Table 8.15 Feeding regimes during trials with Foubé Zebus

Lots	Method of keeping and basic ration	Rice flour	Cotton cake
I	Grazing on foot (straw) water, minerals	–	1 kg
II	Grazing on foot (straw) water, minerals	Ad lib.	0 kg
III	Grazing on foot (straw) water, minerals	Ad lib.	1 kg
IV	Grazing on foot (shavings) water, minerals	Ad lib.	1 kg
V	Loose housed: hay, water minerals	Ad lib.	1 kg

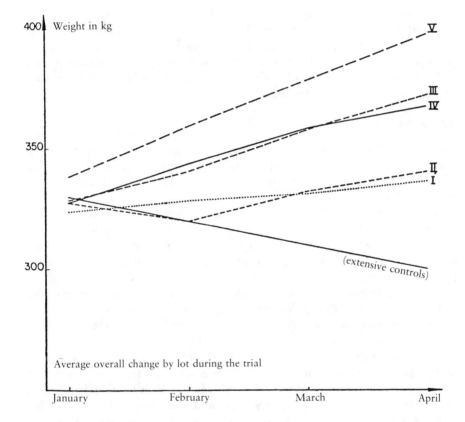

Figure 8.2 Average adjusted growth by lot during the trial

The results are illustrated by the graph in Figure 8.2 which is self-explanatory.

The numbers kept varies from one to several units in small farming enterprises, to tens or hundreds or even thousands of head in industrial feeding lots.

For 20 years, the development of intensive fattening methods has been seen in Africa being practised by farmers during the latter parts of the cropping season and in which the basic ration is constituted of harvest residues (groundnut haulms) and diverse by-products (cereal middlings, cotton seed).

These operations can be developed and improved as a result of numerous experiments which have been carried out. Often, the supplying companies or financial agencies encourage them by providing appropriate short- and medium-term credit.

These techniques should experience considerable development in all the regions where agricultural activities, which produce residues and by-products (rice, cotton, sugar), and traditional livestock rearing co-exist temporarily or permanently. Endeavours have been made in Senegal, Cameroun and in Thailand to develop these activities.

The adoption of farm techniques of intensive fattening is often a logical progression from the development of animal drawn cultivation. In effect livestock rearing and agriculture are often practised by different populations in the tropics. Animal traction, when it is adopted by cultivators, constitutes their first contact with livestock and leads them to use animal husbandry methods inaccessible to traditional stockmen.

Industrial fattening

Very often, the development of certain crops, such as sugarcane, cotton and oil palm, leads to the establishment of industrial processing activities (sugar refineries, cattle cake factories, oil mills) which generate by-products which can be used for livestock feeding.

Too often, unfortunately, the governments are tempted to export these by-products in order to procure foreign exchange. In certain cases, notably those of sugar refineries, the product is too low in value to be exported and nevertheless its use for fattening proves to be a profitable method of obtaining some value from it.

In Cuba, a technique of using the molasses from sugarcane for intensive cattle fattening was perfected, and this is experiencing increasing success in all the sugarcane producing countries, which are generally deficient in meat (Plate 8.23).

Besides giving value to the molasses, this technique shows the advantage of calling upon non-protein nitrogen (urea) in a very significant way and thus economising on the sources of protein (cattle cakes) which can then be reserved for the most profitable enterprises. Furthermore, coarse forage and by-products which are generally unused (groundnut shells) can serve as a basic ration and so find some value.

In industrial fattening methods, the by-products which provide basic rations can be varied (bran, rice flour, waste from fruit canning factories). It is often necessary to cultivate high productivity forage in order to provide part of the protein or energy requirement of the diet. The high productivity tropical forages (*Panicum maximum, Pennisetum purpureum, Tripsacum laxum*) are fed as green forage or alternatively conserved (silage) (Plate 8.24).

In the future, one can foresee increasing use of cassava (roots and leaves) whose use has been made the object of numerous studies for several years in South America; this could bring about an opening up of widespread use of

Plate 8.23   Fattening yards in Cuba

Plate 8.24   Harvesting maize for silage (photo: Rivière-Casalis)

techniques which allow the fattening of livestock with a minimum of external inputs to the enterprise.

Perspectives

Cattle fattening, which is experiencing rapid development, effectively contributes to the intensification and increase of production. It is dependent upon the development of forage resources. It will justify genetic improvement of livestock leading notably to an increase in size of cattle; with the better conversion ratio are the large sized breeds (those transforming food into lean meat).

Fattening of sheep and goats

Sheep and goats, which represent a considerable source of protein, are the object of a flourishing traditional trade for supplying the urban centres but their involvement is still larger in the small markets of the rural areas. Family slaughtering must be taken into account and there is no need for a butcher or a family to be able to eat a sheep.

Traditional fattening of sheep, and to a lesser degree of goats, exists all over the tropics. The 'house sheep', a castrated male, fed on kitchen scraps, rice bran, haulms etc., is particularly developed in the Islamic zones of Africa. This sheep is sacrificed for the festival of Tabaski and its coat is used as a prayer mat.

Different regimes of intensive fattening were compared in Dakar. The characteristics of these regimes and the results are shown in Tables 8.16, 8.17 and 8.18.

The potential for fattening is considerable. Over-fed, sheep can reach 100 kg in a year.

The creation of a fattening system, using large numbers, is theoretically possible but at present is affected by pathological problems: diseases transmitted by ticks, by viruses and above all by vermin.

It seems that the problems start at above the level of 100 head, kept in confinement.

Table 8.17 Feeding regimes during sheep fattening trials

Type of regime	Nature of concentrate	Rate of incorporation of haulm or shell of groundnut %	Theoretical value of the ration				Identification of regime
			FU/kg Dm	DCP/fu	Cellulose % DM	Ca/P	
Haulm-	I	18	0.8	90	17	1.3	F.1
concentrate	II	20	0.85	90	16	1.3	F.2
	III	57	0.65	100	21	2.2	F.3
	IV	59	0.66	110	22	2.1	F.4
	V	59	0.69	100	23	3.3	F.5
	VI	75	0.5	110	34	10	F.6
Shell-	VII, VIII	20	0.75		25	1.3	C.1
concentrate	IX	30	0.65	110	30	1.6	C.2
	X	40	0.56		35	1.4	C.3
		50	0.47	120	38	1.6	C.4
		50	0.42	150	40	1.2	C.5
		24	0.52	125	27	2	C.6

Table 8.16 Types of concentrates used for fattening sheep: composition and estimated value of concentrates

| Lots | Sorghum | Bran | | Cotton by-product | | Fish meal | Molasses | Urea | Min. + Vit. | Value in kg DM | | | Price* | |
		Maize	Wheat	Seed	Cake					FU	DCP	Ca/P	kg DM	1 FU
I	–	65	–	22.5	–	–	10	–	2.5	0.8	66	0.9	18	22
II	–	72.5	–	25	–	–	–	–	2.5	0.9	76	0.9	18	20
III	50	46	–	–	–	–	–	–	4	0.87	66	1	30	34
IV	50	45	–	–	–	–	–	2†	3	0.87	82	1	31	35
V	51	46	–	–	–	–	–	–	3	0.89	68	1.5	29	33
VI	97	–	–	–	–	–	–	–	3	0.9	68	1	43	47
VII	20	61	–	–	15	–	–	–	4	0.94	97	1.1	26	28
VIII	20	55	–	–	22	–	–	–	3	0.93	110	1.25	28	30
IX	38	55	–	–	–	–	–	2.2	4.8	0.85	110	1.2	26	30
X	47	–	48	–	–	0.6	–	–	4.4	0.7	83	2	29	41

* Relative 1976, with costs of processing included.
† Phosphate of urea

Table 8.18 Analysis of results obtained from sheep fattening feed trials

		Sheep used			Growth		Consumption		
Regimes tested	Duration of feeding (days)	No.	Weight (initial) (kg)	Breed	Gain (total) (kg)	Calculated daily liveweight gain (g/d)	Feed (g/d)	DM/100 kg LW	Index of consumption
F.1	63	5	25	Peul–Peul	8.1	129	1200	3.5	8.2
F.2	42	5	24.9	"	4.3	102	1100	3.4	7.0
F.3	90	8	26.6	"	5.8	58	1071	3.2	11.2
F.4	90	8	27.1	"	4.9	51	1108	3.3	12.9
F.5	90	8	27.4	"	6.7	75	1118	3.2	9.0
F.6	52	6	28.2	"	5.9	115	1350	3.9	5.9
C.1	98	9	25.8	Peul-Peul	9.9	100	1403	4.0	10.5
C.2	98	10	26.4	"	11.9	120	1607	4.4	8.6
C.3	98	8	26.0	"	12.3	125	1722	4.7	7.8
	133	6	28.6	Touabire	13.2	99	1665	4.2	9.4
C.4	133	6	29.4	"	12.8	96	1612	4.0	7.8
C.5	133	6	29.1	"	10.0	75	1562	3.4	8.8
C.6	70	10	36.1	Peul-Peul	9.0	137	2276	5.1	8.4

Milk production

Analysis of the problems associated with milk production in the tropics represents a significant part of the current research and publications.

Geography of dairying

A superficial examination of the distribution of the regions reputed for dairying across the globe shows that none is situated in the tropics. The principal milk producing countries, from whence the specialised breeds originate, are all in the temperate zones, with mild oceanic rainy climates – Holland, Denmark, the British Isles, the Channel Islands, Normandy (North France), New England (east USA), New Zealand and occasionally in countries with hard winters – Switzerland, Scotland, Franche-Comté on the french swiss border.

The most widespread specialised dairy cattle breeds, and those which progress the most, originate from these regions: Friesian-Holstein, Jersey, Guernsey, Brune des Alpes, Montbeliarde (Plates 7.39, 7.41 and 7.42).

In the intertropical zone, the cattle populations made up from breeding stock imported from these regions were able to be established and develop each time that the altitude limited the effects of the climate: East Africa, Central and South America, Madagascar.

There thus exists, a priori, a certain antagonism between the concept of highly productive milking breeds and that of warm tropical climates.

Table 8.19 Milk production of some local tropical breeds

Country	Breed	Method of keeping	Production (kg)	Duration (days)
Madagascar	Zébu (Madagascan)	Intensive	6	12
Ghana	West African Shorthorn	?	774 ± 101	295
Cameroun	Mbororo Akou (WF)	?	465	
	Mbororo Djafoun (RB)	?	295	
Senegal	Pakistani Zebus	Intensive	1 147 ± 126	241 ± 7
			735.5	
Nigeria	White Fulani	?	734	362
India	Sahiwal	?	1 597.2 ± 31.2	288.3 ± 3.6
	Haryana	?	1 098.0 ± 39.6	242.2 ± 5.5
	Tharpaka		1 285.5 ± 114.5	248.2 ± 16.9
	Red Sindhi		1 534.9 ± 32.2	284.1 ± 3.8
	Gir		1 125.5 ± 31.7	257.4 ± 4.6
	Kankrej		1 256	353
	Kangayam		643.6	264.0 ± 3.3
Sri Lanka	Sinhala	?	1 255 ± 55	224 ± 20
Mali	N'Dama	Intensive	491.4	
Niger	Azawak	Extensive	445 ± 18	270
			to 624 ± 17	

Factors limiting tropical milk production

Breed factors

Numerous studies have been made with the aim of determining the limiting factors of milk production in a warm climate.

The cattle breeds which originate from the tropics generally have a limited genetic potential for milk production and remain mediocre producers (500–1500 kg per lactation) even when the best possible husbandry conditions are available to them (Table 8.19).

The two best tropical milking breeds are the Sahiwal Zebu, originating from Pakistan, and the Criollo breed, a humpless breed represented in most of the countries of Central and South America.

The best selected bloodlines of these two breeds hardly achieve 2000 kg per lactation, although exceptional individuals have been shown to have attained lactation yields of 4000 kg.

In a general way, and in all the continents, the genetic improvement of local breeds for milk production has essentially been obtained by crossing with breeds which originate from temperate countries. Such operations have been carried out in some cases for centuries (since the eighteenth and nineteenth centuries) and have lead to the creation to new breeds such as the Rana on the Madagascan Plateaux and the Taylor in Pakistan. Most often, the crosses have been carried out during the second quarter of the twentieth century, when industrial development of the tropics initiated the start of urbanisation and the increase of milk consumption made intensification of production necessary (Table 8.20).

Table 8.20 Milk production of European breeds in the tropics

Country	Breed	Method of keeping	Production (kg)	Duration (days)
Madagascar	FFPN	intensive	L1 2 768 (10)	332
			L2 2 109 (9)	319
			L3 3 371 (5)	350
Cameroun	Holstein-Friesian	?	L3 3 202	
	Jersey	?	1 685	
Kenya	Friesian	?	L1 2 452	273
			L2 2 804	282
			L3 3 165	286
			L1 1 897	279
			L2 2 162	288
			L3 2 400	289
Uganda	Jersey Kenya	?	L1 1 704	399
			L2 2 227	331
			L3 2 515	355
			L4 2 019	317
	Jersey USA		L1 2 514	403
			L2 2 585	381
			L3 2 778	353
Nigeria	British Friesian	?	2 012	305
Senegal	Montbeliarde	intensive	1 101	186
			3 066	280
Thailand	Rouge Danoise	intensive	L1 2 305	–
			L2 2 760	–
Zaire	Friesland	?	3 182	305
	Jersey		2 336	266
Madagascar	Normande	intensive	2 155	
Bolivia	Holstein	intensive	3 040.7 ± 123.4	–
		extensive	543.4 ± 97.8	–
	Gir	extensive	375.3 ± 144.7	
Venezuéla	Holstein	intensive	L1 3 828	333
	Brown Swiss	intensive	L1 3 642.9	
			L2 4 256.3	349.4
Brazil	Friesian	?	2 543.9 ± 42.28	329.02 ± 3.94

L (1, 2, 3) correspond to number of lactation (1, 2, 3). The figures in parenthesis indicate the numbers, when they are known.

Until then, in most cases (Africa and Asia notably), the level of production from local breeds sufficed to satisfy the needs of the traditional consumers who were, most of the time, the stockmen themselves.

Exploitation of cattle for milk is, in fact, one of the ancestral features of pastoral economics in Africa and Asia. The major part of the cattle production of these continents is still the premise of traditionally specialised populations, which have only entered the market economy in the course of the last decades and had, until then, lived in symbiosis with their cattle for millenia.

These populations have, all the time, shared with the calves the meagre milk production of their herds' cows. Taking account of the numbers of cattle involved, the total production, which cannot be counted, is probably considerable. The rearing conditions and genetic potential of the herds means that individual performances can only remain limited.

Food resources

The forage potential of the tropics has been discussed in Chapter 5 'Animal production and forage resources'. What should be remembered in relation to the problems of milk production are the following features.

1. The natural pastures of the tropics have significant seasonal variations of productivity and nutritive value.
2. Modern agronomic techniques (selection of forage species, fertilisation, irrigation) enable the attainment of productivity very much higher than the best obtained in temperate countries. Certain forms of forage intensification are therefore applicable in certain cases in the tropics, with very favourable results.
3. Tropical climates are favourable to the production of abundant food energy notably in the form of starchy root crops, but the level of production of forage proteins is not high.

The result of this situation is that, with their particular characteristics, food resources can be favourable for an intensive system of production in the tropics as in the temperate zones.

Climatic factors

The main obstacle to intensive milk production in the tropics is physical climatical factors.

Numerous experiments have shown that a prolonged period in which temperatures are more than 25° C, particularly in humid air conditions, leads to a reduction of dry matter intake by milking cows and, as a consequence, a drop in their production. The incidence of these high temperatures is considerably reduced if cool periods (nocturnal or seasonal) intervene. Experiments have shown that the fall in appetite due to heat is the principal factor in depression of production; this has not been demonstrated when the animals are fed by a fistula into the gut.

High ambient temperatures have another depressive action on milk production by reducing the fertility of the cows, thus lengthening the interval between lactations.

Sociological factors

Herding peoples are often nomadic or transhumant and do not practise agriculture. Their system of production, which does not permit a place for intensive forage production, therefore has limited possibilities for improvement.

In general terms, sedentary stockmen are agriculturalists and rarely exploit their animals for milk, except when they are sedentary pastoralists. Their systems of production involve cattle either for work or equally for the production of meat.

Pathological factors

Considerable progress has been achieved over the course of the last 50 years in the fight against most of the tropical diseases (see Chapter 6 'Animal production and disease'). Trypanosomiasis, where it exists, constitutes a difficulty for dairying in common with the other forms of livestock production and which involves particular efforts (preventive treatment).

The diseases transmitted by ticks (babesiosis, anaplasmosis, heartwater) have been the main justification, for a long time, of the crossing of Zebus with specialised European breeds for milk production. In modern methods of animal production (zero grazing), the need to favour these practices is considerably reduced.

The principal constraints to the development of dairying in the tropics are thus climatic and physiological. There are regions, notably upland ones, where these constraints are lessened or eliminated. Very often in these cases, when the economic conditions exist and particularly when there is a remunerative market, milk production develops (Plates 7.45 to 7.48).

Postscript: economic problems and future methods of livestock production

G. Tacher

Institute of Animal Production and Veterinary Medicine in the Tropics

One of the big challenges of our time will be to feed more than six billion people before the year 2000.

The large countries could provide one would think the shortfall of production at the world level; this would only move the problem because, in addition to the distribution difficulties to which there could be a solution, the aid reliant position of the populations of developing countries would be incompatible with human dignity and would preclude all possibilities of general development, which can only be founded on agricultural development.

These arguments are discussed elsewhere in the concept of self-sufficiency which one finds in practically all the justifications for large programmes. This need for food security is not peculiar to developing countries; it is experienced by all nations. The example of Great Britain in the nineteenth century is worth recalling. Having pledged its future to a reliance on industrial development and a policy of exporting and, in so doing, giving up the maintenance of its agriculture, it partially had to turn back on this option in favour of a certain amount of self-sufficiency.

This is why, as Pierre Uri indicated: *to aid the world to feed itself will be the great task of this end of the century.*

Within the context of the necessary development of agriculture, animal production would take the place of first choice even if only looked at from the narrow angle of the qualitative improvement of rations.

However the development of animal production cannot be only sectorial, it goes beyond purely technical considerations and should be put into the general field of planning, itself directed by politics.

The major problems posed by the development of animal production – should production be intensified?

In its report *Agriculture: Horizon 2000*, FAO estimated that the demand for animal products in the developing countries ought to increase by 4.5 per cent in the coming 20 years. This expansion could provide for 2.2 per cent of demographic growth and for 2.3 per cent of a supposed increase in revenue.

If one relates this to what has happened for the large ruminants over the last 15 years in these countries, the production of meat was only increased by 2.5 per cent and that of milk by 3.0 per cent. This is to say that considerable efforts will have to be made.

When such a gulf exists, the first thought that springs to mind is to modernise and intensify production, notably by a massive injection of investment. Such a suggestion merits examination in both an economic and global context.

Very simply, the economies of the developing countries are dominated by three large problems: unemployment, inflation and a deficit on the balance of payments. They will form the major constraints for the planning of the development of animal production.

Unemployment

The waves of unemployment which begin to submerge the towns of developing countries originate from excessive birth rates, but above all from the poverty of the rural people.

If the increase in production is brought about by a modernisation and intensification of animal production, and technically it could be, this will occur in a capitalist form, that is to say by substituting capital for labour by relatively elaborate techniques which will not permit the use of the rural youth and the unemployed.

Besides, often these techniques cause a transfer from the peasant class towards the well-off classes of the population, classes more open to modern technology. If one wants, for example, an improvement in near to town milk production, it is necessary to bring about a leap in technology, which often can only be done by people with sufficient means who have received a certain level of education. This type of person is found among those sectors of the population already in a favoured position.

In the developed countries, the satisfying of national food needs is achieved by a working rural population representing 5–10 per cent of the total working population.

In the developing countries, between half and two-thirds of the working population work in the rural area and often provide production which is insufficient at the national level.

Modernisation might then permit an increase in production but might never help in the resolution of the crucial problem of unemployment and might even risk accentuating it.

Intensification could moreover have two other major disadvantages.

1. It might be situated in the areas around the towns, which might increase regional disequilibirum.
2. It might not favour the fight to improve the living standards of the rural poor, which could ensure the continuation of the actual vicious circle: the crisis of the rural areas leads to a shrinking of aggregate demand, which in turn is the source of unemployment.

Inflation

Politicians are extremely sensitive to variations of price and food commodities; meat is foremost of the latter.

In the developing countries, nominal salaries are very low and low food prices (food is the main item in the family budget) create a salary which finds itself increased accordingly, in real terms. However, an increase in prices always leads to claims for salary increases.

Trying to stifle this inflation generates tensions, particularly in the towns, and so governments seek to keep prices as low as possible.

This is frequently done without success by fiscal means. For example, very often the government fixes a ceiling price for meat but, because this is too low, it allows a 'tolerable price' which however is often overtaken in its turn by a black market price.

As a result of the lack of success, the government then tries to keep the consumption price at a low level by a series of other measures:

1. subsidies on consumption – for example, in Gabon, 30 CFA francs per kilogram of meat according to the year;
2. liberal import policy – for example, in the Ivory Coast, in 1978, compensated quarters coming from the Argentine and being constituted of 2/3 forequarters and 1/3 hindquarters, had an average import price of 230 CFA francs. The meat was resold to retail butchers at 280 CFA francs and finished up on the market at a retail price of 400 CFA francs on the bone. The wholesale price of locally produced meat was 400 CFA francs for the forequarters and 450 CFA francs for the hindquarters. At the retail level, locally produced fresh beef on the bone was sold at 50 per cent more than the imported frozen product (fresh beef 600 CFA francs per kilogram, frozen beef 400 CFA francs per kilogram).

This liberal import policy stifles the development of local production. That is even more true with exports from developed countries, with which the local product must compete, and which are very often subsidised in a more or less disguised way.

This pressure on prices is thus implicitly a transfer from livestock rearing to the rest of the economy whereas a number of developed countries effect a transfer in the other direction.

Balance of payments

Weakness in the balance of payments is fairly general in developing countries. Now modernisation calls upon either foreign capital for its installation or, and this amounts to the same thing, it calls upon foreign exchange to purchase equipment, various inputs and expertise.

In a general way, these technologies are consumers of energy and if they are substituted for extensive and less productive techniques, but ones which are lower consumers of energy, the balance per kilogram of food produced will always be unfavourable to modernisation. The non-oil producing countries will thus reflect this increase in indebtedness.

In the face of the weakness of internal aggregate demand, it will often happen that part of modern animal production might be agro-exporters. This can seem to be very profitable and does draw certain benefits between the outgoing and incoming of currency. It is necessary, nevertheless, to draw attention to the fact that this type of project is often subsidised in one way or another (if only by a bias in tax allowances) and the foreign exchange which they bring back into the country (exactly as do the cash crops so discredited nowadays) should be used judiciously. They will be beneficial if they are used to increase agricultural productivity, whereas they will be a source of impoverishment if they are used to fund luxury expenditure or imports of consumer goods destined for the already privileged classes.

Finally, this type of project can only be financed by making significant calls on credit. Now in a period which could be classified as normal, the tendency of lenders is to orientate towards the most profitable enterprises for which the return on their investment is the fastest possible. Livestock enterprises are thus penalised because quick return techniques favour short-term projects as opposed to long-term ones.

Different future methods of animal production

It is well known that there are other constraints to the development of animal production but, in simple terms, those which are now discussed dominate the scene. They will affect the various methods of production in different ways.

The rearing of ruminants

As regards world production of meat from ruminants (cattle, buffalo, sheep, goats), the tropical developing countries account for 16 per cent. This proportion has reduced elsewhere by about 1 per cent during the last twenty years.

For the developed countries, ruminant production represents 43 per cent of meat production and for the tropical developing countries the figure is 58 per cent (in Africa, this proportion is 84 per cent because pig and poultry production are less developed than in the other countries).

The essential peculiarity of production in the tropical countries is a very low overall productivity per head. Live cattle produce 12 kg and a small ruminant little more than 3 kg of equivalent carcass per year in these countries, whereas they give near to 80 and 7 kg respectively in the developed countries.

For milk production which has a considerable importance for home consumption of the populations, the difference is even larger than for meat, considering that the productivity per living animal is estimated at 90 litres for a cow in the developing countries whereas in the developed countries it is close to ten times as much.

Animal production in pastoral production systems

The poor levels of the preceding figures should be considered. Livestock rearing is often practised on the most difficult land where no other agriculture could be carried on. If livestock production were not carried on, then there would be no other use made of this land and these countries cannot permit the non-use of resources.

The three constraints discussed previously remain determinants for the future of these systems of production.

1. They favour rural employment. The recent drought in the Sahelian countries showed that once this animal production was weakened, waves of unemployment overtook the towns putting their economies a little more in jeopardy.
2. They are ill-favoured by inflation and by price policies. The price of meat for consumption is as low as possible while the price of inputs, which will be necessary to improve animal production, and the price of goods consumed by the stockmen, increases faster. In these systems of production, the effects are however tempered by the level of home consumption (of which milk is the most significant part) but this, in its turn, retards entry into the national economic sphere and, as such, also restricts modernisation.
3. They are favoured by the balance of payments situation. The relationship of the productivities between animal production in the developed countries and the developing ones is very much against the latter, but if one takes an energy balance, that is is to say the number of kilograms of meat produced in relation to the energy consumed, it would be against the developed countries (the subject would be for debate elsewhere). In the latter, inputs are mainly of a non-renewable energy nature, fertiliser, tractors and

machines, buildings etc., whereas in the former the inputs are of a renewable energy nature (in the Sahel, the only non-renewable energy inputs constitute negligible administrative services and pastoral water supplies). Furthermore, for the immense populations concerned, livestock keeping is equally a way of life, that is to say that socio-economic factors often outweigh economic problems.

Animal production in mixed farming systems

Pressure on the land, which comes from the advance of agriculture under the thrust of human demography, exerts itself first on the best land and tends to marginalise extensive livestock production. In these systems of production, the integration of cropping and livestock rearing, i.e. mixed farming, becomes imperative. The three constraints play different roles.

The integration of livestock rearing and crop cultivation renders the two types of husbandry more viable and more profitable.

1. It enables the use of the by-products of farming.
2. The use of animal traction renders the work less arduous.
3. The animal brings its work and manure to the farming and enables diversification of activities and gives an increase in output from man-power. It brings its produce, either for home consumption or for sale and thus constitutes a financial base for small ruminants.
4. Forage crops, for example berseem clover in the Mediterranean countries or the Middle East, improve the agricultural fields.

All these factors considerably favour employment and the standing of the small farmers in the rural areas.

Pricing policies are in general unfavourable to a certain modernisation. The arguments put forward in the pastoral systems remain valid. Furthermore, intensification happens by an improvement with cereal based feeding. Now cereals are in direct competition with human food and the price relationships are very unfavourable in the developing countries. The ratio between the price of 1 kg of beef and 1 kg of cereals is of the order of 1 : 13 in the United States whereas it is of the order of 1 : 7 in the Sahelian countries. If one extracts from this relationship the general expenses of exploitation and the index of consumption of a ruminant, one notices that in this system of production one can produce meat more profitably in the developed countries whereas it is very difficult to produce it in the developing countries.

The mixed farming system contributes to an alleviation of the balance of payments. The use of manure and animal traction enables saving of foreign exchange which can be used for the purchase of fertiliser, tractors and fuel. It is interesting to note that if the same two million draught animals existing in the developing countries worked only 2 h per day, their energy would represent about eight million TEP, or the annual production of the Petroffina company.

Animal production in modern systems

This is still relatively rare and only develops in certain very particular cases such as close to town dairies and feedlots, when they exist in conjunction with the availability of agro-industrial by-products or with the possibilities of having forage crops at reasonable cost and buoyant internal markets. It has been seen that such types of general economic constraints were enjoyed by this method of production.

The future of ruminant rearing

If there is rationality in man, development of milk production, the best converter of animal resources into cash, ought to have the most attractive future, but rationality is hardly an attribute to this world and since the beginning of antiquity we have seen the cave drawings: man pursuing the bullock at first with his *assegai* (slender throwing spear) and now with his bank notes.

Everywhere where the pressure on agricultural land will still permit extensive methods of livestock rearing, which might be in a pastoral or agro-pastoral system, this ought to remain the basis for development of animal production because it best meets the three major constraints which have been examined.

For certain, it remains a necessity to produce and it is important here to raise an ambiguity which is frequently encountered with regard to productivity: this is too often considered as a result of genetic improvement whereas this is only a very small part of the matter. Genetic improvement is subordinate to improvement of feeding and to the lifting of disease constraints, which seems to be an obvious thing which is too often forgotten. Next it is linked to an absence of risk, a fundamental concept in traditional extensive livestock rearing. In a period of food abundance, due to a favourable climatic phase, one has the impression that stockmen could improve their stock (milk production, growth rate, size etc.) but they know that when bad times return these animals, however perfectly adapted to their environment, would produce less or could disappear more rapidly than those which they have selected on criteria which are not classic (for example, resistance to the dry season, aptitude to travelling long distances etc.). Finally, under very severe environmental, social and economic constraints, it is certain that stockmen run their enterprises by optimising their production without knowing it.

Productivity is, in reality, strongly conditioned by parameters such as mortality or fertility, which are very easily improved if only the stocking rate remains adapted to the food potential, that is to say that it might be increased by commercialisation.

The productivity of sheep can be studied in Saudi Arabia in a desert environment (plant biomass of the order of 22 kg DM/ha), the same productivity is of the order of 16 kg of liveweight per animal present annually in the herd. In the Sahelian countries (plant biomass of the order of 1500 kg

DM/ha), the same productivity is of the order of 8 kg, or less than half. This improvement has been made possible by subsidising the barley which the stockmen largely distribute to their animals, thus reducing the mortality and increasing the fertility. As is well known, it amounts there to a redistribution of oil revenues; the developing countries cannot allow themselves this type of aid to livestock rearing apart from simple health service activities or the distribution of food supplements from local by-products on target at strategic times, which would enable an increase in productivity in a very significant way.

Milk production should be differentiated; that destined for the rural populations, who heighten improvement of livestock rearing productivity of the pastoral and agropastoral systems and where normal principles for the improvement of meat production can be kept; and that milk production destined for urban populations in which the genetic improvement of milking cows is planned in correlation with the use of local agricultural and agro-industrial products and by-products and with the development of forage crops.

Monogastric types of livestock rearing

One should distinguish between traditional livestock rearing and the industrial type.

The problems of traditional animal production are notably those of ruminants. The major obstacle to their development is the difficulty of using a food which does not come uniquely from exploitation of natural vegetation. In these traditional enterprises, the basic food comes in effect from this exploitation and it is nearly impossible for the small farmer to obtain an agricultural surplus to give to his livestock. Simple efforts, identical to those envisaged for ruminants, nevertheless enable augmentation of the productivity of this type of animal production in a significant way.

Augmentation of total meat production will come in the future, however, from industrial or semi-industrial rearing monogastric livestock (pigs and poultry). The main reason for this is simple: numerous countries have pressure on their land such that the development of ruminants on pasture is no longer possible. They thus ought to turn towards monogastric types; these animals have the best ratio of food conversion and their production cycles are the quickest. Another reason will bring about this development: this will be the disequilibrium between overall national production and the aggregate national demand.

This tension will tend to force the decision maker to chose this course of action even though it generates little employment and, conversely, it might be the instigator of inflation because this type of production only develops in the absence of constraints on selling prices.

In reality it will equally engender a deficit on the balance of payments because, besides equipment, the technology of production and its inputs are those of the developed countries which, furthermore, will increase economic dependency.

For example, Senegalese intensive agricultural production is based on the American 'maize–soya' model whereas Senegalese agricultural production is of the 'sorghum–groundnut' type.

If one wishes to develop modern pig and/or poultry production, it will then be necessary to intensify efforts to use technologies adapted with a maximum of inputs from within the country.

The decisions on the matter of the policy for development of animal production will be difficult to take. Logic and solidarity are two factors to use to remedy the crisis, to consider in the development of the rural areas in fighting against unemployment and in giving a new life to the system by raising demand, that is to say in favouring the evolution of traditional animal production. This is incontestably the choice which should be made in the long term.

The drought and desertification have been attributed to too much success in the fight against epidemics.

However, the demand in numerous countries, and principally in the towns, one seeks to fill the food deficiency rapidly; this can only be done by launching industrial rearing monogastric livestock (pigs, poultry) – all operations can be carried out in an industrial and semi-industrial way, but which demand qualified manpower and capital. Certain countries are, because of their climate and resources, privileged in this matter.

One finds there the classic contradictions between the decisions which have to be taken in the medium term and those to be taken in the long term. Rigorous planning resting on a firm voluntary policy will be the key to success.

Very good results have been obtained both in pig production and in poultry production.

Selected bibliography

General works

Coloumb, J., Serres, H. and Tacher, G. (1980) *L'élevage en pays sahélian*. Presses universitaires de France, Paris, 183 p.

ILCA/CIPEA (1975) *Inventaire et cartographie des pâturages tropicaux africains*. Proceedings of the colloquium, Bamako, Mali, 3–8 March 1975, 399 p.

INRA (1978) *Principes de la nutrition et de l'alimentation des ruminants*. INRA, Versailles (route de Saint-Cyr, 78000), 597 p.

McDowell, R. E. (1972) *Improvement of livestock in warm climates*. W. H. Freeman and Company, San Francisco, 711 p.

OCAM (1971) *Colloque sur l'élevage*, Fort-Lamy, Tchad 8–13 December 1969. IEMVT, Maisons-Alfort.

Recherches sur l'élevage bovin en zone tropicale humide. (1980) First international colloquium, 18–22 April 1977, Ministère de la Recherche Scientifique (B.P. 1152, Bouaké, République de Côte-d'Ivoire). IEMVT, Maisons-Alfort, 2 vols, 1026 p.

L'embouche intensive des bovins en pays tropicaux. Proceedings of Colloquium, Dakar 4–8 December 1973 (République du Sénégal, Ministère du Développement Rural – République Française, Ministère de la Co-opération). IEMVT, Maisons-Alfort.

Rivière R. (1978) *Manuel d'alimentation des ruminants domestiques en milieu tropical*. Ministère de la Co-opération, Paris; IEMVT, Maisons-Alfort (Coll. Manuels et Précis d'Élevage n° 9).

Chapter 1

Christiansen, W. C. (1971) *Livestock feeds and feeding in Latin America*. Agricultural Development Paper, Univ. of Florida, Institute of Food and Agricultural Science.

Hrabovsky, J. P. (1981) Élevage Horizon 2000, notamment dans les pays en développement. *Revue mond. Zootech.*, **40**, 2–16.

McDowell, R. E. (1966) *Problems of cattle production in tropical countries.* Cornell International Agricultural Development, Mimeograph 17.

FAO (1981) *Agriculture: Horizon 2000* (P.O. 92–5–20 1080–7).

FAO (1988) Production Yearbook **42**, 1988. FAO, Rome, 306 p., 123 tables.

FAO (1978) *Laits et produits laitiers: projections des disponibilitiés, de la demande et du commerce en 1985: projections relatives au produits 1985,* FAO, Rome, (FAO/ESC; PROJ/78/).

FAO (1979a) *Projections pour 1985 de la production de la demande et du commerce de la viande.* Groupe intergouvernemental sur la viande Rome, 7–11 May, 1979 (C.C.P.: ME/1979/4).

FAO (1979b) *Utilisation des céréales dans le secteur de l'élevage: tendances, facteurs et questions de développement.* Groupe intergouvernemental sur la viande, Rome, 7–11 May, 1979 (C.C.P.: ME/1979/6).

Thurston, D. H. (1969) Tropical agriculture, a key to world food crises. *Biol. Sci.*, **29** (1).

Chapter 3

Johnston, J. E., Hamblin, F. B. and Schrader, G. T. (1958) Factors concerned in comparative heat tolerance of Jersey, Holstein and red Sindhi-Holstein F_1 cattle. *J. anim. Sci.*, **17**, 473–9.

McFarlane (1956) Urinary sodium potassium ratios in a hot environment. *Med. J. Aust.*, **3** (4), 139–40.

Rückbüsch, Y. (1977) *Physiologie, pharmacologie, thérapeutique animales.* Maloine, Paris, 424 p.

Chapter 4

Archambault, J. (1960) *Les eaux souterraines de l'Afrique occidentale.* Berger-Levrault, Nancy, 1 vol.

Funel, J.-M. and Laucoin, G. (1980) *Politiques d'aménagement hydro-agricole.* PUF, Paris, 212 p. (coll. Techniques vivantes. Développement en zones arides).

Bureau de Recherches Geologiques et Minières (1975) *Notice explicative et cartes de planification pour l'exploitation des eaux de l'Afrique sahélienne.* Fonds d'aide et de co-opération de la République Française: 1 vol. 21 × 29, 117 p., maps 1/500 000 (9 colours).

Bureau de Recherches Geologiques et Minieres (1976) *Notice explicative et cartes de planification des ressources en eau souterraine des États membres du Comité interafricain d'études hydrauliques.* Série Hydrologéologie, vol. 21 × 29, 118 p., 3 maps 1/500 000.

Serres, H. *Essai de bilan des politiques d'hydrauliques pastorales.* Gerdat, 42, rue Scheffer, Paris, IEMVT, 10, rue Pierre-Curie, Maisons-Alfort, 1 vol. 21 × 29, 139 p.

Serres, H. (1980) *Politiques d'hydraulique pastorale.* PUF, Paris, 122 p. (coll. Techniques vivantes. Développement en zones arides).

Chapter 7

Anderson, V. L. and Kempthorne, O. (1954) A model for the study of quantitative inheritance. *Genetics*, **39**, 883–98.

Bichard, M. and Smith, W. C. (1971) Cross-breeding and genetic improvement. In: *Pig production* Proc. 18th Easter Sch. Agric. Sci. Univ. Nott., 37 –52.

Braend, M. (1971) Haemoglobin variants in cattle. *Anim. Blood. Agric. biochem. Genet.*, **2**, 15–21.

CIPEA (1979) *Le bétail trypanotolérant d'Afrique occidentale et centrale.* Addis-Abeba, CIPEA–ILCA. Vol 1: 155 p., Vol 2: 311 p. (CIPEA BP 5689).

Cockerham, C. C. (1954) An extension of the concept of partitioning hereditary variance for analysis of covariance among relatives when epistasis is present. *Genetics*, **39**, 859–82.

Cockrill, W. R (1974) *The husbandry and health of the domestic buffalo.* FAO, Rome, 996 p.

Epstein, H. (1971) *The origin of the domestic animals of Africa.* Africana Publishing Corporation, New York, vol. 1, 573 p., vol. 2, 719 p.

Falconer, D. S. (1982) *Introduction to quantitative genetics.* Longman, London, 340 p.

Francis, J. (1966) Resistance of zebu and other cattle to tick infestation and babesiosis with special reference to Australia: an historical review. *Br. vet. J.*, **122**, 301.

IEMVT, Ministère de la Co-opération (1980) *Les petits ruminants d'Afrique centrale et d'Afrique de l'Ouest. Synthèse des connaissances actuelles.* IEMVT, Maisons-Alfort, 295 p.

INRA (1976) *Amélioration génétique des animaux de ferme.* Application aux bovins. CNRS, Jouy-en-Josas, 159 p.

Joshi, N. R., McLaughlin, E. A. and Phillips, R. W. (1957) *Les bovins d'Afrique. Types et races.* FAO, Rome.

Kone, K. (1948) Le boeuf du lac Tchad de la région de N'Guigmi. *Bull. Servs. Elev. Ind. anim. A.O.F.*, **1** (2–3), 47–64.

Maule, J. P. (1953) Cross-breeding experiments with dairy cattle in the tropics. *Anim. Breed Abstr.*, **21** (2), 105–21.

Mason, I. L. and Maule, J. P. (1960) *The indigenous livestock of eastern and southern Africa.* Farnham Royal, Commonwealth Agricultural Bureaux, (Tech. Communication n° 14), 240 p.

Mason, I. L. (1951) *The classification of West Africa livestock.* Farnham Royal, Commonwealth Agricultural Bureaux, (Tech. Communication n° 7), 39 p.

Osterhoff, D. R. (1975) Haemoglobin types in African cattle. *J. S. Afr. vet. Ass.*, **46** (2), 185–9.

Popescu, C. P., Cribiu, E. P., Poivey, J. P. and Seitz, J. L. (1979) Étude cytogénétique d'une population bovine de Côte-d'Ivoire. *Rev. Élev. Méd. vét. Pays trop.*, **32** (1), 81–84.

Proceedings of the 1st World Congress on applied genetics. Madrid, 1974.

Serres, H., Capitaine, P., Dubois, P., Dumas, R. and Gilibert, J. (1968) Le croisement Brahman à Madagascar. *Rev. Elev. Méd. vét. Pays trop.*, **21** (4), 519–61.

Chapter 8

Adeneye, J. A. and Adebandjo, A. K. (1978) Lactational characteristics of imported British Friesian cattle in Western Nigeria. *J. agric. Sci. UK*, **91** (3), 645–51.

Bianca, W. (1965) Cattle in a hot environment. *J. dairy Res.*, **32**, 291–333.

Bodisco, V., Manrique, U., Valle, A. and Cevallos, E. (1973) Tolerancia al calor y humedad atmosferica de vacas Holstein, Pardo suizas y Guernsey. *Agron. trop.*, **23** (3), 241–61.

Branton, C., McDowell, R. E. and Brown, M. A. (1966) *Zebu–European cross breeding as a basis of dairy cattle improvement in the USA.* Southern Co-operative series. Bull., 114.

Charray, J., Coulomb, J. and Mathon, J. C. (1977) Le croisement Jersiais-N'Dama en Côte-d'Ivoire. *Rev. Élev. Méd. vét. Pays trop.*, **30** (1), 67–83.

Coulomb, J., Gruvel, J., Morel, P., Perreau, P., Queval, R. and Tibayrenc, R. *La trypanotolérance. Synthèse des connaissances actuelles.* Ministère de la Co-operation, Paris; IEMVT, Maisons-Alfort, 1977.

Doutressoulle, G. and Traore, S. (1949) L'élevage dans la boucle du Niger. *Rev. Élev. Méd. vét. Pays trop.*, **3** (1), 17–28.

Dupire, M. (1970) *Organisation sociale des Peuls.* Plon, Paris.

Gallais, J. (1975) *Pasteurs et paysans du Gourma. La condition sahélienne.* CEGET, Paris.

Gilibert, J., Razakaboana, F. and Dubois, P. (1973) *Résultats du Sahiwal á Madagascar.* IEMVT, Tananarive, 25 p.

Kiwuwa, G. H. (1974) Production characteristics of Friesian and Jersey dairy cattle on privately owned farms in Kenya. *East. Afr. Agric. For. J.*, **39** (3), 289–97.

Madsen, O. (1976) Red danish cattle in the tropics. *Wld Anim. Rev.*, **19**, 8–13.

Maricz, M. (1958) Résultats des croisements d'absorption des races Friesland et Jersey à la station de Nioka. *Bull. Inf. I. N.E.A.C.*, 7 (3), 133–64.

Oliveira, R. M. de, Fontes, C. R., Silva, H. C. M. da and Silva, T. (1977) Alguns factores de meio que afetam a produçaô de leite de um rebanho holandès Preto e Branco. *Arqos Esc. Vet. Univ. fed. Minas Gerais*, **29** (1), 69–76.

Pearson de Vaccaro, L. (1973–5) Some aspects of the performance of purebred and crossbred dairy cattle in the tropics. Part 1. Reproductive efficiency in females. *Anim. Breed. Abstr.*, 1973, **41** (12), 571–89. Part 2. Mortality and culling rates. *Anim. Breed. Abstr.*, 1974, **42** (3), 93–103. Part 3. Growth, size and age at first calving in Holstein Friesians and their crosses. *Anim. Breed. Abstr.*, 1975, **43** (10), 493–505.

Phipps, R. H. (1974) The performance of imported Kenyan and American Jerseys in Uganda. *East. Afr. Agric. For. J.*, **34** (4), 381–5.

Technical Centre for Agricultural and Rural Co-operation (CTA)

The Technical Centre for Agricultural and Rural Co-operation (CTA) was set up in 1983 in Ede/Wageningen, in the Netherlands, under the second ACP-EEC Convention (Lome II) between the ten Member States of the European Economic Community and 69 African, Caribbean and Pacific States (the 'ACP').

The Convention was renewed in 1984 and the number of ACP States now stands at 66 with twelve European countries.

The aims of the CTA are to collect and circulate scientific and technical information, facilitate the exchange of information, promote technical popularisation, and encourage research, training and innovation in the spheres of agricultural and rural development and extension. It contributes to studies and publications, organises specialist meetings, assists the documentation centres of the ACP States and has a question-answer service at their disposal.

Headquarters: 'De Rietkampen', Galvanistraat 90, Ede, Netherlands. Postal address: CTA, P.O.B.380, 6700 AJ Wageningen, Netherlands,
Tel.: (08380)–20484
International line: 31–8380–20484
Telex: 30169 CTANL

Agency for Cultural and Technical Co-operation (ACCT)

The Agency for Cultural and Technical Co-operation (ACCT), an intergovernmental organisation set up by the Treaty of Niamey in March 1970, is an association of countries linked by their common usage of the French language, for the purposes of co-operation in the fields of education, culture, science and technology and, more generally, in all matters which contribute to the development of its Member States and to bringing peoples closer together.

The Agency's activities in the fields of scientific and technical co-operation for development are directed primarily towards the preparation, dissemination and exchange of scientific and technical information, drawing up an inventory of and exploiting natural resources, and the socio-economic advancement of young people and rural communities.

Member countries: Belgium, Benin, Burundi, Canada, Central African Republic, Chad, Comoros, Congo, Djibouti, Dominica, France, Gabon, Guinea, Haiti, Ivory Coast, Lebanon, Luxembourg, Mali, Mauritius, Monaco, Niger, Rwanda, Senegal, Seychelles, Togo, Tunisia, Burkina Faso, Vanuatu, Vietnam, Zaire.

Associated States: Cameroun, Egypt, Guinea-Bissau, Laos, Mauritania, Morocco, St Lucia.

Participating governments: New Brunswick, Quebec.

Index